Audrey Wilkes

RADAR

A WARTIME MIRACLE

Other books by the Authors

Colin Latham
An ABC of Radar

Anne Stobbs
One-Oh-Eight Miller
Dear One-Oh-Eight

RADAR

A WARTIME MIRACLE

Recalled by

Colin Latham & Anne Stobbs

AND BY MEN & WOMEN WHO PLAYED THEIR PART IN IT FOR THE RAF

FOREWORD BY
SIR EDWARD FENNESSY, CBE

SUTTON PUBLISHING LIMITED

First published in the United Kingdom in 1996
by Alan Sutton Publishing Limited, an imprint of Sutton Publishing Limited
Phoenix Mill · Far Thrupp · Stroud · Gloucestershire

Reprinted 1996 and 1997

Paperback edition first published 1997

British Library Cataloguing in Publication Data

A catalogue record for this book is available from the British Library.

ISBN 0–7509–1114–X (hardback)
ISBN 0–7509–1643–5 (paperback)

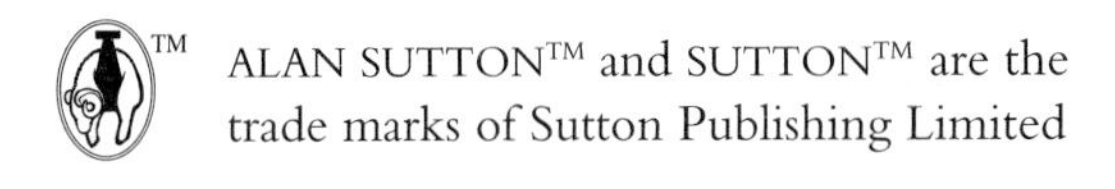

Cover illustration: from a photograph of an East Coast CH station (Courtesy of Yorkshire Evening News*).*

Typeset in 11/13 Bembo
Typesetting and origination by
Alan Sutton Publishing Limited.
Printed in Great Britain by
Butler & Tanner Ltd, Frome and London

Contents

Text throughout the book, unless otherwise attributed, has been written by Colin Latham.

Foreword

Sir Edward Fennessy, CBE

Staff member Bawdsey Research Station, 1938, and Staff Officer No. 60 Radar Group RAF, 1940–6

At a secret gathering in Berlin on 26 February 1935, Hitler officially created the German Luftwaffe, appointing Goering as its commander-in-chief. Thus he gave formal status to the plans for a modern air force which Erhard Milch, Von Seeckt and others had been preparing for years – an air force designed to destroy all who opposed Hitler's ambitions. A week later he revealed this potent threat to the world.

Little did Hitler and all the top Nazi chiefs gathered for this momentous occasion know that on that very same day, a Morris van was parked in an English meadow near Daventry. Inside, peering intently at a cathode ray tube, was Robert Watson Watt,[1] head of the Radio Department of the National Physical Laboratory, and his assistant, Arnold Wilkins, together with A.P. Rowe from the Air Ministry. As they watched the screen they saw an echo appear at 8 miles range coming from a Heyford bomber which was reflecting radio energy from the BBC Daventry transmitter. From this simple but effective demonstration was to come the weapon which would play such a crucial role in the defeat of the Luftwaffe, to which that very day Hitler and Goering, with much pomp and ceremony, were giving official recognition.

There could have been no greater contrast: in Germany, the assembled Nazi might; in the English meadow, Robert Watson Watt and colleagues – the only guest, Watson Watt's young nephew, taken along for the ride by his uncle and parked on the grass bank by the hedge.

Rightly, Colin Latham and Anne Stobbs have entitled this fascinating book *Radar: A Wartime Miracle*, for miracle it indeed was.

In 1934 Great Britain lay wide open to destruction from the air. Many concerned with air defence believed in the dictum 'The bomber will always get through.' Indeed, with the speed and operating altitude of the modern bomber and with no means of detecting its approach except sound-locators, it was a hard fact that had to be accepted. The only defence, our air strategists argued, was offence. Build an even stronger bomber force than any enemy who might attack us, they urged.

1 Robert Alexander Watson Watt adopted the hyphen when he was knighted in 1942. He became Sir Robert Watson-Watt FRS.

One man did not accept this policy of despair. He was a civil servant in the Air Ministry Directorate of Scientific Research – Mr A.P. Rowe. In 1934 he wrote a paper stating that unless means were developed to counter and defeat the bomber, Britain would lose the next war. Robert Watson Watt responded to this challenge, and in the famous Daventry demonstration of 26 February 1935 he showed the way. Sir Henry Tizard and Air Marshal Sir Hugh Dowding gave Watson Watt full backing, and within six months Britain had the basis of a radar defence system. By the outbreak of the war in September 1939, our skies were guarded by a chain of high-power radar stations extending from the Isle of Wight to Scotland.

But more significantly, this revolutionary new weapon had been integrated into Fighter Command, whose controllers and pilots had been trained and exercised in its use as a vital combat weapon.

Thus, when war came, the Commander-in-Chief of Fighter Command had a battle-ready weapon with which to scramble and control his few but brave young fighter pilots and defeat a numerically superior enemy, and with the Battle of Britain won, to thwart Hitler's plans to invade Britain.

It was A.P. Rowe's paper in 1934 that caused Watson Watt to suggest that radio could be employed to defeat aircraft: a proposal that came only just in the nick of time to save this country from the devastating onslaught of the Luftwaffe bomber fleets.

For those of us who lived and fought through those desperate days it was indeed a miracle.

Colin Latham and Anne Stobbs have performed a remarkable task in compiling this unique record of the still-vivid memories of so many men and women who played their part, not only in the crucial days of 1940 but throughout the war, where radar in its many roles contributed so much to the achievement of ultimate victory.

E.F., 1995

Preface

Colin Latham

'Miracle' is a strong word, appropriate for strange and wondrous events. How, in these 'high tech' days of colour television, mobile phones, satellite communications and much more, can we justify using it for something as commonplace as radar has now become?

The answer is twofold. Firstly, for the wonder, in the early days, of 'seeing' intruding aircraft long before they reached our coasts; and secondly (which is the more apparent now), that government departments, civilian scientists, industry and the armed services should have collaborated so closely and effectively – and in secret – to achieve so much in just a few short years.

Radar has by now become a fact of everyday life, important in civil as much as in military applications. In this book we attempt to describe some aspects of how it was first used by the RAF, but we are not unaware that it was also a boon to the other services. Following the initial experiments of the early years, not only the RAF but the Navy and the Army were backed by dedicated teams of scientists developing equipment for their particular needs.

Anne Stobbs and I are deeply indebted to all who have contributed to this book with their personal stories, and to those who, by correspondence and discussion, have assisted us in so many ways. I am especially grateful to Marconi Radar Systems for the use of historical material from the company archives. Without such enthusiastic interest and generous aid from many quarters – both at home and abroad – the job could not have been done.

I have found, in the course of the task, that I have learned much about this vast wartime radar scene of which I was not previously aware because, at the time, many aspects were outside my sphere of activity. I hope that, in a similar way, readers of my vintage may find points of interest in parts of the contents outside their own experiences. I hope, too, that those who were not there may better understand why we are proud of what was achieved and may agree that 'miracle' is no exaggeration.

Anne Stobbs

In May 1991 a host of men and women who had worked in one capacity or another on wartime radar assembled for a reunion in Coventry. The occasion was the brainchild of Alf Cassidy, a Canadian ex-radar mechanic from Ontario who thought it was time the people who had worked in the very secret world of radar came together and celebrated what an incredibly good job they'd done.

Radar was such a dark secret throughout the war that it tended to remain so;

few people ever talked much about it, even after the war, and it was rare to meet somebody else who had been involved with it.

But Alf Cassidy thought the time had come to put a stop to all that and to try to winkle people out of the woodwork and give them a chance to meet old friends and talk over events of long ago.

The first reunion was a huge success. Alf brought a planeload of fellow Canadians with him, and there were other folk from New Zealand, the USA, Australia and South Africa. There have been two more reunions since then, and another is in the pipeline for 1996.

One of the reasons for their success was the fact that – all those years later – ex-radar folk discovered that they were among friends who spoke the same language, laughed at the same jokes and shared the same memories. There was a wonderfully relaxed, joyful atmosphere pervading the gatherings, and the general level of intellect was much what you might expect from such a carefully-selected trade as radar had been. (Radar mechanics had been in one of the top non-flying grades in the RAF, with radar operators only one grade lower, and the standards of education and of integrity were very demanding.)

I think we had tended to take all this for granted at the time, and to some extent it wasn't until we all met each other again, more than forty years on, that some of us began to appreciate what an exceptional bunch we really were, and how clever the RAF had been to pick us all out of the common herd so discerningly!

There were books on radar to be bought at the reunions, and people began to understand and appreciate the broad canvas which many had never really known about, and of which each of them had formed only a tiny but vital part.

In fact, many books have been written about the radar war-within-a-war which was fought with such intensity, and fascinating books a lot of them are. But nobody, so far, has written a book telling it the way it was from the point of view of the people who were actually *doing* it. They couldn't, because they didn't have the material.

But we have it now. We have it from some of the backroom boys who were quietly boffining away throughout the war, inventing, adapting and perfecting the radars, and at the same time trying to put a spanner in the works of enemy radars. And we have it from those clever mechanics who were servicing the hardware, and from the operators who twiddled the knobs – mostly on lonely, inhospitable hilltops all over Britain. And we have it from the chaps who learned how to fold up the aerials, pack them on the backs of lorries and take them overseas – to the Middle East, the Far East and eventually to Europe in the wake of the invasion forces.

We have it from ex-WAAFs who – some straight from school – had to buckle to and learn all about cathode ray tubes and goniometers and sine waves and 'trips to fils' and many more strange, scientific mysteries.

Some of the memories from some of these people come crowding back within the pages of this book; and to link each group of memories, Colin

Latham has explained what each type of radar was and how it was used. Who better than he to do it? He was an instructor at No. 9 Radio School, Yatesbury, and after the war had a distinguished career with Marconi Radar Systems, retiring as Chief Engineer, Airspace Control Division.

So let Colin instruct us again. And let's read the stories told by the radar bods of fifty years ago.

Introduction: Radar and the RAF

The word 'radar', coined in America during the Second World War, is now firmly established in many languages and has become truly international. This is not inappropriate since, in common with many scientific advances, the concept of radar – though far less its practical realization – arose at more or less the same time in different parts of the world. The term is an acronym from *RA*dio *D*irection *A*nd *R*anging, and the palindromic form of the word gives a clue to the essential process of the reflection of radio waves.

Thus radar, as it is commonly understood, is a technique for detecting and determining the position of a distant object by means of reflected radio waves.

Starting with the work of James Clerk Maxwell, a Scottish physicist, in the nineteenth century, the phenomenon of radio-wave reflection has been observed throughout the history of radio communication. Some experimenters merely regarded it as a nuisance when it interfered with their work, while others, perhaps the more adventurous, attempted to exploit it. Notable among these was Christian Hülsmeyer, a talented German engineer, who in 1904 patented his Telemobiloscope – a form of obstacle-detector having both a radio transmitter and receiver. It was to be carried on board ship and arranged to ring an alarm bell if reflected signals should indicate an unseen obstacle. This was a brave attempt at such an early stage, but evidently, despite his efforts, trials failed to convince ship-owners of its practical value.

Marconi, lecturing in New York in 1922, said he had noticed the effects of reflection of radio waves by objects miles away, and he speculated that by the design of suitable equipment the presence of ships could be revealed in fog or thick weather. And the French liner *Normandie*, famous for luxury travel in the 1930s, was fitted with a radio obstacle-detector to guard against possible collision in poor visibility.

All these were steps in the direction of radar, but there was to be far more to it than mere obstacle-detection. Interception of a suspect aircraft's track would not only require accurate and frequent plots of range, bearing and height, but positive identification as well.

The technical literature places on record several radar-like experiments, with varying degrees of success, in Britain, America and other countries in the interwar years, but most petered out through lack of financial support or interest from the military authorities. Only the Germans, it seems, took it at all seriously as part of their determined re-armament programme, though not without some problems, since they appear not to have enjoyed the close and at times informal user–industry cooperation so characteristic of Britain.

By 1934, when a few alert-minded individuals in the British government took serious note of Germany's re-armament and determined to improve Britain's early-warning capability in case of air attack, we were fortunate in having a flourishing radio industry. Commercial radio services were well established, and domestic radio had come a long way from the early days of the BBC in the 1920s, when rudimentary receivers, many of them home-built with only slight technical knowledge, were much used and proudly displayed in homes throughout the land. A wide variety of well-designed radio receivers had become available from a large and professional radio manufacturing industry, and the world's first high-definition television service was soon to open and serve the London area from Alexandra Palace. Intercontinental radio communication by short-wave radio was highly developed.

With this level of proven technology to hand and war clouds gathering over Europe, it was natural to seek a radio solution to the feared threat of attack by German bombers. Little faith could be placed in our existing early-warning devices – feeble sound-locators which had to rely, unrealistically, upon a quiet environment and at best gave only slow and general warning with no positional data.

Perhaps enough radio-frequency power could be generated and directed at intruding aircraft to stop them – even to form a 'death ray'? When that question was put to the scientists who would know – at the Radio Research Laboratory, Slough – the answer was firmly negative; but, as will be seen, it triggered the development of radar.

Thus, while Britain entered the war with an air force numerically far weaker than Germany's, she possessed a unique defensive organization. Efficient early warning would minimize the need for standing fighter patrols and conserve our precious men and machines for the most effective response.

Radar was to serve all three branches of the armed forces in the war. Following the initial pre-war development of basic radar equipment at Bawdsey Research Station, near Felixstowe, development teams were set up near Swanage (TRE),[1] Christchurch (ADEE)[2] and Portsmouth (HM Signals School). Although these separate establishments catered respectively for the special requirements of the RAF, the Army and the Navy, much cross-fertilization of ideas took place, and in some cases equipment first conceived for the use of one service found application in another.

Each service benefited from radar, but none more than the RAF. Radar proved a vital factor in the Battle of Britain and in the nightfighting that followed; it aided Coastal Command in the battle against U-boats in the Atlantic, and the many radar-like navigational aids and beacons transformed the

1 Telecommunications Research Establishment at Worth Matravers near Swanage (transferred to Malvern mid-1942).

2 Air Defence Experimental Establishment, later ADRDE (Air Defence Research and Development Establishment) at Christchurch (transferred to Malvern in 1942).

accuracy with which targets could be pinpointed for bombing and supply dropping.

To cope with all this new technology, the RAF needed to expand. New operational skills had to be acquired, both in the air and on the ground, and unprecedented levels of technical backup brought to bear on the vast number of new installations. Priority was given to the recruitment of technical personnel and to training in electronics.

Work on radar in wartime presented many challenges, both in the air and on the ground, at home and overseas. A great spirit of common purpose was engendered among those concerned, irrespective of their rank or seniority. In the following pages an attempt has been made to convey the atmosphere of those remarkable times by describing the workings of the main RAF equipments – with some emphasis on the ground side – and through a variety of personal reminiscences.

CHAPTER ONE

The Zeppelin Spying Mission, 1939

Len Dobson, *Radar Operator during the early days of RDF at Douglas Wood*:

In 1935 I joined the Boy Entrants scheme of the RAF and did a wireless operators' course at Cranwell, from where I was posted to No. 8 Flying Training School, Montrose.

In April of 1939 I received a posting to an Air Ministry Experimental Station at Douglas Wood, about 10 miles north of Dundee, where we were billeted in Carnoustie. Douglas Wood was one of the new RDF stations, and it was so secret that nothing was available in writing regarding the operation of the station. I just had to obtain information from the airmen already there.

Len Dobson

At Montrose we had been using long wire aerials between poles about 80 ft high, but at Douglas Wood there were four wooden masts with dipole aerials approximately 100 in long (a quarter of the wavelength of

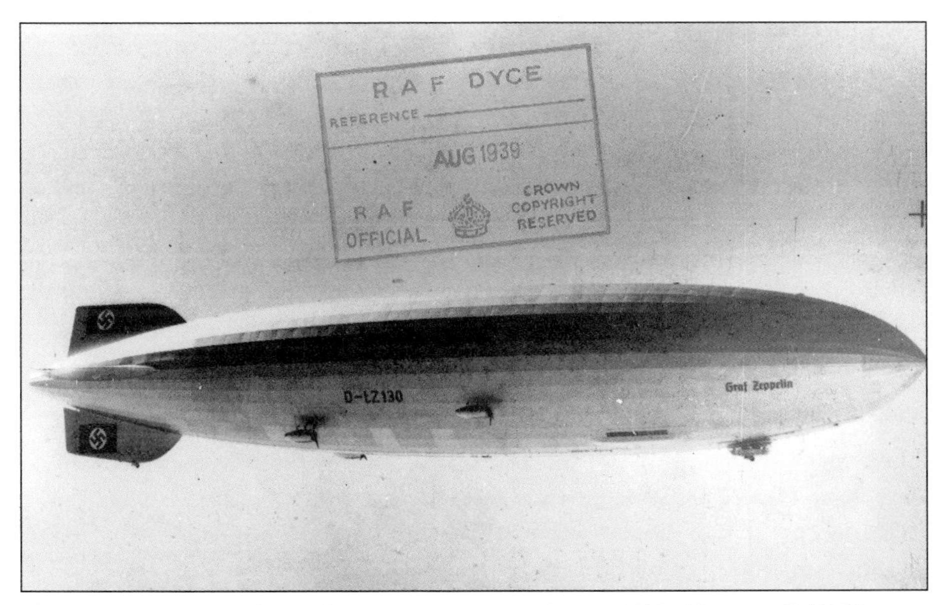

The LZ130 Graf Zeppelin on her spying mission in August 1939. (Courtesy RAF Museum, Hendon)

around 10 m). Aerials at 80 and 240 ft with sensing reflectors were fed into a temporary wooden hut with some sandbags around it and connected to a type of receiver I had never seen before – an RF5, which provided a visual indication on a cathode ray tube (CRT) of distance, bearing and height of aircraft flying up to approximately 100 miles away.

At Montrose I had dealt only with aural signals; the first time I was taken into the receiver hut I thought it contained television equipment, and I expected to see a picture. It was very disappointing when all we saw was a horizontal line on the cathode ray tube!

The ground wave of the transmitter (Tx) appeared at the start of the timebase on the receiver (Rx) tube, causing a downward deflection of the trace, as did an aircraft (though with a smaller deflection). In that part of the east coast there were very few aircraft flying, and it was quite an occasion when we reported a flight of three aircraft one day.

Some 50 yards away there was another wooden hut close to another 240 ft mast, and this contained an MB1 transmitter connected to a temporary transmitting array on the mast. This transmitter was gradually brought on air, and as far as I can recall, was some 400 kw on full power, which was considerably more than I'd been accustomed to at Montrose.

In those early days we understood RDF to stand for 'reflected direction finding'. Previously, when I had been on wireless, there had been a method of direction-finding on high frequency known as 'Huff Duff', which required the cooperation of both an air operator and a ground operator, and was often out of range at 35 miles.

As we were all wireless operators, none of us had been trained on maintenance. But we just had to get on with it, as it was absolutely essential that the equipment be kept in operation to give early warning to our aircraft and enable them to investigate any strange aircraft approaching our shores. It wasn't until the summer that a wireless operator mechanic was posted in.

Some 500 yards away, in a separate compound, were the transmitter masts – some 360 ft high and constructed of strong steel latticework. In April 1939, one-and-a-half masts had been completed, gradually increasing to four during the summer. I remember going over to the Tx site and trying to lift some of the steel lengths, but I couldn't move them. On a clear day I would sometimes climb the transmitter or receiver masts, and I'm sure I could see as far as East Lothian.

The Flight of the Zeppelin

There came a memorable day on Thursday 3 August 1939. I had just come on duty when I saw what I felt sure was a response at over 120 miles, bearing almost exactly on our line of shoot – our best transmission direction, which was 114°.

The plot was passed to Headquarters Fighter Command (HQFC) at Stanmore, who asked us to keep plotting. The response came slowly towards us and appeared to be moving at about 60 m.p.h. What was it? HQFC told us nothing, but asked us to keep passing positions. When asked how many aircraft, I had to say between 50 and 100. I'd never seen such a huge response.

With the situation in Europe as it was in 1939, could this be an invasion fleet with protective balloons above it? And why was it coming directly towards us, and why was it moving so slowly? By 1430 hours it was quite near the Bellrock Lighthouse and must have been visible to the lighthouse keepers, but of course we had no contact with them.

Then the response appeared to change course and start to move in a direct line towards the next RDF station – Schoolhill. At about 1500 hours it changed course again and proceeded in a north-easterly direction parallel with the Aberdeenshire coast. Then gradually the response faded.

I was on duty until 2130 hours on 3 August, and at about 2100 this large response appeared again about 100 miles to the north-east, coming down almost due south. Plots were again passed regularly to HQFC, and it was only the next day that they confirmed it had been the Graf Zeppelin (later, this was identified as Zeppelin LZ130) and they were sure it had been trying to find out the purpose of the tall masts which had appeared all down the east coast.

Unknown to us, the people in the village of Muchalls had seen the airship some 8 miles off the coast, and the information was telephoned to the HQ of the Royal Auxiliary Air Force at Dyce, who had despatched a Magister aircraft to investigate and take photographs. The pilot had apparently also decided to loop the loop round the airship.

It's astonishing in retrospect to realize that there were only six of us at Douglas Wood working a twenty-four-hour watch system and responsible for early-warning cover for about a hundred miles of coastline while the Germans were overrunning one European country after another. I can recall early IFF (Identification, Friend or Foe) experiments being carried out between Leuchars and Douglas Wood, with boffins arriving in September 1939 to test out new ideas, such as using red, yellow and blue filters[1] together to enable us to see echoes at Dunkirk through 'railings' (see Glossary) and sine wave interference.

BACKGROUND TO LEN DOBSON'S STORY

Note: The following passage was adapted from 'I see the cat but he can't see me', C. Latham, *Marconi Radar Systems News and Views*, July 1992.

Len Dobson's first hand account of observing – by radar – the Zeppelin's journey up the English east coast gives a fascinating insight into the very beginning of the British defensive radar system.

[1] 'Colour Filters': the fluorescent screens of radar displays used double phosphors, differing in duration of 'afterglow' and colour, such that persistent echoes produced a colour different from that of transitory interference. Filters helped observers to discriminate between genuine echoes and interference.

At that time – a month before the outbreak of war – Britain had already installed long-range early-warning radar stations, virtually as a continuous chain, from the Isle of Wight to the north of Scotland.

That these were not only operational but were feeding continuous plot and track data on offshore aircraft movements into centralized filter rooms linked to Fighter Command airfields represents one of the major engineering and organizational achievements of the century.

The whole integrated system had been achieved in secret during the incredibly short period since the beginning of 1935. Until then, no satisfactory method of early warning had existed, and memories of the bombing of London in the First World War, less than twenty years before, were still uncomfortably strong. Germany was re-arming rapidly; aircraft had become much more powerful and faster; something had to be done, and done quickly.

By early 1935, developing 'death rays' using super-high-power radio transmissions was ruled out, but detection of aircraft by reflection of radio waves was thought practicable. In fact, interference from aircraft had often been observed to affect short-wave radio and experimental television transmissions. Were these merely freak occurences, or, if properly organized, could they be relied upon?

Hence, in February 1935, the classic Daventry experiment was mounted.

Mobile receiving equipment with a cathode ray tube display was taken to a country spot – well away from local interference – in a Northamptonshire field not far from the BBC's Daventry short-wave transmitter. An RAF Heyford bomber was ordered to fly back and forth over a pre-planned course, while a small party of officials, led by Robert Watson Watt, stood by as scientist Arnold Wilkins demonstrated the effect of the passing plane on the CRT. As his calculations had predicted, reflection was consistent and unambiguous.

This was not really radar, since neither range nor bearing were indicated, but it was sufficiently convincing for a vigorous development programme to be authorized.

First at Orfordness, and before long at Bawdsey, pulse transmissions made possible the measurement of range, and directional receiving equipment – not unlike that already established for normal radio direction-finding – gave indications of bearing. Further work, using specially developed aerials, led to height measurements.

Thus it became possible to locate, in three dimensions, the position of aircraft at considerable distances. Ranges were improving all the time, and the building of Britain's first chain of early-warning radar stations went forward apace. Thus it came about that Len Dobson, one of the first RAF radar operators in that tense pre-war period of 1939, was engaged in surveying the air traffic around our coasts. War had not yet come, but it was in everyone's mind.

Meanwhile, the Germans had also been busy developing radar. The radar equipment technology of their pre-war designs may, in fairness, be judged as advanced by comparison with ours, in so far as they opted from the first for shorter wavelengths (down to 50 cm) and more directional aerial systems. In those respects, they anticipated the general trend of radar design.

On the other hand, the vast defence system which Britain installed, with its multiple radar stations, high-quality landline communications, filter rooms and control centres, was on a comprehensive scale quite unparalleled elsewhere.

The Zeppelin LZ130 which Len Dobson plotted was specially fitted out as a flying radio laboratory whose mission was to detect any British radar transmissions. That it failed to do so has often been commented upon, and many have speculated on the likely outcome had the mission succeeded. Would all our radars have been neutralized, either by attack or jamming, on the outbreak of war? If so, the Battle of Britain would almost certainly have been lost and Hitler's 'Project Sealion' – the invasion of Britain – put into effect. The course of history would have been very different.

The technical reasons for the spying mission's failure have been examined elsewhere, but the main conclusions may be summarized as follows:

The British radars of 1939, the type known as CH (Chain, Home) worked – for good reasons – on wavelengths of around 12 m. At such wavelengths, aerials are necessarily large – indeed, impracticably so for precise beam-forming. Consequently, they did not produce a narrow beam like a searchlight, to be moved about and directed at different parts of the sky, as did the German radars of the time, and as was soon to be general radar practice in the war. Instead, the CH radars had static aerials and operated as invisible floodlights reaching out over the sea. All aircraft within the illuminated area were potential radar targets, and echoes from each could be plotted in turn by the CH direction-finding receiving system.

With a continuous chain of such stations, and with the coverage area of each overlapping the next, the Zeppelin's coastal journey was one of total and continuous irradiation. Furthermore, since the 25-per-second-cycle pulse rate of CH stations was in every case derived from the common 50-cycle mains supply frequency, it appeared to the German technical crew that the radiation was some form of interference rather than a radar transmission.

This 'interference' was the more violent for two reasons: firstly, the signal received at the Zeppelin, so close to the powerful radar transmitters, must have been of enormous intensity, probably overloading the input circuits of the sensitive German receivers. Secondly, the CH transmitters had no harmonic suppression, and so the radiation extended over a wide range of frequencies. As a result, CH pulses were likely to break through no matter how the receivers might be tuned.

This was not the end of the German radio observers' difficulties, because the very presence of the airship's enormous structure caused yet more distortion of the powerful radar transmissions.

Furthermore, by pure coincidence, over in Germany a series of ionospheric probing tests was in progress to assess long-distance radio communication frequencies, and these happened to include the waveband on which British radar worked. Although the technical leader had requested the suspension of these tests during the Zeppelin's spying mission, it appears his plea had been ignored.

While it was claimed that the German tests spoilt the mission, it is questionable whether they would have had much effect, since the received intensity must have been very low compared with that from the radars. The airship was quite close to the radars but a long way from Germany.

From the technical viewpoint, it is easy to sympathize with the German radio crew. No doubt under pressure from their masters to probe and report on British transmissions, they were utterly misled by what they received. It has been said that, noting the repetition rate of the 'interfering' pulses, they suspected their source to be sparking and arcing of the British electricity grid distribution system.

And all the while, their position was being tracked by operators such as Len Dobson, and reported to the filter room.

Thus CH, the first operational British radar, may be said to have won the first round even before the war began! Although several CH stations in the south-east were attacked in 1940, Germany did not persist in her attempts to destroy or jam them. Presumably their potential – to be proved throughout the Battle of Britain – was not recognized.

WAS THIS THE DAY GOERING LOST THE BATTLE OF BRITAIN?

Sir Edward Fennessy

Sir Edward Fennessy, CBE:

On 3 August 1939 the CH stations on the Essex and Suffolk coasts detected a massive radar echo approaching from the east. Some 30 miles from the coast it turned northwards. Fighter Command then plotted it as it flew up the east coast to Scotland. At that time we assumed it to be the Graf Zeppelin LZ127, but we now know it was her sister ship, the LZ130, engaged in a radar spying mission.

Len Dobson gives us above a firsthand account of his own experiences in tracking this event, and this is followed by a précis of Colin Latham's very thorough research into why the Zeppelin mission failed.

The mission, planned by General Martini, Chief Signals Officer of the Luftwaffe, was to detect and measure the signals from the large radio stations Germany had observed us constructing along the east coast and which Martini believed might be for radar detection purposes.

At Bawdsey and Fighter Command, the flight caused considerable concern, for we assumed our CH stations had been detected and measured for frequency and other characteristics, and we concluded that their destruction would be a major priority for the Luftwaffe when war came. Bawdsey, we considered, would be the first to be dealt with.

By September we were at war, and we awaited an early attack; but none came. Meanwhile, we proceeded rapidly with converting the early CH stations – then housed in wooden huts with the minimum of protection – to more solid brick buildings with considerable protection. We also built mobile reserves in readiness.

In July 1940 came the Luftwaffe attacks on Fighter Command airfields and other targets. Attacks which, with the aid of the CH stations, Fighter Command intercepted with increasing success. But at 60 Group,[1] we awaited an attack which we feared would destroy our CH cover.

Then, on 12 August 1940, the attack we feared came. In the morning Dunkirk, Dover, Rye and Pevensey were all bombed, causing considerable damage, the heaviest at Rye and Pevensey. In the afternoon fifteen Ju88s dive-bombed Ventnor, delivering their full bomb load of 500 kg bombs within the site, causing much damage and putting the station off the air for several weeks. But thanks to the heroic efforts of the men and women who manned the stations, all – with the exception of Ventnor – were operating and plotting to Fighter Command before midnight.

Next day we awaited the return of the Luftwaffe for a second and finishing blow, which would almost certainly have put us out of action for weeks – an attack which would have denied Fighter Command cover from the Isle of Wight to the Thames, leaving a gap through which the Luftwaffe could have poured its fighters and bombers against a blinded Fighter Command. However, except for the heavy raid on Poling on 18 August, no attack came.

But why did the Luftwaffe fail to follow up its initial assault without a knockout blow?

Several years after the war I met General Wolfgang Martini, wartime Commander of Luftwaffe Signals and Radar, and we discussed both the Zeppelin mission and the attack on the CH stations of 12 August 1940. He told me that in 1939 he was very concerned that we had an operational radar system along the east coast, but that the negative results of the Zeppelin mission had eased his concern. However, when Fighter Command began to achieve such success in July 1940, he became convinced – despite the Zeppelin results – that we now had an effective radar system operating from the CH sites. He urged Goering to destroy the stations before launching Eagle Day, planned for 13 August (Eagle Day was to be the opening phase of the massive Luftwaffe attack designed to destroy Fighter Command and thus allow the invasion to be launched).

Goering was dismissive of the role of radar in the air battle but reluctantly allowed Martini one day of attacks. This was 12 August. Three days later, at a conference of Luftwaffe commanders, Goering ordered that as the attacks had not put the radar stations out of action, no more time was to be wasted in such raids. So the attacks we awaited and feared never came. And with the vital help of the CH stations, Fighter Command fought and won the Battle of Britain.

What might have been the outcome had Goering destroyed our radar cover?

[1] 60 Group RAF, located at Leighton Buzzard, was responsible for all ground-based radars and navaids.

Was Goering's order of 15 August not to attack further and destroy the CH system perhaps the reason that he lost the Battle of Britain? And what far-reaching historical consequences might have stemmed from Britain's loss of that battle?

I still recall General Martini's expression of disbelief when I told him that fully operational CH stations plotted the Zeppelin from the Thames to Scotland in August 1939. I am sure he realized the part which the failure of that mission may have played in the defeat of the Luftwaffe in 1940, for Martini was an able and astute officer who knew that the radar stations should be destroyed as an initial step in the battle, but he had lacked the evidence to convince Goering. A successful Zeppelin mission might well have given him that evidence.

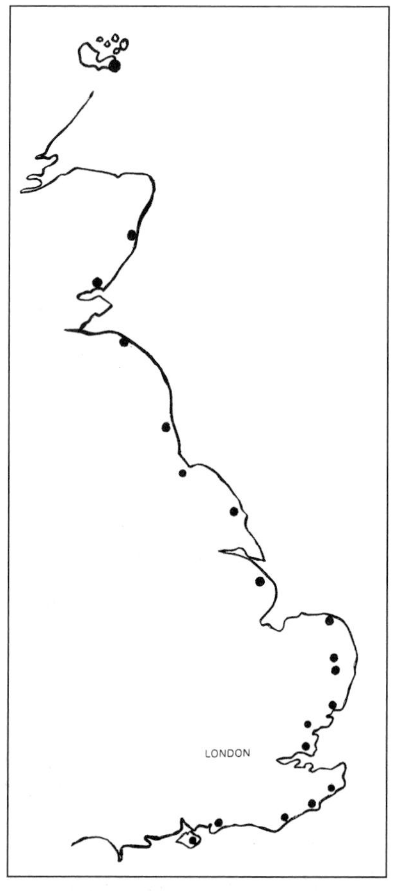

The early-warning radar chain in August 1939. (Stations may be identified by referring to the main map on p. 223.)

CHAPTER TWO

Chain, Home (CH)

AMES TYPE 1 – Air Ministry Experimental Stations Type 1 – were known as 'CH' since they were the first stations of the 'Chain, Home'. (It should be noted, however, that the general term 'Home Chain' was eventually taken to include many other and later radars.)

THE BEGINNINGS

The 'Daventry experiment' of 1935 has already been mentioned, but let us pay tribute to Arnold Wilkins, the scientist who successfully carried it out. But for his thoughtful approach and careful setting-up of the equipment, the CH programme might never have materialized. The term 'Daventry experiment' is misleading: 'demonstration' is a better word. How could Wilkins provide convincing evidence of consistent radio-wave reflection by aircraft using only simple, mobile equipment set up a few miles from the powerful 49 m broadcasting station at Daventry? Would not the strong direct signal swamp any relatively weak re-radiation from an aircraft? Had the transmitter been sending pulses (as would the yet-to-come radars), he could have discriminated easily between the powerful direct transmission and the comparatively weak reflected signal; but there was no such convenient aid, since the BBC radio transmission was continuous.

Wilkins's clever solution was to set up two receiving aerials, spaced about half

Ventnor, Isle of Wight, CH station where height finding was not possible.

a wavelength apart, one feeding directly into a sensitive receiver, and the other likewise but via an adjustable phase-shifting network. By adjusting the phase, he was able to cancel out the signals from the two aerials so that the oscilloscope connected to the receiver output showed zero signal. He then set the phase slightly off the zero point so only a vestige of signal showed – just enough to monitor that the system was alive. Now, when the test aircraft came within range – 8 miles has been reported – the relatively weak reflected signal, coming in at a different angle, produced in the aerials two signals with a phase relationship different from that of the direct transmission and therefore uncancelled by the phasing network. As a result, the reflected signal caused substantial deflections of the trace and positively demonstrated the aircraft's presence as repeated runs were made. The official observers were convinced, and immediate development funding was authorized.

THE CHAIN TAKES SHAPE

In the next few years Watson Watt's enthusiastic leadership, Wilkins's technical prowess and the efforts of a growing technical team achieved promising radar trials with the RAF. Pulse techniques were refined and contracts placed with selected companies. Starting with Bawdsey, twenty-one 'east coast-type' CH stations were set up from Netherbutton (Orkney) to Ventnor (Isle of Wight), all feeding their plots, by voice, into centralized filter rooms via high-quality landlines. Meanwhile, Dr E.G. ('Taffy') Bowen had joined the team to lead the seemingly impossible task of developing airborne radar, and good progress was made by others on radars for the Army and the Navy. The miracle had begun – and all in secret!

Once war started, the chain was extended westwards with more stations, slightly differently equipped, but of similar performance. Both versions were known as Air Ministry Experimental Stations, Type 1 or, colloquially, just 'CH'.

Note: Discussion of wavelength, power, etc., appears in the Appendix.

GENERATING THE RADAR DATA

To be effective in an early-warning defence system, a radar installation needs to interpret aircraft echoes in terms of distance and direction and, if possible, altitude. Distance and direction – known in radar parlance as 'target range' and 'bearing' – will, initially, be provided in relation to the station's own position; but to be of use in a remote central filter room these data must be converted into national grid references, with height as an added bonus whenever possible. In addition, identification – i.e. whether friendly or hostile – is highly desirable.

Our world has two characteristics of importance for radio communication and radar. Firstly, the atmosphere is an excellent electrical insulator, in which radio waves travel freely at very nearly the same constant velocity as in space. Secondly, the surface of the earth itself is generally a fair electrical conductor and therefore reflects radio waves impinging upon it.

In order to provide accurate information, an early-warning radar (sometimes called a 'surveillance radar') has to be checked and calibrated in terms of its ability to measure ranges, bearings and heights.

Range is not difficult to obtain with accuracy; it amounts to a straightforward measurement of elapsed time between transmitting a pulse and receiving its echo. Fortunately, the natural constancy of the velocity of radio waves can be relied upon; so accuracy is a function of the quality of the timing and display circuits. These may be checked, quite quickly and straightforwardly, by an operator or mechanic, using an in-built stable calibrator unit which provides accurately-spaced 'cal-pips' on the radar display. This has rarely been a problem in radar design. By contrast, the calibration for bearing and height accuracy is far more complex and time-consuming, involving extra staff and trials with aircraft, as described later.

Bearing accuracy can be more difficult because returning waves (the echo) may encounter contours, such as the slope of a hill, before reaching the receiving aerial. In such a case some or all of the received signal will be reflected from a direction other than the true one, and the radar's direction–finding system can indicate a false bearing.

The technique of direction-finding on CH resembled methods previously established in general d/f (direction–finding) radio work using the *radiogoniometer* (a device for measuring the angle of arrival of a radio signal, *gonio* from the Greek 'angle', more familiar in the words 'hexagon', 'octagon', etc.). The actual 'gonio', as the radiogoniometer was known by CH workers, was a fine piece of precision engineering (little larger than a big tin of soup) mounted close to the radar receiver. Within it was a rotatable pick-up coil placed within a set of fixed coils: the fixed coils were connected by long cables to a set of static aerials high on a mast, and the moving coil supplied the input to a sensitive radar receiver.

A control knob, with a pointer and scale calibrated in degrees, enabled the radar operator to find the direction of arrival of echo signals and hence their bearings. In rotating the gonio coil it was as if the aerials themselves were being turned. The natural pick-up characteristics of the aerials (simple horizontal half-wave dipoles) was such that little change in maximum signal strength occurred over a wide spread of angles, but the position of zero signal was quite sharp. Hence, in taking a reading of bearing, it was usual to 'd/f to a minimum', the pointer being offset accordingly.

Height-finding is more difficult still. Here we are concerned with the sloping path down which the echo signal comes from aircraft to ground. If we can assess this 'angle of elevation', if we already know the range, and if we allow for the curvature of the earth, the height of the distant target may be calculated. That sounds complicated, but on CH this was assisted either by reference to prepared charts or, especially, by the Electrical Calculator (see p. 21).

Unless a radar aerial is able to form a radiating beam so narrow that no appreciable amount of energy impinges on the ground, the radiation in the vertical plane will be affected by reflections. To form beams so constrained that this does not happen requires that the vertical dimension of the aerial – of whatever type and form, and there are many – is very large compared with the wavelength. Later in the history of radar development, this was commonly

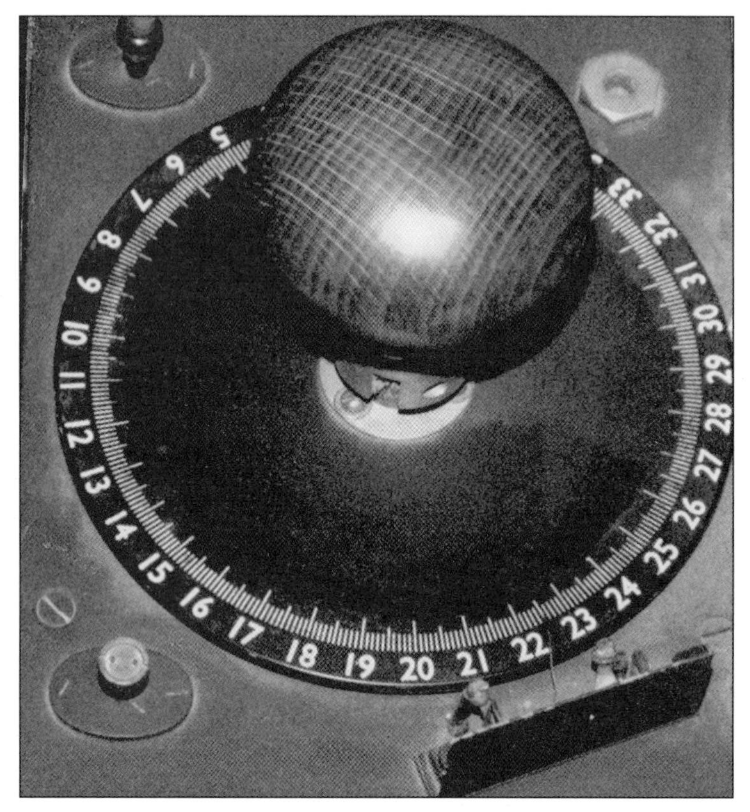

Goniometer knob and degree scale, conveniently placed for the operator's left hand.

achieved; typically, aerials measuring 20 ft or more from top to bottom were (and still are) used at 10 cm wavelength, making the aerial's 'vertical aperture' some sixty or so times greater than the wavelength. To get a similar ratio with CH, working on about 12 m wavelength, the aerial would have had to be well over two thousand feet from bottom to top – clearly not a practical proposition!

As a result, targets in the sky received from the CH transmitting aerial both the direct ray and the slightly longer indirect reflected ray. In such a case the relative path lengths change with angle of elevation, causing signals to increase or decrease according to whether they happen to be in or out of phase, and so, at any given range, the field strength varies with elevation. A set of 'lobes', with gaps between, is formed, their positions depending on the relationship between wavelength and aerial height above ground (see diagram, p. 13).

So far, we have considered the case of a transmitting aerial where the lobes represent areas of radiation; for a receiving aerial, lobes are formed in exactly the same way by ground reflection, but instead they represent areas of signal pick-up.

For a radar working at a given wavelength, the radiation pattern – i.e. the position and shape of the lobes – can be varied by switching to aerials at different heights. Further, through knowledge of the individual lobe patterns of aerials at different heights, and by comparing the echo signal strength from each, the angle of elevation of the target can be assessed. Then, knowing that and the range, height can be calculated.

That was the principle behind the CH heightfinding process. Alternative sets of aerials, both for transmitting and receiving, were available and could be selected at will, by remote control, from the radar operator's console. The comparison of signal strengths was done with the gonio; when it was switched to the heightfinding role its fixed coils were fed from receiving aerials at different heights, and the pointer reading at the position of minimum signal could be interpreted as angle of elevation.

It will be seen that a gap occurs in the radiation pattern near ground level; consequently, low-flying aircraft will not be detected until very close. The geometry of the reflection process is such that the height of the lowest lobe can be decreased only if the ratio of aerial height to wavelength is increased. With CH aerials, supported by high towers, little more could be done about aerial height. The eventual solution lay in the use of a shorter wavelength for low-cover radars such as CHL and CHEL (Chain, Home, Extra Low) (see Chapter Three) which would work in parallel with the existing CH radars.

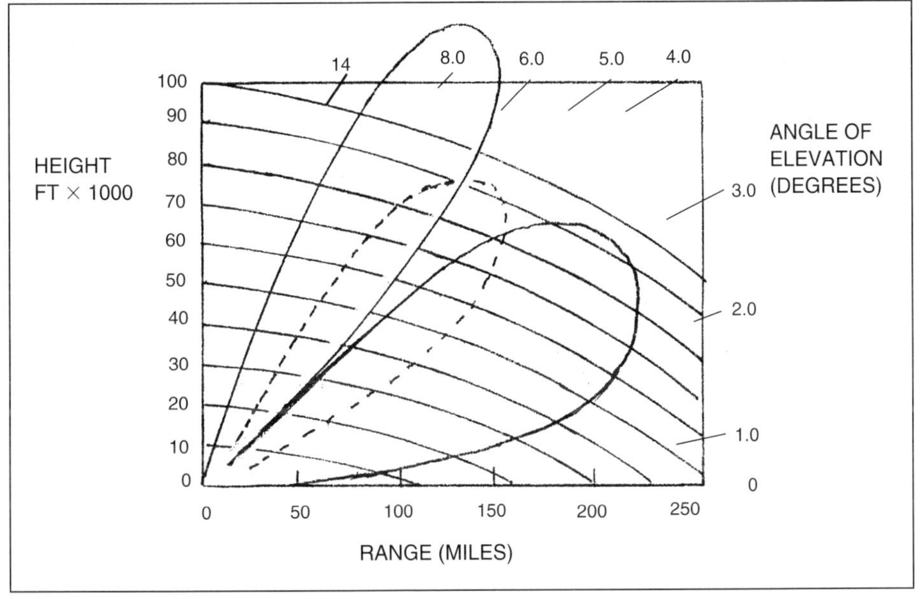

Lobes formed by ground reflection. The solid lines show the main lobes of a typical CH station as produced by the main aerial array at the mean height of 215 ft. The severe null at 5° was overcome by an alternative array at 95 ft, giving the dotted lobe, which could be switched into service as required. Neither array covers the lowest angles of elevation. For them, a greater ratio of aerial height to wavelength was the only solution and was found in the development of the shorter wavelength CHL and CHEL equipment. (CH wavelength, c. 12m; CHL, 1.5m; CHEL 0.1m)

CALIBRATION

To sum up, unavoidable ground reflection was both a drawback and an asset for CH. It could cause inaccuracy in bearings, yet it provided a means of heightfinding. This had two consequences for CH: firstly, it was essential to pick suitable sites, and secondly stations needed to be calibrated by aircraft flying at known bearings and heights. Specialist, roving calibration parties would attend to this when stations were newly commissioned, and at intervals thereafter.

For CH stations, normally sited near the coast, a flat or slightly sloping terrain, at least on the seaward side, was desirable. Even so, the reflective nature of the ground might well vary in different directions; hence the need for flight trials so that the accuracy, both of bearings and of heights, could be checked. Where necessary, corrections were noted and wired into the Electrical Calculator. The number of calibration flights would depend on the site, but usually many were made by an autogiro on circular and radial tracks at constant heights. Two-way ground-to-air R/T (radiotelephone) contact was maintained between the aircraft and the radar station during such trials. On the majority of CH sites, satisfactory performance in terms of bearing accuracy and heightfinding was achieved by these means, but it was not always possible. Ventnor, for example, proved unsuitable for heightfinding because of its surrounding terrain.

IFF

So much for the determination of range, bearing and height by CH stations; what of the identification of aircraft – friendly or hostile? The development of IFF (Identification, Friend or Foe) systems passed through several phases in wartime. (It has continued to evolve ever since. Nowadays, similar but much more complex systems are embraced by the term 'secondary radar' and are used to identify civil aircraft as well as military.)

It was realized at an early stage that friendly aircraft would need to carry a means of identifying themselves on CH displays, and the first solution was a simple aerial whose tuning continually traversed the band of frequencies used by CH stations. Each station, in plotting the aircraft, would see an extra-large response every time the aircraft's IFF aerial resonated with the radar's frequency.

This simple arrangement was not sufficiently decisive and gave way to one in which a small airborne receiver/transmitter gave out a pulse when it received CH pulses. Again, this was not the full answer: for one thing it was inconvenient because, in order to respond properly, the airborne equipment could only be set up for correct sensitivity after the aircraft had become airborne. But another and more compelling reason was that radars other than CH were coming into service on other (shorter) wavelengths. How could the airborne unit respond to all of them?

The solution was to design a common IFF system to be added to any radar and working within a specific frequency band, 157–187 MHz. CH stations, like others, would have a set of such MkIII gear. It consisted of special aerials, a small pulsed IFF transmitter (interrogator) and IFF receiver (responsor), whose output

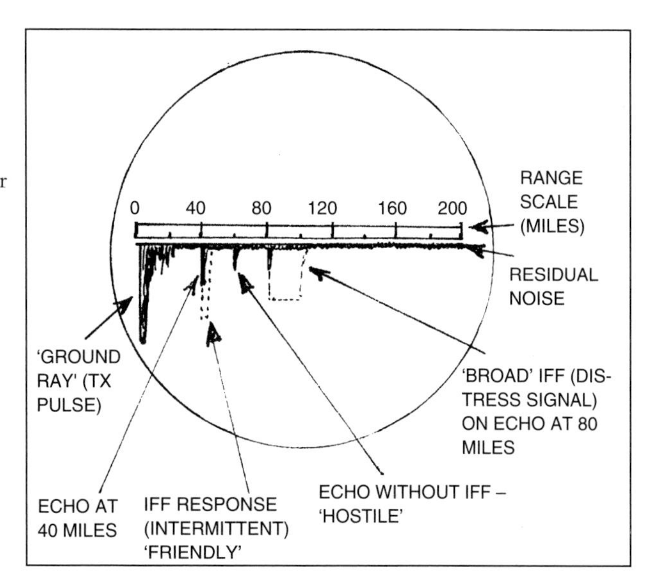

Typical cathode ray tube radar display, showing echoes and IFF responses. Alternative forms of IFF presentation included a parallel trace immediately above the radar trace, with IFF signals shown as upwards deflections over the relevant echoes. Nowadays, decoded SSR signals appear on the PPI display in alpha-numeric form, close to associated echoes.

was fed to the main radar display and aligned with the radar echoes to which the aircraft's identifying pulses referred. (See above for typical form of display.)

Note: Although the range of the IFF system needed to match the radar's, its transmitter could be relatively small since only one-way transmission was involved (see Appendix).

CH AERIALS

In an early conception of the CH system, enemy jamming was foreseen, and each station was to be capable of working on any one of four spot radio frequencies within the 20–50 MHz range (15–6 m wavelength). Stations were therefore planned to have four self-supporting transmitter towers, each with a spot-frequency aerial array, plus four towers for the corresponding receiving aerials. Steel was used for strength on the 360 ft Tx towers; wood for the 240 ft Rx towers to prevent the sensitive direction-finding dipoles being affected by a conducting metal framework.

However, it became necessary to improve the transmitting radiation pattern and the solution was to employ much larger 'curtain arrays' of dipoles and reflectors slung in the spaces between towers. By then the concept of four frequencies had become unnecessarily idealistic; most static CH stations operated on one or two frequencies within the 22–30 MHz range (*c.* 12 m wavelength), and the MRUs (Mobile 'Radio' Units) – used temporarily while some main stations were under construction – operated at around 45 MHz (7 m wavelength). Two of the new curtain arrays, main and standby, could be slung between three towers, the middle one being common to both arrays. Thus it came about that some CH stations had only three 360 ft towers, while others retained the four. In some cases the spare tower was used to support other and later equipments.

The foregoing applies generally to CH stations of the east coast type. These used a large transmitter with water-cooled, demountable, continuously-evacuated valves. When the chain was extended west of Ventnor, the use of two curtain arrays was becoming established, and most of the newer stations incorporated them as their first and permanent fit. These arrays were each supported by a pair of 325 ft guyed steel masts. For receiving, a pair of 240 ft wooden towers, similar to those of the east coast, was adequate.

East coast sites varied in area from 10 to 25 acres, but west coast sites were much more dispersed, generally with separate buildings for main and standby equipments, and totalled some 100–150 acres. Although the west coast stations also differed from the east coast type in having somewhat lower-powered transmitters (with air-cooled, sealed-off valves), they were similar in most other respects, and radar performance was generally comparable.

With its static aerials and low PRF (pulse recurrence frequency) of twenty-five pulses per second, it is not hard to see a hereditary link between Type 1 and the techniques of radio direction-finding that had been established, from the late 1920s onwards, by Watson Watt's Radio Research Laboratory in their work on the detection of electrical storms. CH certainly differed markedly from all later radars, which generally employed scanning aerials and much higher PRFs in the

A typical East Coast CH Station with four 360 ft transmitter towers on the left and the 240 ft receiver towers in the distance. (Courtesy of *Yorkshire Evening News*)

A typical West Coast CH station.

region of several hundred pulses per second. It is perhaps not surprising, therefore, if some latter-day technical historians should regard Type 1 as being merely a transitory design, soon to be eclipsed, and to proceed to question whether its introduction was wise.

Such a view ignores completely the immense urgency under which the chain was set up. CH provided a quick and certain response to the need for a reliable long-range early warning system at a time when no other was available; and it continued to do so, not only throughout the war but into the 1950s, despite its inability to detect low fliers unless at very short range. The considered value of CH is summed up in a document issued in 1942, 'for the information of engineers of Allied Governments'. The document reads:

> In spite of the developments in very high frequency and centimetre apparatus, the CH station, with its high performance on medium and high-flying aircraft and long range height measuring facilities, remains the backbone of the UK early-warning system and is not likely to be superseded during the present war. The MRU (Mobile Radar Unit) in spite of its bulky nature, has proved its worth in both home and overseas service and this apparatus has no rival as an early warning device for bases and defended areas overseas.

CH PERFORMANCE

Radar performance, as anyone who has been involved in flight trials will know, can be hard to predict or define with certainty because of the many factors involved. Some, such as site characteristics, are fixed; others – like efficiency of observers, state of maintenance of the equipment and type and attitude of target aircraft – are variable. A conservative assessment of average CH performance given in an official 1942 document suggests pick-up ranges, from a high site, of 130 miles on an (unspecified) aircraft at 15,000 ft, falling to 45 miles from a sea-level site on an aircraft flying at 3,000 ft. Another report of trials with a single Anson aircraft from a CH station sited well above sea level gives 120 miles with the aircraft at altitudes above 3,000 ft, falling to 53 miles at 1,000 ft and 18 miles at 500 ft. No doubt, many with experience of operating CH will testify to greater ranges on tight groups of aircraft and on particular occasions.

Range accuracy is quoted as plus or minus 1 mile at all ranges, and height as plus or minus 500 ft at medium ranges, but worsening at greater distances. Bearing accuracy is given as plus or minus 2° under 'normally favourable conditions' (but far less accurate on weak, long-range echoes).

To those who were called upon to maintain CH equipment (initially, re-mustered wireless tradesmen of the RAF and, from the onset of war, newly-recruited engineers and radio enthusiasts) it presented a totally new experience. Transmitters and receivers were larger and more complex than most had seen before, and offered enormous scope for individual adjustment and setting up to achieve optimum performance. Most mechanics took to the work with enthusiasm and relished their new-found expertise. For the east coast transmitters, familiarity with vacuum pumps and water-cooling plant was needed, but usually soon acquired by those with a feel for engineering. The receivers provided satisfying opportunities for careful and methodical setting up, using controls that worked smoothly and precisely. For those for whom vertigo was not a problem – or who painfully learned to overcome it – maintenance on the towers could be a daunting but thrilling task. Doubtless many, grappling with tools or test gear while just managing to hang on several hundred feet up, have reflected upon the irony of their official trade description: 'Radio Mechanic, *Ground*!'

A wide variety of CH station equipment included the following essential elements:

- a powerful transmitter, sending out 25 pulses per second, coupled to a transmitting array floodlighting a broad area in front of the site out to an effective range of some 200 miles;
- a sensitive receiver fed via a direction-finding goniometer from a static receiving aerial array of crossed dipoles (to detect reflected signals during the transmitter's 'quiet' period);
- a radar range display and a scale of degrees on the goniometer to indicate bearings of targets;
- alternative receiving aerials (installed at different heights) which, when fed into the goniometer, gave readings of the angles of elevation of targets;
- an Electrical Calculator to produce (1) national grid reference plots from ranges and bearings as seen from the station, and (2) target heights from combination of angle-of-elevation and range data;
- secure landline equipment (a high-quality telephone system) for two-way communication with the remote filter room;
- the IFF transmitter ('interrogator') and receiver ('responsor').

ABBREVIATED TECHNICAL DESCRIPTION OF THE MAIN CH EQUIPMENT

East coast CH transmitters Type T3026: four predetermined frequencies in the 20–60 MHz range; continuously-evacuated valves; pulse length 5–40 microseconds; h.t. 25 kV; peak pulse power output up to 450 kW. Type T3026A: similar but only two predetermined frequencies; h.t. up to 35 kV and output up to 700 kW; pulse width remotely controlled from receiver (on some stations, transmitters were modified for powers exceeding 1 MW).

West coast and mobile transmitters (prefixed MB – 'Mobile Base') Type T3018A (MB2) sealed-off, air-cooled valves; two wavebands covering 22–60 MHz; pulse length 6–9 microseconds and 12–17 microseconds; h.t. 24 kV; power output up to 300 kW depending on frequency and tuning. Type T3018B: similar but pulse width selectable from receiver. Type T3104 (MB3): similar to T3108B but with simplified control panel.

CH receivers (prefixed RF for 'Receiver, Fixed', or RM for 'Receiver, Mobile'. The Type RF5, as used on the early fixed stations was progressively replaced by improved versions (RF6/7/8) of the basic receiver concept. The term 'receiver' included not only the superheterodyne receiver itself but the master pulse timing circuits for the station (normally derived from the 50 Hz mains supply via an adjustable phase shifter and 'spongy-lock' circuit) and an integral display console.

The display was produced on a 12 in cathode ray tube (CRT) in the form of a horizontal linear range scan with downwards vertical deflection. Great care was taken in the design of the balanced deflection, shift and astigmatism-correction circuits, to ensure that good focus could be achieved – by careful adjustment of preset controls – at all parts of the screen. Adjacent to the display was the control knob for the goniometer, whose rotatable search coil provided the input to the first radio-frequency stage of the receiver proper. Sundry key switches enabled gonio and range readings to be fed to the Electrical Calculator for conversion to plots in grid reference form and to heights in thousands of feet.

The superheterodyne receiver itself often evoked reactions of surprise and joy when first encountered by those mechanics whose previous experience had been gained on more orthodox designs for wireless communication, or for domestic radio and television. The number of stages, the facilities and the extent of the layout were all exceptional.

One question often posed is why push-pull radio-frequency stages (peculiar to CH) were used? The answer has been given by Mr Sidney Jefferson, the EMI receiver designer who joined Watson Watt's team in the early days and who drew up the specification for the CH receivers, to be manufactured by A.C. Cossor Ltd. The design arose from concern about 'paralysis' of the receiver following the very high-power local transmitter pulse. By using a balanced input from the goniometer, the transmitter pulse would be damped on both half-cycles as the two valves of the first stage were alternately driven into grid current. Other design features guarding against paralysis – which, if unchecked, would result in the inability to detect short-range echoes – included careful attention to time constants in the circuits and stabilization of bias voltages.

The receiver comprised three push-pull radio-frequency stages, push-pull mixers (fed from a separate local oscillator), five single-ended intermediate-frequency stages at 2 MHz, a full-wave detector and push-pull output to the Y-deflection plates of the cathode ray tube. Three pre-set bandwidths of 50, 200 and 500 kHz enabled the operator to select that most suitable for prevailing conditions in conjunction with appropriate choice of transmitter pulse length.

Anti-jamming palliatives included:

- two narrow-band tunable filters within the receiver pass-band to minimize continuous-wave interference (Intermediate Frequency Rejection Units, spoken of as 'Iffroo', for IFRU);
- the Intentional Jitter Anti-Jamming Unit ('Idge-Adge', for IJAJ) against pulsed interference;
- the Anti-Jamming Blackout Unit ('Adge-Boe', for AJBO) against frequency-modulated interference;
- transparent colour filters over the screen to minimize or eliminate unlocked transitory interference;
- a loudspeaker – an unusual but most valuable fitment on a radar receiver – which aided identification of the form of interference.

The CH receivers, well designed and soundly constructed, were widely respected by those who used them. The operator's task could be uniquely satisfying, in that he or she had a variety of controls to hand and could exercise

A CH operator in action, with her left hand resting on the gonio.

personal skill in several ways, including dealing with interference and estimating raid strength. The first detection of a weak, long-range echo and the use of the best methods to enhance the response and develop a track was both gratifying and exciting.

THE CH ELECTRICAL CALCULATOR

Note: Much of this section is based on information provided by ex-Post Office engineers S.H. Sheppard and A.D. Sinclair.

Of all the complex and curious pieces of equipment associated with CH radar it is doubtful if any, in terms of mystique, exceeded the good old CH 'fruit machine' – the Electrical Calculator. To some extent this was because those who understood it – the CMEs (Calculator Maintenance Engineers) – were a select few who quietly and mysteriously managed to keep it in working order so that other technical staff rarely needed to become involved. The comprehensive RAF radar mechanics' courses, which explored electrical theory in some depth and covered all aspects of the radar equipment and its ancillaries in detail, glossed over the 'calc', saying merely what it did but not how! It was special, and most CMEs were ex-GPO engineers in uniform, as will become evident.

Providing due allowance was made for inaccuracies arising from ground reflections, a CH receiver/display system provided range, bearing and angle of elevation in relation to the station's own position. But at the filter room, where the outputs of many stations were combined, plots were required in the form of a common grid reference, together with heights in thousands of feet above sea level.

Such a data stream could be generated locally at each CH station by plotting ranges and bearings on a map suitably overlaid with the national grid and reading off the coordinates, by employing height-conversion charts based on the known transmitter lobe patterns, and by taking into account any bearing and height corrections previously obtained from calibration of the station.

However, it was realized early in the development of the CH system that such a workload, even with an optical converter to assist in applying corrections, would be tedious and cumbersome, and especially so at busy times. Consequently, the Electrical Calculator was developed to perform those functions automatically. Much use was made of telephone technology – relays and uniselector switches, both ratchet and motor-driven, as employed in automatic telephone exchanges.

The principle of the Electrical Calculator was conceived by Mr G.A. Roberts, a scientific civil servant, and the detailed design and development entrusted to the Circuit Laboratory of the Engineer-in-Chief of the Post Office. The initial production of forty-two machines, two for each of the twenty-one east coast CH stations, was carried out by the Post Office Factories Department, and a later order, put out to industry, covered the west coast sites.

Prototype testing was done by engineers of the GPO Circuit Laboratory, many of whom not only became responsible for installation but remained on site as permanent CMEs to maintain the equipment and to apply the necessary cross-connections resulting from station calibration. This action ensured that appropriate corrections were made for plots at all bearings when calculating grid references and heights. The effect of the earth's curvature was also taken into account in height calculations.

Today, the job done by the 'calc' would be a doddle for a compact unit using digital computing technology; but its bulk was then a small price to pay for a unique and vital function that materially assisted raid reporting.

The electrical calculator.

Alan Sinclair *writes*:

Alan Sinclair

The first calculator was received in the lab for inspection and testing on 20.11.39 and testing was completed on 9.2.40. Installation, at Poling in Sussex, commenced on 26.2.40 and was completed on 20.3.40. With increasing experience, testing and installation times were reduced because on 21.6.40 the 21st calculator was in the laboratory to complete the east coast programme. The laboratory staff was insufficient in numbers to cope with a large programme and technicians were borrowed from other areas – telephone exchanges etc. Many of these became CMEs.

The prototype calculator installed at Poling was followed by Staxton Wold, in Yorkshire. Manual plotting and height conversion was used where stations were on the air before a calculator was in operation but once one was working, grid references and height were automatic. An extra rack was added later to cope with extended height coverage.

I did not become involved until early 1940 when I was one of a team of young (very!) men installing a calculator at Swingate, Dover. Later I helped install the High Street, Darsham (in Suffolk), calc, eventually becoming the CME there, first as a PO technician and later in uniform as LAC!

This is how the first CMEs were 'recruited': arriving for work at the Lab on Jan 1st 1940, about a dozen of us found a note attached to the 'signing on' book. The note stated that 'the following personnel will report to Air Ministry, Kingsway for enrolment in His Majesty's Royal Air Force'.

Having signed our lives away at our first port of call, we were sent off to Acton for medicals and then on to RAF Uxbridge for enrolment.

It was late afternoon when we arrived and the offices were closed – as were the gates behind us. We had to stay overnight and queue to make calls to our startled families who, of course, knew nothing about it. We were duly sworn in the next morning and returned home. We were made RAFVR (RAF Volunteer Reserve) and called up the following September (1940). We did no square bashing and were not even taught how to salute correctly. I suppose we picked up such 'etiquette' as was essential in the next five years!

Stan Sheppard *adds*:

Stan Sheppard

The Circuit Laboratory were aware that the project was coming along and I was 'earmarked' to undertake the work, put in the 'reserved' category to exempt me from call-up to the Forces and subjected to positive vetting by the Intelligence services. In due course I was given a DR1 pass for access to any secret establishment as necessary. I was involved in installations at Poling CH and a number of others including Netherbutton. Then came a period as a member of a checking party touring the East Coast chain reporting on tests before returning to the

Laboratory for work on follow-up equipment for radar, including CH plot transmission by teleprinter and mechanized ground-to-air commands for OBOE.[1]

Eric Dyson, *CME*:

Eric Dyson

I was first called up into the Army, Royal Signals, and had a very short tour of France (Calais and Dunkirk) as a radio mechanic, but was then fished out for this new-fangled radiolocation stuff, by virtue of my civilian employment as a Post Office engineer. We were called CMEs, which originally stood for 'Calculator Maintenance Engineer' – the calculator being the rather primitive electromechanical computer used on CH stations which worked out the true azimuth and height from that 'seen' by the radio waves. Direct and reflected waves reached the aerials of CH stations, and the reflected waves were distorted by the slope of the hillsides near the stations and thus the need for calibration and correction. The 'calc' whirred into action when the operator pressed the button, and was often known, particularly on southern stations, as the 'fruit machine'.

Later on, when GCI stations came along, they still needed engineers with the same sort of training to look after telecommunications, but these had no calc, so CME on these stations came to stand for 'Communications Maintenance Engineer'.

Many of the people who were brought in to work on communications and calculators from the Post Office remained on installation and modification work, travelling from site to site, and it was deemed that they could do the job more effectively as civilians. That way, they didn't have to contend with RAF discipline re movements, postings, etc.

But when they were left on a station on maintenance, they were then put into uniform. They lived on the B sites (domestic sites) and worked on the A sites (operational sites – the two sites were usually at least a mile apart) like everyone else, and it was pure luck whether one ended up in civvies or in uniform.

There were other trades in much the same position – transmitter, receiver, calibration and aerial parties, apart from regular Air Ministry and research establishment people.

FILTER ROOMS

The original concept of a plotting room common to several radar stations stemmed largely from the difficulty of obtaining precise bearings, especially at the longer ranges, from CH. With such a closely-spaced chain, many intruders'

[1] Not all such advanced projects were implemented: needs changed rapidly in wartime. GPO engineers made many contributions to radar, including CH aerial switching systems, central landline synchronization of pulse transmissions ('one-in-one' system) and circuits for Gee ground stations. Mr Sheppard was one of many civilians who worked intimately with the RAF, a situation unparalleled, we believe, in Germany.

tracks would be plotted – accurately in range but not so well in azimuth and height – by more than one station.

Thus, by means of range cuts and by combining and filtering the plots of several stations, the overall accuracy of data was enhanced before transmission to Sector Operations, Fighter Command. At a filter room the WAAFs, who placed the updated coloured counters on a large plotting table, were each in direct and continuous telephone contact with the tellers at the CH stations.

The filter room best known to many radar operators was at Stanmore, which coped with the busy south-east area. As the chain developed and the number of stations increased, it became impracticable for one filter room to handle them all, so several others were set up in different areas of the UK including 'Western', located near Box, Bath, for stations of the south-west chain, Preston for the north-west and Newcastle for the north-east.

Filter rooms also handled data from CHL and CHEL (see Chapter Three), either directly or via a parent CH, depending on the disposition of the radar stations plus, in some cases, visual plots from the Observer Corps.

Avis Parsons *(née Hearn),* **MM**, *Flight Sergeant, CH Operator and Instructor*:

[As told to Anne Stobbs]

Avis's life had an unpromising start. I doubt if anyone would have forecast, when she was a child, that one day she would go to Buckingham Palace to be presented with the Military Medal by King George VI.

She missed a lot of schooling through ill health, so the odds were against her ever getting into radar in the first place! But the early bird catches the worm, and Avis was certainly an early bird in the WAAF.

Directly after Munich, when she was 23, she joined the Auxiliary Territorial Service (ATS) at RAF Halton, near where she lived.

Avis Parsons

There were only five trades in all, and equipment was the only one offered to her. But in June 1939 the WAAF [Women's Auxiliary Air Force] was formed, and Avis automatically became one, since she was attached to an RAF station.

The Commandant's wife, Mrs Dacre, stood her up against a wall and warned her that at 4 ft 10 in she was short of the minimum height and had little hope of getting into the WAAF. Fortunately for the RAF, she was proved wrong, and Avis became a proper WAAF in March 1939. In August she had an interview at Halton, and they asked: 'Could you work through the night? Could you stand air raids?' (The latter was a significant question, as it turned out, but how could one possibly answer it?)

Within a week she had to report to Halton and from there was sent to digs in Leighton Buzzard for a two-week plotting course at 60 Group. She had no uniform apart from shoes and a shirt or two. From there she moved to Fighter Command Headquarters at Bentley Priory, where she worked in the Filter Room, moving the 'tiddlywinks' around. Air Chief Marshal Sir Hugh Dowding – from up aloft in the gallery – complained one day that he could see Avis's knickers. It is hard to imagine how he achieved this feat, from far above her, but Avis was deeply embarrassed when told. (Perhaps he wasn't called 'Stuffy' for nothing!)

Soon, in May 1940, they were issued with their proper uniform, although Avis's was miles too big for her (she weighed about 6½ stone). They had no drill training of any sort, these 'early birds'.

Presently, the Powers That Be asked for volunteers to go on a radar course at Bawdsey. When she arrived there, Avis was overawed. However, she passed, together with twenty-three other WAAFs, of which twelve were sent to Dover and twelve to Poling. They were the first WAAF radar operators on the Chain. At Poling she found only male operators and civilians.

(Watson Watt himself went on record later on to show his admiration and approval of women radar operators. At a press interview in September 1941, he said: 'Anti-hamfistedness is women's greatest attribute in war work, whether it is radiolocation or potato-peeling. It was impressed on me very early in life that men peel potatoes but women scrape them. There is the same difference in radiolocation. Women are clamouring to go into the front lines and it may be the women who will win a war that incompetent men have got themselves into.')

Avis moved into a new world. At first (in November 1939) they were billeted at Arundel Castle and waited on by a butler. In due course the civilian operators disappeared and reappeared in uniform; then they disappeared again – replaced by the girls. They were on a four-watch system, with three WAAFs to each watch. It was a terrible winter; both the Luftwaffe and the RAF were more or less grounded, and this gave the girls a chance to settle in, though there was very little on the screen.

Operating a CH (which Poling was) entailed three operators working at the same time: one on the set, one on the plotting table (passing plots to Stanmore as well) and one recording the plots. At that time each CH station worked in partnership with its own CHL, with all CHL plots being passed through the CH station, making heavy work for the operators. Later, when more telephone lines were laid, the CHL passed its own plots straight through to the filter room. Poling's CHL was Truleigh Hill, so Avis and her friends would wear two headsets at once and definitely had to keep their wits about them. They little knew it, but they had just six months to learn their trade before the Battle of Britain started.

All of a sudden, in May 1940, the screen began to fill. Until then, no one had ever seen more than about a dozen echoes at a time. They had to learn to work fast and furiously. For the next three months they worked at becoming highly proficient at their job.

One day they were told that Air Marshal Dowding was coming down to the station. The day before, Avis was chosen to demonstrate to him what they were capable of, and during a dummy run, she picked up a hostile with ease, d/f-ed it to perfection, tracked its approach, passed her plots, and the whole operation went like a marriage bell. Needless to say, the following day, she sat at the set with Dowding bending over her watching every move, and absolutely nothing happened at all! Not a vestige of a trace of a plane, just an empty screen. Poor Avis – it seemed nothing ever went right for her when that man was around.

Then, on 16 August, their 'parent' station, Tangmere, was bombed, and that same week Ventnor CH was attacked. (Poling at that time was such a tiny, primitive station that it had no facilities of its own, but used Tangmere's.)

On 18 August Avis went on the 1–6 watch, and they were told by the sergeant to make the changeover quickly. 'We've picked up a mass,' he said. There was a brand new receiver block which had never been operational before, but the sergeant said: 'One of you get in there fast and pass the CHL plots!'

Avis went. There was nobody in there but herself. She put both headsets on – one for Truleigh and one for Stanmore – and began passing plot after plot from one to the other. She was desperately busy. Suddenly, the telephone rang and the sergeant from the CH block shouted: 'Duck!' – codeword for 'Take cover.'

Avis said: 'I can't – I've got too much information coming through.'

'OK,' said the sergeant, 'I'll leave it up to you.' So she was not *ordered* to go to the shelters, but neither was any offer of help forthcoming.

By then the dive-bombers were approaching. Somebody came into the ops room – a civilian – Avis had no idea who he was. She simply passed him one of the headsets and said: 'Just repeat what I say, will you?' Suddenly, all the bells on the PBX telephone exchange in the corner started ringing at once. The din was deafening. A bomb had fallen close to the main switchboard and shaken the receivers off their hooks! But soon that noise was drowned out by the terrible scream of Stukas dive-bombing the radar station and the whistle and explosion of the falling bombs.

The operator at Truleigh spoke into Avis's ear: 'Poling – that plot is right on top of you!' Avis said: 'Well, I don't need telling that – the bombs are coming down on top of my head!' and went on passing CHL plots to Stanmore. By this time everybody from the CH block had gone to the shelters. Avis believes that if she had gone outside to head for the shelters herself, she would almost certainly have been killed. ('In any case,' she says, 'I wasn't really sure where the shelters were!')

In that moment Avis thought about her family. She had always been small, but her mother had often said: 'You'll never amount to anything, Avis.' She thought: 'Why run when you are most needed?' Yet the screaming of the Stukas outside was 'bloodcurdling' (her word).

Thirty bombers had dropped a total of ninety bombs. The receiver block was demolished; the roof of the hut was later found to be resting on the RF5 receiver itself (so it was just as well that the others had made for the shelters). One of the receiver aerials had been chopped off. When eventually an officer came in and ordered the evacuation of A-site, and at last she went outside, Avis saw his beautiful Lagonda car smashed to pieces. Avis and three other WAAFs were rushed down to B-site by a very senior officer with red tabs.

A lot of unexploded bombs had to be cleared away afterwards, and Poling went off the air for precisely two days. A mobile reserve was erected in Angmering Woods, in two big caravans, one for the Tx and one for the Rx, with a small 9 in

CRT screen instead of the standard 12 in. Avis says: 'It wasn't quite as efficient, but it filled the gap you see. There was a dirty great hole in the chain!'

She was on the 1–6 watch in there on 20 August. Finding herself with the headset on, taking the plots again from Truleigh Hill, she picked up another load coming for them at Poling, and this time she was frightened. Fortunately, they were intercepted.

The following January, Avis – a corporal by then – met a friend of hers who said: 'Do you know that you have just been gazetted for the Military Medal? I just heard it on the wireless!' Avis scarcely believed this, but presently the WAAF Admin Officer sent for her and told her that she had been put in for the decoration the previous November by the CO; it had been recommended by the CO of 60 Group and approved by Dowding, no less! And in March 1941 she went to Buckingham Palace with her mother (who had said she'd never amount to much), and when His Majesty asked her what she had been doing at the time of the raid, she replied that she'd been working on telephones. Nobody was to be told about radar – not even the King! (And in any case, it was perfectly true!)

Only five other WAAFs were awarded the Military Medal. Avis was later posted to Cranwell and promoted to flight sergeant. Her job there consisted of acting as a kind of adjutant to the WAAF officer in charge of radar training. Her duties involved taking parades, colour hoisting, etc., for which she had no training whatsoever, having missed out on all the usual drill. Marching in front of a squad

The party held at Poling to celebrate Avis Parson's Military Medal. Avis is in the centre.

one bitterly cold day, she arrived at their destination, turned round and found most of the squad had disappeared! As a drill sergeant, she wasn't a huge success.

But she was a huge success at Poling that day in August 1941.

Bobbie Martin *(née Roberts), CH Operator*:

I enlisted in the WAAF on 23 September 1939 as a 'Clerk, Special Duties', which sounded interesting to me. We were issued with a minimum of kit – respirator, service raincoat and a beret. I spent a brief time at Leighton Buzzard before going off to HQ Fighter Command at Bentley Priory, Stanmore, in the Filter Room as a plotter.

Bobbie Martin

At that time the Filter Room table covered only the south-east corner of England – presumably the area covered by the then limited deployment of operational CH stations.

About this time we obtained a little more uniform – a WAAF skirt and grey stockings. Gradually, we were given our full entitlement of uniform.

In the Filter Room I was receiving plots from Poling. In the quiet watches of this 'phoney war' period I learned a lot about Poling, and it sounded rather a nice place to me. From Stanmore, some of the WAAF volunteered to be trained as CH operators and, for this purpose, we were sent to Bawdsey. From there, in the last weeks of 1939, the girls who passed were divided between the stations at Poling and Dover, and I asked for Poling.

When I arrived there, the admin and living quarters had not been completed, so the WAAF were billeted in Arundel Castle. Here we lived in grand style. The food was marvellous, prepared by a Belgian lady chef: breakfast was laid out with dishes of all kinds – kidneys, bacon and eggs, fish – almost anything you could want. There were about twelve WAAF billeted at the castle and we had a sitting room in a circular tower which belonged to one of the Howards. It had a big fireplace in it, and we used to go down to the cellars with a large basket to collect logs and bring them up in a lift. There were Red Cross dances held by the Duke and Duchess of Norfolk in the castle, to which we were invited, always under the watchful eye of the housekeeper, who seemed to have some responsibility for us. We were expected to greet the duke and duchess during the evening, and always to say goodnight to the housekeeper when we went to bed.

When the camp was ready for us in the spring of 1940, we had to leave the castle and come down to earth with a bump! But with our numbers increasing all the time, some of us had to be billeted out in nearby houses, and I was in a cottage almost opposite the CH station. I was living there at the time of the German attack, and fortunately I wasn't on duty when the dive-bombers came. But Avis Hearn was, and it was she who continued to pass the CHL plots from Truleigh Hill to Filter Room and earned herself a well-deserved Military Medal.

After the bombing, we continued operations temporarily on a different radar, with separate transmitter and receiver aerials which, while pointing in the same direction, were mounted on different huts. This was achieved by someone turning the Tx aerial, keeping a meter at zero – quite a difficult task, winding the aerial turning gear and at the same time winding the old gramophone!

It was in August 1940 that a phone call from the Queen Bee[1] was overheard, in which she said that some operators were needed at Worth Matravers, near Swanage, but with the warning that there were some two hundred mad scientists there. A friend and I promptly said: 'Right, that's for us!'

TRE had by then moved to Worth from Dundee and the CH station had recently become operational. There was plenty of activity on our screens at that time, with the enemy bombing raids on the big cities which started in September 1940, including Coventry on 14 November. Many of the squadrons flew over us, and we could see them clearly on moonlight nights.

At Worth I first met my future husband, a TRE scientist, when he was busy fitting some experimental equipment to the CH. We were planning to get married and take a furnished house in Swanage when the Powers That Be decided to move TRE to Malvern! They also decided to move *me* to the Isle of Anglesey, in Wales. Typical of the way things happened in wartime, but we did get married, and in August 1943 I left the WAAF, after nearly four years' service, as I was expecting my daughter, Rosalind.

Anne ('Freddy') Kaye *(née Grisewood), Flight Sergeant, CH Operator*:

Anne Kaye

I joined up at Adastral House at the beginning of 1940. We stood in line for our medicals, giving our names, and when I gave mine, the girl behind me asked if I were any relation to Freddy Grisewood, who was a well-known broadcaster at the time. I admitted proudly that he was my father, and straightaway was christened 'Freddy', which I've been called ever since.[2]

Our interviews were pretty rapid – in fact, the whole feeling was that they were in a hell of a hurry. All they asked was who our parents were and what we had done at school: we were then told to sign the Official Secrets Act and divided into radio operators or plotters. Nobody had the slightest idea what it was all about (I had visions of going mad learning Morse Code).

After a fortnight's square-bashing, we were on our way to Yatesbury

[1] Senior WAAF officer.

[2] The girl who christened me 'Freddy' for life was called Joan Ellacott (now Mulcaster). We later met again at Cranwell, where we were both instructing, and after the war she came to my wedding. Joan remustered from radar and became a Signals Officer in Bomber Command. After the war, she had a most distinguished career designing costumes for films and television. It was she who finally tracked me down and we met again after fifty years! It was also Joan who put Colin Latham in touch with me, who persuaded me to dredge all this stuff out of my somewhat rusty memory!

in Wiltshire. It was dark when we arrived, so we didn't appreciate the loveliness of the countryside there until the following morning. It was a grand spot, but we had little time to enjoy it, as the instructors were in such a hurry to train us and get all the stations manned.

It all seemed pretty straightforward: sitting in front of a CRT and d/f-ing the echo, twiddling a knob which controlled the gonio until the echo disappeared; reading the range; estimating the number of aircraft from the leading and trailing edges – all taken down by another WAAF on the recording console and plotted by yet another on the big map. Not very difficult really.

We had only three weeks to get the hang of it, plus a very sketchy outline of the theory of RDF. They certainly were in a hurry!

Postings came through – Stonehaven for me (School Hill), in Aberdeenshire. This must have been a major blunder on the part of the powers that be, for when we arrived after a ghastly journey, with crowds of drunken sailors getting in at Edinburgh, they had no accommodation for us and had to billet us in a lovely hotel in Aberdeen! Unfortunately, they soon realized this was a luxury they couldn't afford, and we were all posted again.

I went to Rye, which was the greatest fun. It was still a very primitive station, with the Rx and Tx blocks just wooden huts, the underground blocks being as yet unfinished. We were being bombed quite frequently, and two WAAFs in the Tx were killed. (Luckily for me, I was in the Rx that day, and all that happened was a clock fell on my head! We all prostrated ourselves on the floor under tables, but kept on going, of course.)

After the bombing, we went underground, and the equipment was modernized slightly. It was exciting when the tube was jammed with enemy aircraft which all seemed to be coming our way. There were nights when nothing much happened and we took turns sleeping on the floor or brewing mugs of tea.

Radar got much more sophisticated later on, but not while I was at Rye; all that time we were still unable to tell the height of aircraft.

As the Battle of Britain raged overhead, German pilots were shot down into nearby fields and picked up by the RAF Regiment and brought to our guardhouse to be interrogated. Being able to speak German, I was often sent for to translate. These lads were in a shocking state, and their gear was very second-class compared with the equipment our boys had.

One day I was on sentry duty with a ruddy great Lee Enfield rifle outside the guardroom, when Nobby Clark, a Calculator Maintenance Engineer, came along and said he needed to go to Rye and would I like to come too on his 500cc Norton. He happened to be on a charge at the time, but was going to risk it as he knew the CO was off camp.

I got someone to take over from me, and off we went. Unfortunately, Nobby took one of the corners too fast and we had a spectacular crash. I went flying over the hedge but was OK, but poor old Nobby broke two toes and was carted off to Rye Hospital.

Shortly after this, I was posted to Cranwell as a corporal instructor. I wonder why! It was great being a corporal; the rank of LACW (Leading Aircraftwoman) hadn't come in by then, so I went straight to corporal from ACW/1.

Sad though I was to leave Rye, Cranwell proved even better, especially for a sports-mad person like me. There were squash courts, tennis courts, hockey pitches and a theatre in the college, so I was able to play and act to my heart's delight. The training was fun too, as we were now getting the conscripted bods who were a bit older, and had mostly been electricians, etc. They knew a damn sight more about things than we did, but of course they hadn't had the RDF experience.

It was a hedonistic life, and I adored it. The place was swarming with Canadians, Australians, Free French and so on, so there was plenty of male company for all the super dances. We put on a play called *Outward Bound*, which I thought was a very odd choice since all the characters were dead except for one young couple who were only half-way there! I played one of those, and I was amazed it went down as well as it did. Nowadays there would have been catcalls and things thrown.

I stayed at Cranwell for a year and then was posted to RAF Dry Tree, Goonhilly Downs, in Cornwall – super address and super station. By then I'd risen to the exalted rank of sergeant, with a whole watch to myself. As they were all blokes I had a great time, and they looked after me like brothers. We all became great friends and swam and played tennis and drank a lot of beer together and sang rude songs in the pubs.

To my astonishment I was made up to Flight Sergeant and asked if I'd like to join a team of three to go round stations and calibrate them. I hadn't the faintest idea what this meant, but of course I said yes. It sounded fun, as we would come under nobody's jurisdiction, and no kit inspections or parades, etc.

Without any hesitation, we were hurtled off to Downderry – another super station – and told to get on with it. Next morning we were issued with flying suits – lovely, I'd always fancied one of those – and told to climb the receiver tower! I was landed with the theodolite, which was strapped to my back. Up we went. (Luckily heights had never bothered me.)

We were supposed to vector on to an autogiro which was supposed to be circling round the station, and take readings which we passed down to our mates in the Ops Room. The WAAF Sergeant took the readings down as well, which we had to transfer to a map when we got below. And what did the Flight-Lieutenant do, I ask myself? I think he did most of the brainwork afterwards. It took on average about three weeks to calibrate a station, always depending on the weather and how many times our auto-giro pilots ended up in the drink (this happened regularly, as they were being flown by pilots who were resting after being on ops!) We were in touch with them by R/T, and some of the conversations should have been recorded for posterity. (On second thoughts perhaps it's just as well they weren't!)

One day we were up the tower on some Welsh station, and when it came time to descend, the WAAF Sergeant with me suddenly froze. She had completely panicked and literally couldn't move. Nothing would shift her. In the end I had to call for a hefty mechanic who came up, and between us we managed to manhandle her all the way down. She never went up again, poor darling, and we had to get a substitute.

While I was on calibration, I was asked to compère *Middle East Merry-go-Round* at the Criterion Theatre for the BBC! There were three of us – one from each service. Meg Merrifield was a Wren and Sally Rogers an Auxiliary Territorial (but really from ENSA, so Meg and I didn't think she counted!).

Once every three weeks I would go up to London and have a brilliant time compèring this programme. All sorts of exciting people came on it, like Richard 'Stinker' Murdoch, AC2 Ronnie Waldman, Arthur Askey, and loads more (I got paid £5 for this!). I then had to catch the milk train back to whatever station I was on and get back up those towers.

Somewhere around this time I had a short spell on GCI (Ground-Controlled Interception) at Exminster. I was there long enough to see what it was all about: how to vector your pilot on to the enemy aircraft. It was great fun. They used Mosquitoes for this, and as a special favour I was taken up in one to see how it worked. The plane was jam-packed with gear, so you had a jolly uncomfortable ride squatting on top of all this.

Then D-Day came and *Middle East Merry-go-Round* came to an end – shame. We, the 'cali' teams, were hurriedly sent back to operational stations to become radar ops again – I was sent to Downderry again (west of Plymouth) and put on watch under a Corporal Clayton, who became one of my greatest friends (I still see her, as she lives in my part of the world).

It was strange to be back on the old gonio again. D-Day itself was a fantastic sight, with the tube packed with a solid echo. There wasn't a great deal we could do, as it was all our lot going out, and hardly any enemy activity at all. It was more exciting to nip outside and take a visual on all the planes and shipping starting what we hoped would be the beginning of the end of the war.

After all the excitement died down and calibration had stopped, VE Day arrived and I thought it was time I did something different. There was a radar mech's course starting at Downderry so I joined that. I must have been mad, as it was frightfully technical! (However, I can still draw a circuit with flip-flop valves, condensers, resistances, and so on. Fat lot of good that's been to me!)

The course went on to RAF Thame, where I met Colin Latham, co-author of this book. I remember many happy evenings in the pub in Thame. But one day, in the middle of a particularly difficult lecture, a corporal came in with some papers in his hand, which he gave to the civilian lecturer. He said: Flight Sergeant Grisewood, you may be pleased to hear that these are your demob papers. You should report to 78 Wing forthwith!'

We had a splendid party that night. In some ways I was sad to go, but the war was over and it seemed pointless to go on.

Joan Mulcaster *(née Ellacott), CH Operator and Instructor*:

Joan Mulcaster

I joined the WAAF on 21 June 1940 at Victory House, where I met 'Freddy' Grisewood (now Anne Kaye); from here we walked – a great straggling crocodile of women – down Kingsway to the tube, en route for West Drayton, where we were to be kitted out, drilled, and allocated our trades.

When they doled out the uniforms, they had run out of the ones for tall girls, so I had to be content with a navy blue cotton overall meant for fatigue duties. And thus – glamorously dressed in overall, grey lisle stockings, blue shirt and collar, black tie, flat, laced shoes and a cap – I went before my selection board the following morning.

I marched rather self-consciously into a room containing a long table behind which sat what seemed to be hundreds of people heavily loaded with 'scrambled eggs' (gold braid). Actually, there were about half a dozen, but I felt very uncomfortable with six pairs of eyes boring into me, clad as I was like Mrs Mopp.

But I must have done all right, because later that day a WAAF sergeant came and announced our results, and I had been selected as a 'Radio Operator on Special Duties'. It sounded intriguing, and I was later to realize that this was the most interesting job possible.

After completing my training at Yatesbury, I was posted to AMES Canewdon, near Southend – a real RDF station! Shortly after my arrival, the war started to hot up: in fact, I was on duty when the first wave of enemy aircraft appeared on our radar screens and the first plot of the impending invasion which started the Battle of Britain was passed to the filter room at Stanmore.

There was never a dull moment. When we weren't on duty plotting enemy aircraft, we were off duty cycling to Southend to the cinema or going to local dances in the evenings. I celebrated my 21st birthday in the local pub there.

I was very happy at Canewdon, and it was a blow when, after only eight months there, I was posted to Cranwell, where I was to be an instructor. I was miserable! After the real thing, it was a terrible come-down to be manning a CRT with artificial echoes on it!

Before going to Cranwell, I had to return to Yatesbury for a four day course on instructing, and there I met my old friend 'Freddy' Grisewood, equally fed up. But at least we went to Cranwell together, and the social life there did compensate us a little. There was a station cinema; dances were held twice a week in an enormous hangar next to the college. The air cadets at the college were training for their wings and were forbidden to mix with us riff-raff; but they used to remove the white flashes from their side-caps, stuff them in their pockets, and come and join the throng.

I stayed for 2½ years at Cranwell, but the endless, repetitive instruction got me down in the end, and I decided to go for a commission as a signals officer in Bomber Command. 'Freddy' and I remained friends, and I attended her wedding in 1947.

Roy Smith, *Radar Mechanic*:

Roy Smith

At Stenigot there was another bunch of people in separate huts who would never talk about their gear – just that 'it was 7K'. We wondered why we should need two different lots on one site, and why should one be so secret. I didn't find out until I was sent for 'J Watch' training. Then I was posted back to Stenigot for three to four months and expected to keep my mouth shut!

One evening in May 1942 when I was sole duty mech in the Rx block, little was happening and the WAAFs were anxious to get spruced up for a dance that evening. Would I take over the tube? they asked. 'OK,' I said, so they promptly disappeared to the wash room. I started to get friendly echoes. 'Did Filter Room want plots?' I asked. 'Yes please,' was the reply. So I made a start and more and more echoes appeared. Hundreds of them! Everywhere! But not an operator to help! 'Just plot the four corners,' said Filter Room, so I struggled on until finally one of the girls came back and threw a fit at what she saw. But she calmed down, took over, and presently all was well. It turned out to be Britain's first thousand-bomber raid – made possible by Gee.

The station's line of shoot was in the direction of Hamburg, and this was valuable when we were asked to ignore all other echoes and plot a photo-reconnaissance aircraft for as long as possible. It flew over us at 30,000 ft, and by using the timebase length control, it fell off our trace at 346 miles (just short of Hamburg). We picked it up at about the same point on the way back, and I suspect this might have stood as a range record for quite a while.

Geoffrey Coucke, *CH Radar Mechanic*:
Scene: R Block, RAF Great Bromley CH – AMES Type 1
Date: Summer of 1942
Equipment: Receiver RF7

Geoffrey Coucke

During an unaccustomed stint one day on the receivers (my usual venue being in T-block) I observed the operator trying to track through a massive dose of interference, bravely doing her utmost without complaint or reference to the supervisor.

My experience on this equipment was minimal, but on quizzing the WAAF on the tube, I gathered that this problem was longstanding and that lots of eminent experts had investigated inconclusively. The supervisor confirmed this, and I suggested that some sort of action should be taken. The condition was intermittent and not much of a problem in a time of low activity, but I felt that it was unacceptable and, in my small and very ignorant way, decided to make my own investigations. But where to start?

As a mechanic, I first tried to check over all the controls and cabling which might have had bad or indifferent connections. It could have been easier for the operator to change to the alternative Rx, but the supervisor decided that she was happy to continue using the running one. (I later discovered that this would not have helped at all, and could, in fact, have delayed the eventual diagnosis.)

I hovered behind the operator to try to 'catch' the interference as and when it manifested itself (as I was assured it would do). For ages all was well, but at the hourly changeover of operator, I noticed that the trace-slip did occur a few moments after the new operator came on. What could this signify? She made no manual moves other than the usual left hand on the gonio and right hand on the range knob.

After a boring hour of nothing happening, a fresh changeover produced the same phenomenon shortly after the new operator took her seat. At least there was a pattern which I could get my teeth into. During the next hour I attended to other matters, requesting the WAAF to advise me should the effect re-occur. It did, for a few minutes once or twice during this 'dog watch' between 3 and 4 a.m. The operator and I both made notes of the time, including those of the changeover periods. The supervisor was meticulous too, and her notes listed all personnel entering and leaving the Ops Room. By comparing the two we had to come to the conclusion that the trouble always occurred at these times of entry and exit. No one came from nor went to the block during the watch hours, so it had to be an internal movement. So why did the Ops Room door open? The obvious reason was for access to the toilet. This was a curious find, and I suggested a test. I would make this trip and the operator was instructed to call out if the display was affected. This did happen, so we were getting somewhere!

I decided to turn the light on and off in the toilet. Proof was now indisputable – the interference came and went when the toilet light was switched on and off! This, of course, explained the changeover manifestations. The penny had well and truly dropped!

At first I wondered if the hanging chain was acting as a tuned dipole! Changing its length by folding it and manipulating the light switch failed to cure the problem, as did checking the wiring within the switch base. About all that was left to try was to change the light bulb, which I did. Hey presto! the mysterious interference had disappeared – for good!

The block had been built in the late 1930s, and the bulb in the loo was of the vacuum type, with a longish glass envelope containing a zig-zag filament set in a circle around a long glass rod. (This was a very common type of bulb before the rather more compact design which uses a coiled-coil filament.) I can only conclude that this bulb, when switched on, gave out some electromagnetic radiation, either on the radar frequency or on a harmonic of it.

In due course I learned that Wing had ordered the removal and destruction of all these old-fashioned Tungsram brand of light bulbs on all radar stations.

A year after my Sherlock Holmes triumph in solving 'The Mystery of the Trace-Slip', I was off to a rather more adventurous life on the Continent with a mobile GCI. This took me to Normandy, Belgium and Holland, with a nine-month stint on the Belgian coast, between Ostend and Blankenberge, where I found that Coucke relatives were thick on the ground (as they were in Holland), and I was able to spend lots of time with them, particularly in Bruges. Those were very happy times for me.

Johnnie Johnson, *CH Operator, now living in New Zealand*:

When the Germans tried (successfully) to jam our screens by dropping loads of foil strip ('window'), I worked out a method of disentangling the true echoes from the false. I was a keen type, and I'd found out that if one turned the strobe up to full brightness (yes, it did occur to me to wonder how long the tube might last!) and then suddenly turned it down, all the false echoes vanished, leaving behind clear definitions of the real thing.

Johnnie Johnson

And so we come to the great night of panic at Canewdon, when the Germans threatened an almighty whack at London. I took over my watch with an alleged 600 planes on the screen. *Every* CH station was recording this number (big flap at Stanmore) – all flying stations alerted. My screen was saturated by a very thin lined echo which just shrieked 'false – false', I would have thought, to the most average of operators. I turned up the strobe to maximum brilliance then down again – all the thin bits vanished and I very quickly counted the clearly-defined blips which were left. I came up with a count of twenty-four! My figures *had* to be passed by the officer i/c watch, and the boffins at Stanmore queried my minuscule figure and went on querying it – who was this operator who disagreed with estimates from all other CH stations within miles? Would the officer check, and so on. I just plodded on until the end of my watch while the mighty at Stanmore tore out large chunks of hair.

Eventually, as the night wore on, the figures were revealed – the Observer Corps (those poor, cold buggers out there) had counted fourteen planes (how they missed my other ten, goodness knows!) Yes, it was a skyful of 'window'. I'd probably get a medal, I thought. Or might they make me an Air Vice-Marshal? I might be called to Stanmore to give lectures . . . ?

Would you believe, that proved to be the last raid on England, or certainly on London – their swansong before they folded. I didn't get a medal, nor even a Mention in Despatches. I sulked on my next watch and kicked the set when I went off duty.

Ray Barker, *Radar Mechanic*:
Danby Beacon (CH)

My arrival at Danby Beacon, on the North Yorkshire moors, in the middle of the grim winter of 1941/2 was memorable. There were three of us heading there from Cranwell, and one – Percy Graham – had an Austin 7 for which he received

Ray Barker

permission and petrol to transport us there. On reaching Yorkshire, we found the narrow roads piled high with snow – higher, in some places, than the car.

After leaving Malton I don't think we passed another vehicle, and conditions grew worse. Eventually, we met a snowplough team who told us that the road ahead was completely blocked. They suggested another route, which we decided to take, even though we could already see the station's towers. This proved equally impassable, so at this point we made a momentous decision. We would drive across the moors in a direct line straight to the towers!

To this day I cannot believe how lucky we were to survive that journey. The car decided to blow an engine casing plug, causing clouds of steam and considerable loss of water. Emergency repairs were carried out with a penny and an eraser to wedge it in position, followed by handfuls of snow pushed into the still-warm radiator.

Eventually, we did arrive at the T-block side of the compound, and we then discovered a cleared road just about 8 ft below us! We had been travelling over deep, frozen snow which had even defied the Army's attempt to relieve the station!

We found a way down with the Austin and turned down to the A-site guardroom along a carved-out road signposted 'Jankers Pass', with station transport buried along its edges.

A very surprised Corporal SP (Service Policeman) wondered where we had come from, and directed us down to B-site, where the arrival of this small vehicle and its occupants caused a great deal of wonderment.

Danby had suffered a terrible winter; in fact, it was at least three weeks before we first encountered Poverty Hill (the official route to the camp). Transport to and from watch had proved very difficult for them, with watches having on occasion to remain on duty for long periods. I heard of people who had set off from A-site, walked round in circles for some considerable time, only to find themselves back at A-site again! It was the first time I'd ever seen snowstorms travelling horizontally, with such force that it was almost impossible to breathe. Sometimes it was necessary to hold a groundsheet in front of you or walk backwards.

We were introduced to the equipment, the likes of which we had never known existed, let alone been trained on. But it didn't take us long to realize what a wonderful piece of equipment had been placed in our care. And yet no one, not even the documents, told us how to isolate the Tx completely from the mains, with the result that one chap suffered a terrible electric shock (which also set his pullover on fire) inside the h.t. transformer compartment, which carried 440 V between phases.

Yet once we understood them, we became extremely fond of those transmitters; they were affectionately called 'Annie' and 'Betty', and they always responded to careful coaxing and sympathetic handling.

The receivers were more familiar to us from our Cranwell days. Only one of them was operational, the second one not having been calibrated. In some respects this was fortunate, as the machine had a most peculiar fault. Given all the tests, it presumably worked perfectly, but it would not receive an echo. Searching for this elusive fault was a pastime for all technical staff from the CO down. Then one day a signal arrived saying that the calibration party was due to arrive to put the set into commission. Bags of panic all round. I was on duty, and I spent the whole night in R-block chasing this elusive gremlin. After hours of work with the signal generator and oscilloscope, I at last discovered the root of the problem. It was nothing more than a single dry joint in the buffer amplifier. I was treated as a saviour by the CO, and I'm convinced that this single operation had more to do with my promotion to corporal than anything else!

Some time later, when I was on a mobile on the north-east chain one evening, there was a terrific gale which nearly blew the station apart, tearing the canvas covers of the GP wagon to shreds.

I later heard from a friend (Tony Convey, Canadian Sergeant Radar Mechanic) what had happened at Danby Beacon that same night. The curtain array, slung between the steel towers, was billowing out with each gust of the wind. To hold it in place, cables led down to each corner of the towers, and slotted slabs of concrete could be added. As the winds increased, Tony had added slab after slab to hold the aerial. Suddenly, a strong gust of wind lifted the slabs up to the top of their guides and they broke free. Sparks and static flew everywhere and he took off and ran for safety. He returned to T-block and switched to 'stacked array', which was attached to the tower. He later learned that the storm had knocked out most of the radar stations, but Danby had done well considering its very exposed situation.

One evening, Danby operators were plotting the return of our bombers from a raid, all showing IFF, when suddenly Middlesborough (only about 15 miles away) was badly bombed. This was the first intimation we had that the enemy had access to IFF.

Bobbie Baron *(née Whitelaw), CH Operator, and later Mechanic*:

One of the main events of my radar days was when, at Danby Beacon, I was able to re-muster from an operator to a trainee mechanic. The shortage was so acute that until there was a vacancy on a course, I was transferred from R Block to T Block, where my reception into that bastion of male supremacy was mixed, to say the least. I think it was agreed that I would at least be useful to make the tea and do the cooking on night watch.

Bobbie Baron

Their doubts were certainly confirmed on one of my first watches as an untrained mechanic; we had just changed transmitters, and I was given the job of gradually winding down the high voltage on the enormous valves of the one just taken off the air, leaving the other to carry on pumping out the energy. I can remember so well leaving the duty mechanic to deal with the frantic phone calls from R-block about the trace and echoes going berserk at their end and his desperate attempts to find the fault, while I dutifully went round at the correct intervals, turning down the little handles. Fortunately, I realized my terrible mistake just a few seconds before anyone else did and was able to start wildly winding them up again before they realized that I was working on the wrong transmitter and was busily putting the station off the air. I had to admit that the abuse which poured over me was quite justified.

I was delighted to find that one of the responsibilities of a mechanic was to climb the towers, checking on dipoles, etc. So one day I persuaded Freddie Smith, one of the mechanics, to take me aloft on one of the 360 ft towers. To Freddie's horror, I insisted on going right to the top, where I went out on to the platform and started to dance up and down in rhythm with the natural movement of the tower. Freddie was yelling all sorts of instructions at me, including something about a thing called 'resonant frequency', and when I finally came back to earth, he gave me a stern lecture about why armies break step on bridges and told me that I could have shaken loose all the nuts and bolts, causing the entire tower to collapse. (I had a feeling he was exaggerating a bit.)

I was eventually transferred to Tannach, near Wick, to start my training, continuing later in Downderry, Cornwall, and finally Thame, in Oxfordshire, where at last I qualified as ACW Whitelaw, Radar Mechanic (though still LACW as operator!).

Of course, by that time the war was over! All the hard work seemed a little pointless, but I enjoyed the training and did quite well, much to the surprise of some of the instructors, who still tended to think of the trade as a male preserve.

Workshop practice was the worst. Many a piece of dratted paxolin was hurled across my bench while I struggled with files, micrometers and numerous other shaping and measuring devices to obtain the correct results. Eventually, I learned to control all the tools with at least adequate efficiency and could wield a soldering iron with the best of them.

Wherever I was posted, I was always the only WAAF mechanic, as we were few in number, but this could be fun, once I had overcome the varying degrees of horror, amazement and disbelief from my fellow mechanics, particularly from some of those recently returned from several years overseas, who were still getting over the shock of finding WAAFs on radar stations at all!

One of the worst of these was a Flight Sergeant Cliff Baron, i/c mechanic at Danby (where I returned in late 1945). He was so shattered at being given a girl to add to his crew that he packed me off on leave at once! But he got over the shock eventually and eighteen months later, we were married.

Knowler Edmonds, *CH Operator*:

Personnel on small radar stations, both technical and non-technical, became attuned to the special, uneven rhythm of watchkeeping. Meal times and sleeping times were vital elements in sustaining crews in their preparation for the irregular hours of duty and off-duty.

The job of operating a sophisticated radio weapon in defence of one's country had its added piquancy, and the enthusiasm of radar watch crews everywhere created a special bond of fellowship and comradeship, perhaps unequalled in other RAF units.

A change of watch in R-block at four primary times each day was achieved with minimum fuss and with professional efficiency. In a CH crew, the first and most important position was that of the operator on the CRT; so the incoming operator would stand by and receive a thorough briefing on the location of aircraft traffic currently being observed and reported to Stanmore Filter Room. To help in visualizing the activity, a mental picture was gained from studying the plotting table, where routes and aircraft identity tags were memorized.

Knowler Edmonds, with fiancée Gretta Lovelady

The incoming operator came in wearing his or her own headset, so the release of one jack-plug and the installation of the new one took but a second. The new operator would inform Stanmore of the changeover, then proceed with locating and calling the echoes, followed immediately by punching two buttons designating the goniometer setting – all in a smooth, unbroken succession.

Meanwhile, other crew members were taking their places at the all-encompassing, long console, consulting their outgoing colleagues as to the 'state of play', and jack-plugging their headsets into the internal line system. By this means the map plotters, the recorder and the CRT operator could all speak to each other, and to Stanmore when needed. Generally, the only two voices the plotters at Stanmore wanted to hear were those of the operator and the plotter for a full, all-round picture of flying activity in the area. A fourth seat at the console was occupied by the supervisor, who controlled the whole performance of the watch and also had a direct telephone line to a supervisor at Stanmore for emergencies.

Thus, the departure of the outgoing watch was hardly noticed!

The 'Calc'

One of the little miracles for its day in the midst of this hive of bustle and pursuit was the 'computing' of a map location indicator brought into use by the operator's two buttons pressed after a goniometric setting had been achieved. The operator would locate the echo, identifying whether hostile or friendly (IFF), d/f it (by tuning it down to zero with the gonio), then by pressing the buttons would display a map grid reference on a light-board mounted in the console at the head of the plotter's table. The board gave a range and azimuth as a four-figure grid reference to be found on the multi-squared map, when a chinagraph pencil would be used to mark the spot, with an identity number alongside. Subsequent plots were observed and written in the same way, each plot joined by a line, thus pinpointing the route the aircraft was taking, together with any changes in elevation.

This sequence of information was written down by the recorder, using specially detailed forms, on every occasion confirming the action the station had taken. All this progression was also dictated to Stanmore, who displayed the information with marked counters on their larger map, thus giving an overall picture of activity to flight commanders observing from an atrium above.

Usually, an operator was relieved from CRT duty after one hour (or less if the frenzied nature and activity of aircraft traffic became overwhelming). The new operator would be familiar with map locations and would quickly identify echoes, locating them and attempting to separate them for identification, his or her whole attention being focused on the trace to the exclusion of all else in the room. It was mentally draining, and the hour off the set was often used for a quick sleep (on the floor or the first-aid stretcher!). Cups of tea or coffee were welcome revivers before it was time to return to the Ops Room, and on night watches eggs and bacon or some such food were fried up (known as the 'tea swindle').

Bill Badcock, *CH Radar Mechanic, Orkney and Shetlands*:

Bill Badcock

We left Aberdeen that cold and foggy afternoon in the late autumn of 1940, bound for Lerwick, in the Shetlands. The vessel was the *Ben McCree*, a ferryboat that normally plied between Liverpool and the Isle of Man in holiday times.

It was quite unsuitable for a North Sea journey in a storm. It rolled like a barrel and made about 5–7 knots at best. I believe there were about two hundred servicemen on board, and there was no accommodation except the decks. As the storm got worse, water poured on deck and we were squashed into the lower deck. I finished up as near the engine room as I could get, for warmth and dryness. It was the most horrific journey, and many times during the long and frightening night I thought that if we sank and drowned we'd all be better off. We had iron rations – corned beef sandwich, chocolate and biscuits – but I don't think many of us could eat. The crew made some tea, but most of it spilt before it could be drunk.

We had to stand off Lerwick most of the day before the weather cleared enough to enable us to proceed to Balta Sound. The unloading of the essential equipment was number one priority – cooking equipment, beds and bedding, two or three vehicles and all the spares. We 'borrowed' a farm gate to use as an improvised sledge to move crates and boxes, all of which had to be manhandled.

The domestic site had Nissen huts but little else, and these were just as the riggers and builders had left them. I noticed that they were all anchored with several cables over the top, which were most definitely needed, as we found later when gales reached 100–120 m.p.h. for hours on end. It was quite impossible to walk upright when wearing a sheepskin coat!

Towards Christmas (though I don't think there was one that year) we had very short days. It was dark from 4 p.m. to 10 a.m. – high winds and snow. The locals said they never had much snow, and that we must have brought it!

We radar chaps were glad to have much to do in getting our CH station on the air; the non-technical chaps nearly died of boredom; in fact, one went berserk and had to be sent back. (Others tried this, without success.)

With the station on the air and the watch system going smoothly, we settled down and the first enemy action was noted. Daily, at first light, a German Condor flying boat came over us on a photographic flight, looked round and departed. Until then our CO, a regular, had treated us gently – no bull, just get on with the job, which we did. Then he made what turned out to be a mistake. He decided to hold a flag-raising parade first thing every day. The next time the Condor came over, he shot up both sites! No casualties, but some damage done, the worst of which was to the technical site ablutions, made out of driftwood for our convenience and comfort (quite illegal, of course, but a real boon, as the domestic site ablutions were cold, inadequate and overcrowded in the early morning. The most you could hope for was some privacy behind a rock that hadn't been used before!).

Well, the Condor gunner must have thought our little hut on the edge of the cliff had sinister significance, for he shot it many times. The seat – lovingly shaped with primitive tools – was cut in two. I shudder at what would have happened if an occupant had been there at the time.

At the same time, a small bomb was dropped on one of the wooden masts, which exploded close to the base and blew away the lower portion of one of the legs. Two radio mechanics happened to be at the top at the time, doing some maintenance. They lived to tell the tale, and it is on record that their descent time has never been equalled.

After that we had no more visits, apart from small boats from Norway during the night, carrying people escaping from the Nazis. They were passed on to the Navy for sympathetic processing. The spring of 1941 was quiet and pleasant by comparison, and I passed my spare time fishing in the burns – small trout were plentiful and easy to catch on a hand line – and trapping rabbits on the cliff to add to our menu. We also tried eider duck, but these were definitely for the bedding and not for the pot!

Freddie Smith, *CH Radar Mechanic and unofficial historian of Danby Beacon (a CH and Type 700 (Loran) station)*:

Danby Beacon, up on the North Yorkshire Moors, was an interesting radar station in many different ways.

Freddie Smith

One of its many claims to fame is that its CH was responsible for the first German aircraft to be shot down in England (a Heinkel), by Group Captain Peter Townsend on 3 February 1940. Shortly after the CH station was completed and operational, the duty operator saw on his cathode ray tube a blip and then another: unidentified aircraft 60 miles or so out to sea, approaching the Whitby coast. His information was passed by landline to the Filter Room, who then activated the RAF fighter station at Acklington. Moments later, Blue Section Hurricanes were airborne, and at 0940 hours the enemy plane was shot down.

(In June 1995 a commemorative stone was dedicated on the site, marking this event and also the radar station itself. Quite a number of ex-Danby bods were on parade up the Beacon that day.)

Like other radar stations, Danby was like a small town, with its own police force, two fire tenders, a small library, equipment section, garage with mechanics and drivers, cookhouse and two sick quarters with wards, consulting rooms and trained personnel. All these had to be manned and maintained. Guard duties, fire patrol, first-aiders, spud-bashing, general duties and training all had to be done, and everybody had to take part.

All our water at Danby came from a big underground lake, via a borehole and water pump. The whole area had been a grouse moor before the Air Ministry commandeered it, much to the owner's annoyance. All the time that it was a radar camp, sheep grazed all around us, and the WAAFs used to feed some of the lambs with milk from babies' feeding bottles.

A rather unusual feature at Danby which I remember very clearly was the searchlight, situated just outside the gates leading to A-site. It had a bastard of a generator which was almost guaranteed to give a hernia to all who tried to start it. The secret was to use a small piece of wood to wedge open the choke lever. This was invariably lost just before the mechanic had to start it, although I seem to recall that sometimes a WAAF operator and assistant had to do it themselves.

On the opposite side of the road stood a long, wooden peg painted white. Having 'struck' the light – no, not with your fist or suchlike, but having touched two carbon rods together (with special controls outside the lamp casing) – a brilliant beam was created. This was directed at the peg, and then the beam was raised and lowered a number of times, then dowsed. Another station nearby (I think Goldsboro') also had a light and did the same thing. Aircraft in difficulties could see the two beams, and where they crossed was the nearest airfield. Some of our girls were quite overcome when a message was received thanking them for our help.

A posed photograph of the staff in the CH radar operations room, Danby Beacon. (Courtesy of the *Yorkshire Evening Post*)

It was interesting at Danby to have two entirely different radars on the site. All personnel on the station shared their off-duty hours, their meals, their liberty runs and everything else, but never once did I learn from any of my fellow-mechanics what their radar was, although some of them were my really close friends. I used to hear one or two CH types grumbling that the '700 bods' were a snooty lot, but even they would admit that it was the correct thing to do to preserve total secrecy.

To reach the site at Danby you had to climb Poverty Hill from the village, and very often in winter you had to climb it on foot when the transports couldn't make it. The winter of 1944/5 was rough, and I well recall the watch being unable to be relieved. A deep snowdrift had formed around the pill box just beyond the 700 site, and the transport with the nightwatch on board ploughed into it. They all did their best to dig it out but it proved impossible, so they all walked back to A-site and went on watch while the driver went back with a second vehicle, whereupon that one promptly ploughed into the drift formed by the first one! At that point all hopes of relieving the duty watch were abandoned and they had to carry on through the night.

The Lodge in Danby village is now the North Yorkshire Moors Centre (National Trust) and well worth a visit for any ex-radar bods who find themselves in the area.

CH AGAINST THE V2

We began the story of CH with its secret tracking of the Zeppelin; this is the little-known story of how, at the other end of the war, it was also of great value against Germany's final terror weapon.

All too often, in the development of new equipment, unforeseen snags arise; indeed, the enthusiasm of experienced engineers, striving to make progress, is usually tempered by the realization that their solution may inevitably fall short of the ideal. But just occasionally, fortune smiles, and what at first appears to be an undesirable or useless design characteristic becomes an unexpected bonus when circumstances change. So it was with CH.

As described earlier in this chapter, the effect of ground reflections at metric wavelengths with practicable aerial heights was a lack of much-needed low radar cover and unnecessarily high angles of radiation (see diagram on p. 13). Whatever use could there be for all that energy at altitudes where no aircraft could possibly fly?

The answer came in September 1944, when the first V2 landed in Chiswick. Unlike the slow, low-flying V1, the new flying bomb travelled at supersonic speed and completed its journey from launch pad to target in a matter of minutes. Thus, effective early warning was out of the question. But its high trajectory – culminating in the region of 150,000 ft – took it through the sensitive upper lobes of CH radars, so that as it passed, echoes could be received in short bursts.

The threat of attack by rocket had been foreseen in Britain, through intelligence reports, for some time. Watson Watt and those of his team who, in peacetime, long before the days of radar, had plotted the sources of brief lightning flashes with

CRDF (cathode ray direction-finding) were quick to realize that a form of its application to CH was a basis for assessing the location of the launching sites.

With the dispatch typical of wartime Britain, where scientists, civilian firms and service personnel worked closely together, project 'Big Ben' sped forward, and very soon the south-east CH stations were equipped to monitor the rockets as they attacked London. Simultaneous observations and photographic recordings at different CH sites provided data which, when analysed, led to the definition of new targets for Bomber Command. That was the way to stop V2.

For work on 'Oswald' – the special equipment fitted to CH for 'Big Ben' – very experienced operators were required. Two of these record their memories here.

Valerie Sullivan *(née La Niece), CH Radar Operator, worked on 'Big Ben'*:

Valerie Sullivan

In the autumn of 1944 I was posted from Danby Beacon to Stoke Holy Cross, Norwich. On the train between Peterborough and Norwich, an American GI informed us that some mysterious rockets – 'not buzz-bombs' – had been dropping without warning on and around London and East Anglia. He did not know what they were or where they came from, just warned us that we could be blown up at any moment!

All too soon we were told, officially, about the mysterious rockets. The reason for our posting to Stoke Holy Cross was to operate highly-secret equipment, code-named 'Big Ben', which was being developed to track the enemy's latest secret weapon, the V2 rocket. I remember having to sign five copies of the Official Secrets Act and having the need for absolute secrecy impressed upon me, to such an extent that I have never mentioned 'Big Ben' until recent years.

I remember boffins lecturing about the speed and trajectory of the rockets with reference to the curvature of the earth and the speed at which it revolves: 'Just a brief explanation' they said.

Our main objective was to detect a rocket as early as possible after launching so that a system of early warning might be developed and the launching sites pinpointed and bombed.

The set was installed in one corner of the CH block with a vertical screen directly in front of the operator. The screen was quite small, about 9 inches in diameter, with a horizontal trace dropping from top to bottom – almost like a curtain continually falling. There was always a lot of clutter, and it was difficult to pick out a rocket's signal, which appeared like a long, thin piece of string dropping down the screen.

Operators were allowed fifteen minutes only at any one time watching the screen, and during that time one's eyes had to be glued to that screen and not removed even for a second. To glance away would mean being put on a charge, we were warned.

A film was fitted into the set, to monitor the CRT continuously. This was removed when a rocket had fallen, and the film was projected on to a screen in a dark-room nearby. If a rocket was missed through the clutter, Filter Room would inform us and the film would be examined carefully to locate the rocket's signal, which could be picked out more clearly on the large screen. (I thought this was helpful initially, because being told what to look for is not the same as actually seeing it.)

In the early days we probably missed as many as we spotted, but it was a challenge, and I have always felt it was a privilege to have been selected to work on 'Big Ben'.

Gwen Reading *(née Arnold), worked at Bawdsey on 'Oswald' (codename for the equipment used on 'Big Ben')*:

Gwen Reading

I recall 'Oswald' being introduced late in the war, as an additional piece of equipment on CH stations designed to trace V2 weapons.

All our work on radar stations was considered very, very secret; but when 'Oswald' was introduced, we were told that, if possible, the work of tracing V2s was even more secret. It may be because this need for secrecy was so drummed into us that so little has been recorded about 'Oswald'.

I would say that the set was about 4 ft 6 in high, 2 ft 6 in wide and 2 ft deep. The screen we had to watch was small, probably less than a foot square, and set at eye level as the operator sat before it. We were only allowed to watch the screen for fifteen minutes at a time, because it had to be watched so intensely. To blink might mean we could miss a trace.

The V2 rocket showed as a curving, thread-like trace. The trace was ummistakable, and on seeing it, the operator yelled 'Big Ben at Bawdsey' down the line to Stanmore. After a few minutes Stanmore came back with the message 'Change Oswald'. We then reported 'Oswald off the air' and removed the film which was running within 'Oswald'. As soon as a new film was inserted we reported 'Oswald on the air' to Stanmore. Stanmore would then request other nearby stations to remove their films, the idea being that only one set should be off the air at any time. A member of the watch then departed to the dark-room to develop the film. Not very pleasant, finding your way through the black night to the room used as a dark-room (at Bawdsey, our rest room had been commandeered for the purpose). The room was illuminated by one very small red bulb, and in that somewhat creepy atmosphere we processed the film. I remember one occasion when I burnt the film. It had to be wound round a frame and spun over a heater, to speed up the process. I had not latched the frame securely, and the whole thing fell on to the heater.

The supervisors projected the film on to a screen, and I suppose measured the trace and transmitted the information onwards. We were not given details of this part of the operation, but understood that it was used to pinpoint launching sites. We were told that London could have been given a four-minute warning of an approaching V2, but this was never done, I suppose because it would have meant the entire population of London scurrying to shelters to avoid the explosion, which – huge as it was – was only going to affect one area. There was no way of pinpointing where the V2 would land.

CHAPTER THREE

Chain, Home, Low and Extra Low (CHL and CHEL)

AIR MINISTRY EXPERIMENTAL STATIONS TYPE 2 – CHL

CHL (Chain, Home, Low) augmented CH with radar cover at lower angles of elevation as a result of its shorter operating wavelength (1.5 m vs. *c.* 12 m).

The development of CHL, much used by the RAF, stemmed from experimental work started by the 'Army cell' of the Bawdsey Research Station in 1938/9. Experimental radars working at about 1.5 m were developed to enable surveillance of surface vessels in darkness (or poor visibility) and to provide coastal artillery with target bearings and ranges.

Designated CD (Coastal Defence) and CA (Coastal Artillery), these sets demonstrated their ability to detect low-flying aircraft at ranges greater than the horizon limit for shipping and led to the development of similar equipment for the RAF, to supplement the existing early-warning chain. Some sites were designated CD/CHL.

For gunnery, it was necessary to determine the bearings of slow-moving ship targets with high accuracy. This was achieved by a design in which transmitting and receiving aerials, on separate rotating mounts, were directed towards the target of interest. The transmitting aerial produced a narrow 'searchlight' form of beam (in practice, not very narrow – some 25° wide) to illuminate the target. The receiving aerial was also trained upon it, but while its natural beamwidth was of the same order, good bearing accuracy was obtained by the use of 'split'. (Signals from a pair of overlapping receiving beams are compared; the two responses are only of equal strength over a very small arc, which accurately indicates the target's bearing). Performance on surface vessels and submarines was good – up to 25 miles was reported – and on aircraft, up to 70 miles. While the 'split' range display was ideal for the presentation of echoes from shipping, a Plan Position Indicator (PPI) was added to aid the monitoring of fast-moving aircraft.

Determined efforts by the teams of the Army cell, who had moved from Bawdsey to Christchurch on the outbreak of war, resulted in several stations being set up by January 1940, at various locations on the east coast and in the Shetlands. Many radar operators of the early CHL days recall vividly their

A typical CHL installation after the design had become established. The aerial was common to T & R and was power-turned.

CHL receiver; the range tube is on the left, the PPI on the right.

struggles with the hand-turned aerials, the power source being their weary arms acting through crankhandles and bicycle chains.

After the fall of France, many more stations were erected around the British coasts, and from late 1940 there emerged the general form of CHL familiar to most RAF operators and mechanics. Thanks to the development of the common T/R (transmit/receive) switch and the rotating transmission-line joint, it now had a single aerial, no longer swept back and forth by hand but continuously rotated by electric drive (see p. 49, top). The range tube was retained, but a PPI was fitted as standard, both displays being used for the full interpretation of echoes (see below).

CHL aerials were normally mounted on wooden gantries and sited as high as possible to maximize the radar cover at low angles of elevation. Where convenient, clifftop sites were chosen (e.g. Beer Head, Devon), or where no such natural features were available, special high towers replaced the gantries. Alternatively, as at Bawdsey, near Felixstowe, the CHL aerial was mounted some 200 ft above ground on one of the cantilevered platforms of a CH transmitting tower. Attending to the turning gear, hung beneath the decking and accessible via a trap door, was hardly a mechanic's favourite task.

CHL was not equipped to establish heights, but it was sometimes possible to

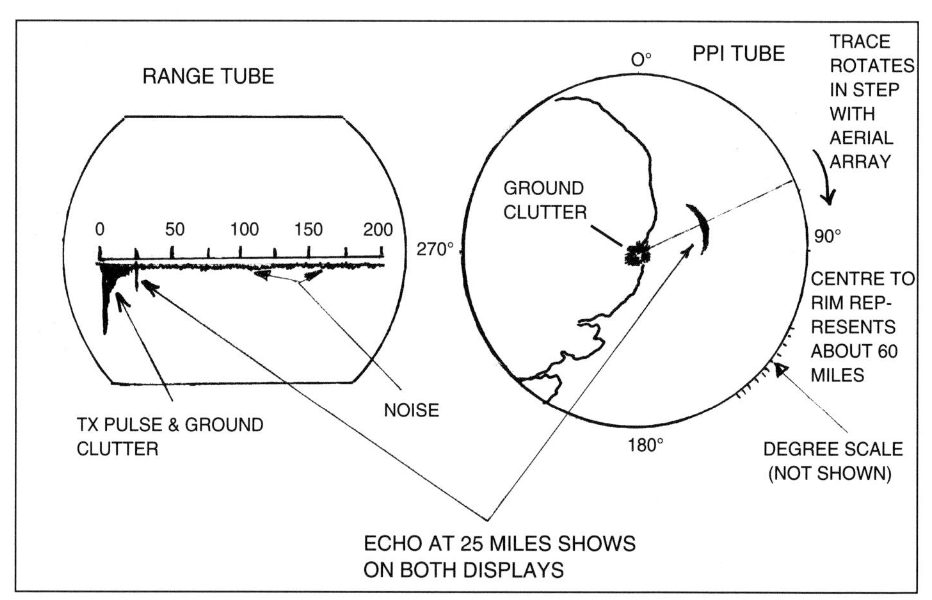

CHL receiver displays. The range tube was normally set to about 180–200 miles and the PPI to 50 or 60 miles as required. Echoes beyond the PPI limit would appear on the range tube only, bearings being taken from the angular position of the PPI trace as the response attained its maximum downward deflection. The intensity of the rotating PPI trace (at 4 or 5 rpm) was set so as to be just visible, with echoes painting up as brighter arcs. However, the beam-width of these 1.5 m radars was such that care was necessary to select, precisely, the centre of the arc as the indicated bearing. Operators were told to 'pick the inside of the middle of the sausage'. Local features such as coastlines and grid reference squares might be drawn on the PPI screen.

make a rough estimate of height by noting the ranges at which aircraft echoes, passing through lobes of known height, faded and reappeared. Plots, normally consisting of ranges, bearings and IFF status, were usually sent to the filter room via the local CH station, which in many cases acted as 'parent' to the smaller CHL station. This was not always the case. Some CHL stations were complete units in their own right, sending plots directly to the filter room.

An innovation in the tactical use of radar was the direct control, at an early stage, of fighter aircraft from a CD/CHL station to intercept mine-laying aircraft. This successful operation presaged the introduction of GCI radars; and, in the event, the 1.5 m ground-based GCI radars, soon to be tested and introduced, owed much to the technology of CHL.

AIR MINISTRY EXPERIMENTAL STATIONS TYPES 14, 52, 53, 54(a), 54(b), 55, 56, 57 – CHEL (CHAIN, HOME, EXTRA-LOW)

The availability of production magnetrons influenced the design of radars for all applications from mid-1940 onwards. The magnetron, producing high power at 10 cm wavelength, not only transformed airborne radar by enabling the transmission of narrow beams from compact equipment, but made possible lower-looking, surface-based radars, with improved target discrimination, for use by the Navy and RAF. It also led to improved gunnery radars for the Army.

I first saw centimetric radar in action at Bawdsey. As a mechanic instructor from Yatesbury, attached to the station to learn all I could about the operational side of CH and CHL, I was also invited to enter a small radar cabin set up on the cliffs overlooking the sea.

With a radar reflector on its roof, the cabin was mounted on a turntable and swung spasmodically to and fro, but stopped obediently when my host banged on the side. The door opened and I was let in. There was not much space for me, since three Wrens were already inside. Two were watching a range display and operating handcranks which turned the whole cabin, while the third was recording plots. Two impressions registered immediately: the gleaming black stockings of the pair who, sitting with skirts above their knees for comfort, worked the radar (why didn't our lovely WAAFs get clothes like that?) and, less erotic but more to the point of my visit, the detailed echoes displayed on the range tube.

This was clearly Admiralty equipment, since the range tube was not calibrated in miles but in thousands of yards. How very odd that seemed. After a brief, friendly greeting, the girls continued to work, inviting me to watch with them as they concentrated on particular echoes by training the cabin accordingly. Echoes showed up sharp and clear, the slightest movement of the cabin changing the size of the response; evidently the beamwidth was narrower than anything I'd met before.

Then, almost due east, a group of fine echoes appeared at about 12,000 yards and disappeared almost immediately, only to show again in ones and twos, but always within a few moments of each other. We could not account for these, so we pressed on with general surveillance of the sea area.

After some minutes we found them again, now at shorter range, and continued to see them for some time, gradually getting closer. When they had come in to some 5,000 yards or less and the responses were stronger – still appearing and disappearing – we decided to nip outside and 'take a visual'. Binoculars provided a wonderful visual – a school of porpoises (or dolphins?) playing happily in the water. Oblivious of the war around them, they moved steadily along, submerged one moment and airborne the next. That was sensitivity and fine target discrimination to a degree I'd never seen before; I was impressed by microwave radar!

The 10 cm Naval Type 271 equipment, developed remarkably rapidly by Admiralty scientists, found its way into a number of RAF radars. Its power output, initially some 7 kW, was raised by successive improvements to 50 kW, and some sets were reputed to produce more – even up to 100 kW.

The next big step was the introduction of Naval Type 277 equipment, with an improved design of magnetron giving up to 500 kW peak power. With 500 pulses per second at the normal pulse length of 2 microseconds, this gave a peak-to-mean power ratio of 1,000:1. Thus the average power output was some 500 W – a respectable figure even now, and especially so in those early days. No wonder the NT277 became a workhorse for a wide variety of radars, naval and RAF alike.

The figure opposite illustrates some of the forms of NT271/277 equipments for the RAF. On coastal sites they supplemented the existing CH/CHL early-warning system and since, because of their shorter wavelength, they gave even better low-level cover, they were called CHEL. NT277 also formed the nucleus of the Type 14 radar (for ranges and bearings) and the Type 13 (for heightfinding), as mentioned in the GCI section (see p. 63).

These wartime centimetric radars heralded the shape of things to come. The majority of postwar radars for general applications, including early warning and heightfinding, have worked on wavelengths between 10 and 25 cm, although there have been some operating at longer and shorter wavelengths, according to their purpose and role.

Why did the advent of centimetric radars not, at a stroke, render the CH/CHL system obsolete? First, the CH/CHL chain was already up and running and, in the main, producing effective results. Second, while the wartime centimetric radars demonstrated the advantages of low cover and good target discrimination as well as accurate heightfinding without the need for tedious calibration, much more work would have been needed for them to replace all other types of radar.

Such work has been the focus of extensive development efforts since the war. Among many improvements and innovations, transmitter powers have increased by factors of ten and more, while receiver noise figures – equally important for the detection of weak signals – have fallen dramatically; aerial design has improved enormously to give better-shaped beams with lower sidelobes, and frequency agility and other measures against jamming have been exploited.

The NT277 wartime centimetric radars had no such refinements – not even basic automatic frequency control to keep the receivers in tune – and they

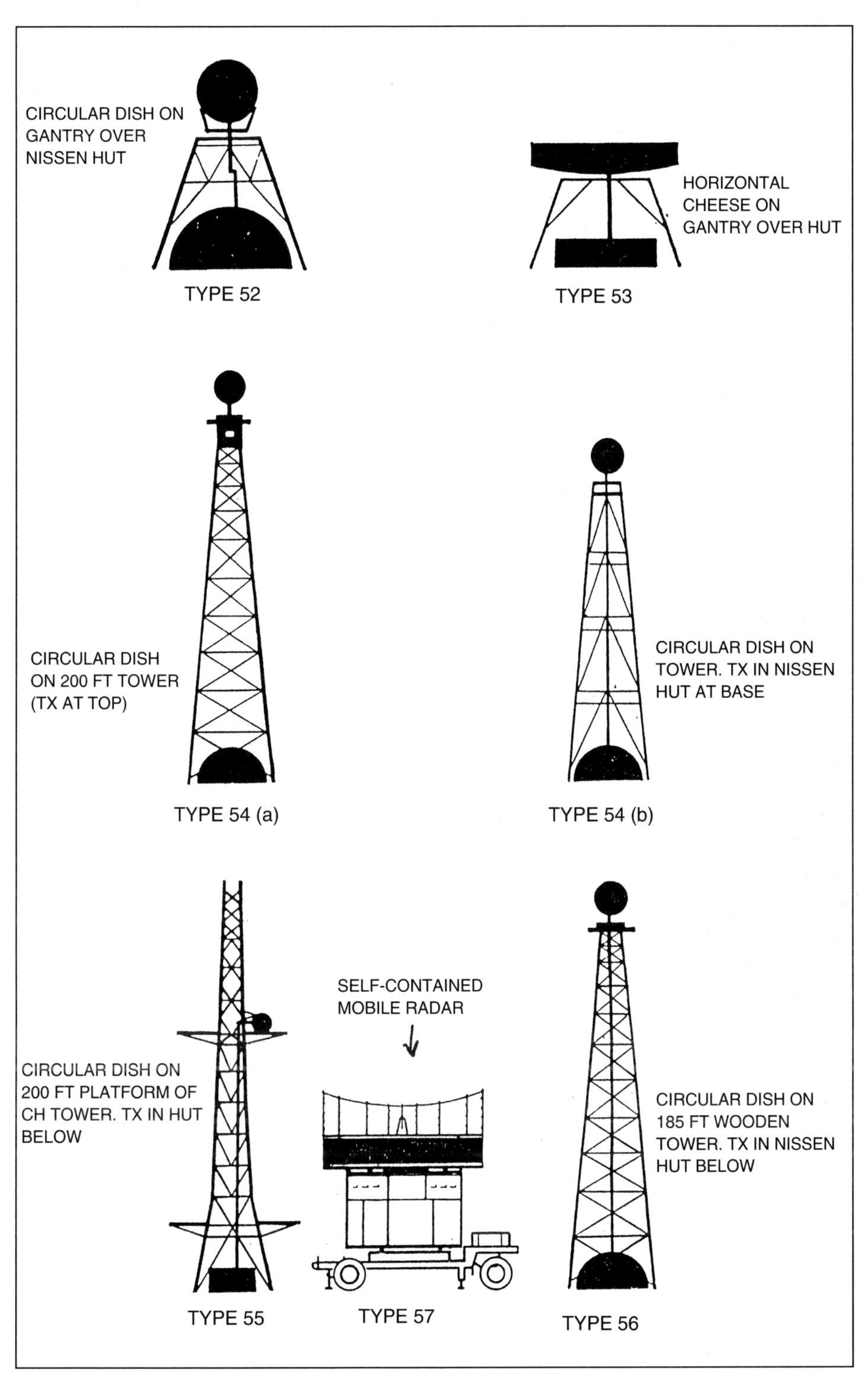

Various configurations of 10cm radars in RAF service. All of them were based on the naval Type 277.

suffered sundry ills, including temperamental thyratrons in the transmitter modulator and unpredictable crystals in the receiver. Yet they made a valuable addition to the total radar system. The span of wavelength from their 10 cm to that of CH represents seven octaves of radio frequency. What a complex early-warning system we had attained, and how highly resistant to complete jamming it had eventually become, with that vast spectrum.

George Capon, *CHL Operator and Mechanic Instructor*:

George Capon

Posted to Glenarm, March 1941. First stop Liverpool to get clearance to travel by boat to Northern Ireland. Arrived in midst of blitz. With another chap, took taxi to quiet pub on outskirts. Very quiet till we got into bed, then ack-ack battery opened fire in field behind pub. End of night's sleep. Next morning reported to weird RAF office in basement of decrepit building in Liverpool. Helped *throw* metal boxes addressed to RAF Glenarm into lorry. Found later they contained new CRTs, all broken! Angry Liverpool ladies threw bricks and abuse at us – why weren't we flying up there and shooting down Germans, instead of walking around town?

Slept in Army rest camp, then next day off to Stranraer and on to boat. Ordered to don filthy life jacket. Sailing delayed for some hours – suspected U-boat in Irish Channel. Arrived next morning in Larne. Helpful civilian, when told I wanted to get to Glenarm, Cookstown, said: 'Take the bus!' Real Irish bus, with crate of live chickens on back seat, stopping at every village shop to chuck out parcel of newspapers. Beautiful scenery up the famous Antrim coast road for 15 miles. We were all billeted in the village – no bed available for me for several days, so shared with Canadian mechanic on different watch! Site about three miles up on clifftop. Four-watch system. Each watch had a soldier of the Royal Artillery and three gunners with them.

The actual site was guarded by a detachment of the Royal Ulster Rifles – these soldiers were nervous and trigger-happy, so going to the latrines during the night was a hazard, and one tried to hold on if possible till daylight! If the sentry heard a crunch on the gravel, he'd take a pot-shot with his rifle and *then* shout 'Halt, who goes there?' We had to make an arrangement that we'd take a hammer and a bucket and bang it for dear life so he'd know it was one of us. But lying up on the cliffs behind gorse bushes at night would be our dear friends the IRA, who were only too pleased to indulge in a little shooting practice when they heard the banging of the bucket.

It was the first site to have a PPI fitted, but no instructions were given on what it was for, so it was only used as an ornament – pretty to look at. It had an old car driving-wheel with handle attached for rotating the aerial, with a motorbike chain connecting – very difficult to manage in high winds. When the wind was too strong, a poor mechanic had to clamber on to the gantry and slip in a thick bolt to fix the aerial steady – a very hazardous job in the middle of the night.

Security was very tight on the station, with passwords changing daily, and now and again we'd be warned by the SPs to keep inside our billets on a Sunday if there was to be a Ceilidh (a sort of Catholic combined hurly game and singsong and booze-up leading to general rumpus). The local yobs were very cowardly – when we came off duty at midnight there was always a gang of them at street corners ready to pick us off. So we would all walk to Bill's billet and see him in safely, then the six of us left would walk to Tom's billet and see him in, and so on until there were two of us who lived in the same billet – home and safe. The brave locals would never dare take us on if there were two of us, but if there was only one of us to six of them, they'd courageously beat the poor chap up.

No operators could ever pass a trade test for promotion to LAC (Leading Aircraftman). Our corporal was only an AC1 (Aircraftman), acting corporal. Our CH station was miles up the coast, and we had no contact with them at all except that we had to go there for trade tests, but as nobody there knew anything about CHL and we knew nothing about CH, we were sunk from the start.

A lot of the billets had no bath, so the chaps were allowed to have one once a week in the so-called hotel in the village. We had a bathroom, so if there was any hot water and you didn't mind being watched by a rat while you were in the bath, it was OK.

We used to do PT in a field full of cowpats, overlooked by Antrim Castle, the home of Lord Antrim. He was away in the Army, but his wife was there, and our PT antics would be watched by her two giggling French maids from a window at the top of the castle.

On Orange Day, there was a dance in the evening, and one of our SPs – a Catholic – was on duty, while his wife went to the dance. When the SP came off duty and found where his wife was, he went to the hall and there was a punch-up. First thing next morning, the CO drove him down to Larne and put him on the boat to Stranraer, for his own safety, leaving his poor wife stranded.

There were pubs galore in Glenarm, some only the front room of a terraced cottage, with no name over the door. We favoured a nice little pub run by a Catholic widow and her red-haired daughter. She always warned us of the approach of any Catholic troublemaker, when we'd drink up and quietly leave. Drinking hours were 9 a.m. to 9 p.m., so we could sink a pint after morning PT before going back to billet for breakfast!

If anyone was given seven days' CB (confined to barracks) it was a real farce. No barracks to be confined to, so we were ordered to report to the local police every day. Easy – a constable was always strolling up and down the village street, revolver strapped to his waist. 'Good morning, Mike.'

'Good morning, lad.'

'Goodbye Mike.'

'Goodbye lad'.

That was some punishment!

Glenarm in the spring of 1941 represented an interim stage in the development of the CHL type of station. Although it was said to be one of the first to have a PPI, nobody had been told how to use it: it merely acted as a bearing indicator for the echoes on the range display. But perhaps that was just as well because, while the latest common T/R aerial had been fitted, it was still not motor-driven. The human power source – crankhandles in sweaty palms – would pause on each echo while its range and bearing were noted, plotted on the board nearby and passed to Filter Room at Preston. Not an ultra-rapid process perhaps, but adequate for the low air traffic density of that region, where the only really regular filter was a high German reconnaissance aircraft.

Preston, which was also Wing HQ, appeared to be satisfied with the modest data flow provided. (Glenarm reported its plots direct – unlike many CHLs, which passed them via a parent CH.)

Like much of life in that part of Ireland then, the mains supply was unpredictable. Power failures were common and everyone, mechanics and operators, was well used to rushing out to the diesel shed, swinging her into life and throwing the switches. Good old Lister diesel engines – what fine service they gave throughout the war.

A respite for operators from the radar displays and plotting table was a stint of 'visual' in the observation post on the clifftop – a sort of gun pit in a dugout. Here, armed with binoculars, you could see the skies for miles in clear weather, and report aircraft movements by telephone to the receiver hut.

Note: George Capon overcame the operators' trade test problem in Northern Ireland by applying to become a mechanic. This entailed a complex and protracted return journey to Yatesbury for a bare half-hour interview. But it paid off: he not only became a successful mechanic instructor, but in August 1943 he met Eva ('Nookie') Hobbs, a WAAF corporal radar operator, who, like him, had come in from operational stations for instructional duties at Yatesbury. Another fine RAF–WAAF marriage, and still going strong after half a century!

E.J.M. Jefferies, *CHL Radar Operator*:

Note: The radar station first mentioned here, Ballinderry, is described, unusually, as 'CHB'. This is an example of how some stations' roles changed as the war progressed. It was installed as a Type 8 – 'Intermediate GCI' – but appears to have reported to Filter Room in the manner of a CH (and some CHLs), rather than directly to a fighter station, as would a normal GCI. Since, unlike a CHL, it was able to provide heights, it was, in effect, giving the data normally provided by a CH, although probably with less maximum range. For operators, it was much like working on a CHL.

Turned down for aircrew on the final eyesight test in 1943, I was offered a choice of ground trades in the RAF, but was at a loss to know which one to go for. A kindly Warrant Officer, seeing my uncertainty, said: 'There's a trade known as RDF Operator. I'm not at liberty to tell you anything about it, but I think you might find it interesting.'

I signed on then and there, and many times throughout my life I've thought of that unknown Warrant Officer who guided me into radar and have blessed him for his good advice.

My first posting after Yatesbury was to Northern Ireland – RAF Ballinderry. This proved a fortunate posting for a number of reasons, the most enduring of which was that within three days I had met my future wife, who lived a quarter of a mile from the camp. We are still happily married more than fifty years on (something else to thank that Warrant Officer for!).

E.J.M. Jefferies

Ballinderry was a CHB (Chain, Home Beam) station, with a strength of only about forty including the CO (a very young Canadian), drivers, cooks, admin. and SPs. The atmosphere at the station was very relaxed. We were in Nissen huts, and although there probably was a main gate beside the guardroom, it was seldom used – we just walked out through a hole in the hedge nearest whichever direction we wanted to go. There was an artificial duckpond made from a tarpaulin – the ducks provided eggs for somebody or other.

The village of Coagh lay in one direction, and A-site in the other, so we were issued with bicycles to go on watch, except for nightwatches, when we were taken in the Bedford truck.

We used to have an arithmetical code for entering the Ops Room – a number under twenty was called out, and you had to respond with the number which would add up to twenty. The only one who found this mathematical feat too difficult was our station dog, 'Spam', who was the result of one of the police dogs misbehaving herself with a local bull mastiff; he used to run behind our bikes as far as A-site and then bark outside the ops block to be let in (he always was!).

A massive permanent echo on the screen was provided by the Mountains of Mourne, which swept down to the sea at a range of 55 miles from us. We sometimes picked up other, unofficial objects on our screen, such as the occasional visit from a very elderly Church Army mobile canteen, which would approach slowly, giving off massive spark interference while still some distance away. The Service Police must have been extremely puzzled when we invariably rang through to them to tell them to open the gate as the Church Army was on its way! They never knew how we knew.

When I left Northern Ireland I was posted to Skendleby, in Lincolnshire, on a CHL unit. I was there when the Heinkel-borne V1 flying bombs started coming in over the North Sea. We were astounded at first to see several hostile tracks coming towards us and suddenly doubling in number. What on earth was happening? we wondered. What was happening, of course, was that they were separating as the Heinkels turned for home while the doodlebugs continued overland, very straight and extremely fast. Soon the Army set up 'Diver Gun

Belts' along the coast and brought very heavy ack-ack fire to bear on anything coming in from the sea below a certain height, without waiting for identification. There was a 'gap' at the Wash and another at the mouth of the Humber, to allow our aircraft a safe route in at low level. I remember seeing a hostile approaching the coast which must have just got into the edge of the gun belt; I never saw an aircraft change course and head back out to sea so fast!

At the time of our very heavy bombing raids in the last year of the war, the numbers of aircraft on the screen at any time could be very great and it was possible to plot only the four corners of the mass, moving as a group and covering many square miles. The largest number I ever plotted we estimated at four hundred plus, and with this amount of clutter, it was impossible to detect IFF. The Germans took to sending up Ju88 nightfighters to infiltrate our bombers and pick off stragglers on their way home. There was nothing we could do, and we felt very frustrated at being unable to help the poor aircrews, who must have thought they were almost safe.

When the war in Europe was finally over, there was an exercise with RAF radar personnel watching the German radar people operating their equipment while Bomber Command made mock attacks on Germany and we operated our gear as usual. We were not told a great deal about this, but it must have been fascinating for those in the know.

I finished the war out in the Far East, driving lorries, but I wouldn't have missed my time in radar for the world, and have always felt privileged to have had the good fortune to take part in a very special organization at a very special time.

Molly Kerridge, *Radar Operator/Mechanic on CH and CHL*:

Molly Kerridge

On a maintenance course at Yatesbury late in 1941, we were the first WAAFs on the mechanics' side of the Radio School. As King George VI inspected my flight, he was heard to say in amazement: 'Mechanics?' Then, after a pause, very condescendingly: 'Oh, *maintenance*!' Until that time no WAAFs had been trained as mechanics, but of course, later on many were.

In 1942 I was at Pevensey, in Sussex, working on CH, and one nightwatch, soon after dawn, we plotted out a mass of aircraft moving towards the French coast. On going outside, I saw large formations of Spitfires and Hurricanes heading out to sea, and we learned later that this was the fighter cover for the ill-fated raid on Dieppe (which was on our line of shoot).

Also in 1942, I was at Hartland Point on CHL/271. The naval equipment (271) was manually operated, and we had Wrens on watch with us. When officers from Wing HQ came to inspect us and we wanted to get rid of them, we let go of the control (accidentally, on purpose) and the cabin went round 360° rapidly in a high wind. Unwelcome visitors got out P.D.Q. – we were used to the motion, but they were not! Mind you, when we got to bed at night we paid the penalty, as the whole bed seemed to be swinging around.

Our RAF Sergeant Mechanic at Hartland was Charles Cox, who took part in the Bruneval commando raid (see p. 112).

At Walton-on-Naze the CHL was on top of the Coastguard Tower. We were plotting Doodlebugs (one landed in the sea at the end of the pier). It was exciting work on watch, and we tended to give no thought to the fact that each one was going to land on some poor soul. But off duty it was another matter: when we heard an engine cut out we dived under the table at lightning speed! I was also at Walton-on-Naze on 6 June 1944, when we saw on the CRT a large mass of shipping moving out from the Thames at dawn. Then we knew that this was the day – D-Day!

CHAPTER FOUR

Ground-Controlled Interception (GCI)

RADARS FOR GROUND-CONTROLLED INTERCEPTION

After the Battle of Britain, when the German offensive against Britain consisted mainly of night-time bombing missions, new and more sophisticated methods of aerial interception became necessary. Thanks to men of vision – notably Sir Henry Tizard and Air Marshal Sir Hugh Dowding – this situation had been anticipated by their encouraging the timely development of special ground-based radars and compact airborne radar sets for our fighter aircraft.

SPECIAL RADARS

Although, in theory, it was attractive to consider the possibility of directing fighters against intruders by using the plots from the coastal early-warning radar chain, early trials soon showed the limitations of this approach. For one thing, CH stations had been designed to look mainly out to sea, but many interceptions would take place overland; and for another, while CHL stations were all-round-looking, they had no means of providing height data (except very occasional rough estimates at certain fortuitous ranges and heights).

Furthermore, the coastal chain was fully occupied with the business of locating and tracking intruders; for effective GCI, specific ground-based radars were required, dedicated to that task alone. They would not report into the general filter rooms, but to their local fighter organization, and they would have direct R/T contact with the fighter pilots. They would concentrate on single intruders – or a small number – and thereby provide rapid streams of updated plots to direct our specially-equipped nightfighting aircraft towards successful interceptions.

GCI EQUIPMENT

Early airborne radars worked at 1.5 m wavelength, but much-improved versions soon appeared in service following the development of the 10 cm cavity magnetron in 1940. On the ground, the 'Final' static GCI radar was the AMES Type 7 and various marks of Type 8 and 15 accounted for transportable and mobile versions.

The ground-to-air link, which permitted direct speech in both directions, was a significant step forward in R/T technology. It worked in the VHF band (*c.* 120 MHz) and gave solid cover throughout and beyond the GCI region. Without such fast and reliable communication, GCI would not have been possible.

The rotating aerial array of 'Happidrome' or 'Final' GCI station (AMES Type 7). Transmitters and receivers are beneath the array, and the operations buildings, also well protected, can be seen in the background.

MODUS OPERANDI

An unidentified aircraft approaching the coast would first be detected at long range by CH and/or CHL, its plots passed to the filter room and its course tracked. When seen by CH, height would be assessed and, as soon as possible, an identity number allocated, preceded – in the absence of IFF response – by 'H' for 'Hostile'. Data would be passed to an appropriately-located GCI station, the intruder 'handed over' and a radar-equipped nightfighter (Beaufighter, or later, Mosquito) would be scrambled from the sector airfield.

With the intruder now within radar range of the GCI station (some 50 miles) the GCI controller was soon able to monitor the movements of both aircraft on his radar screen and commence the skilled task of directing his fighter, by R/T, to within airborne radar range of the intruder (e.g. some 2–4 miles). From then on, the two-man nightfighter crew would take over, homing on to the enemy in darkness with the aid of their airborne radar set.

HEIGHTFINDING FOR GCI

In order to give adequate guidance, GCI radars provided continuous data on the intruder's position, course and height; for this, they had to determine range, bearing and height. As with other radars, range measurement was just a matter of accurate timing; and bearing accuracy was now straightforward, with a rotating-beam aerial and PPI display; only a rapid method of heightfinding demanded a solution.

GCI radars worked on a radio frequency of 209 MHz, so their wavelength was only slightly less than the 1.5 m used by CHL (200 MHz). Much use was made of CHL hardware, the transmitters, receivers and PPI displays being very similar. The main difference from CHL was the addition of heightfinding facilities.

Aerials – rotating, and common to both transmitter and receiver – bore a resemblance to those of CHL, except that the vertical aperture was greater and was divided into sections, each at a different height above ground. This was to permit heightfinding by the principles used on CH – by making use of ground reflections and comparing the strengths of signals from aerials at different heights and therefore having different lobe patterns.

While the underlying principle was the same as CH, the method of comparing signal strengths was quite different. A height/range display, provided in addition to the PPI display, showed echoes as downwards deflections, as on CH; however, in the heightfinding mode, signals from upper and lower sections of the aerial were displayed alternately, while, in synchronism, a small amount of horizontal shift was applied to alternate traces of the display. As a result, each echo was shown as a pair of responses side by side. The space between them could be set by the operator to a convenient distance – perhaps ⅛ or ¼ in – and it was then easy to estimate their relative amplitudes. Height could be assessed quickly by applying the observed ratio of amplitudes of the two signals, plus the range, to a height-conversion chart mounted immediately in front of the display.

SITING AND CALIBRATION

As with CH, the dependance upon ground reflections implied the need for calibration by flight trials and care in site selection. GCI stations, not necessarily sited near the coast, were required to be all-round-looking. Thus they were best erected, where possible, well within flat land areas, so that the heightfinding capability would not vary greatly whatever the direction of activity.

Under overseas conditions in wartime, ideal siting might not always be possible, nor thorough calibration; consequently, a limitation in absolute accuracy might have to be accepted. However, it must be remembered that in this system, where both intruder and interceptor were monitored by the same radar and displayed simultaneously on the same PPI, errors in height would apply equally to both aircraft, especially as they came closer together. In other words, relative height accuracy – most important when directing one aircraft towards another – was maintained: absolute accuracy is obviously desirable, but not so vital as if separate radars had been used to plot raider and interceptor (e.g. the German system).

As interceptions progressed, intruder and fighter echoes became closer on the PPI; positive identification of the latter was provided by IFF Mk 3G – a version using special airborne equipment with an extra output at 209 MHz, the GCI radar frequency. At the controller's request to the fighter pilot, 'Canary, please,'

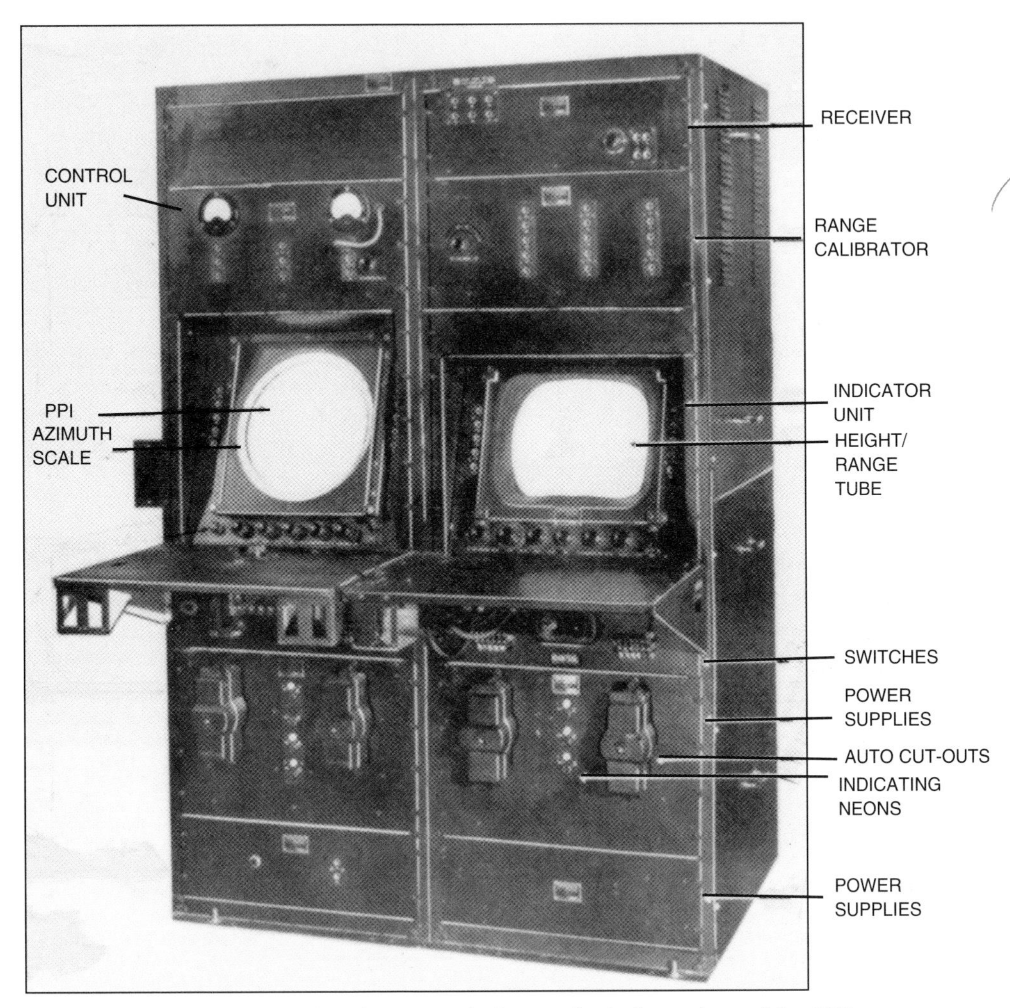

CGI receiver and display console. This consisted of two racks similar to those of the CHL system. The desk below the height/range tube carried height conversion charts. The automatic power cut-outs were vulnerable to tripping by contact with the operators' knees.

the airborne set would transmit a signal that appeared against its echo on the radar screen as a 'crown of thorns' (see p. 64, bottom).

Microwaves Enter the GCI Arena

The advent of the cavity magnetron, making possible high-power transmitters at 10 cm wavelength, not only transformed airborne radar but was also a boon for ground-based radars. The shorter wavelength permitted the use of new aerial

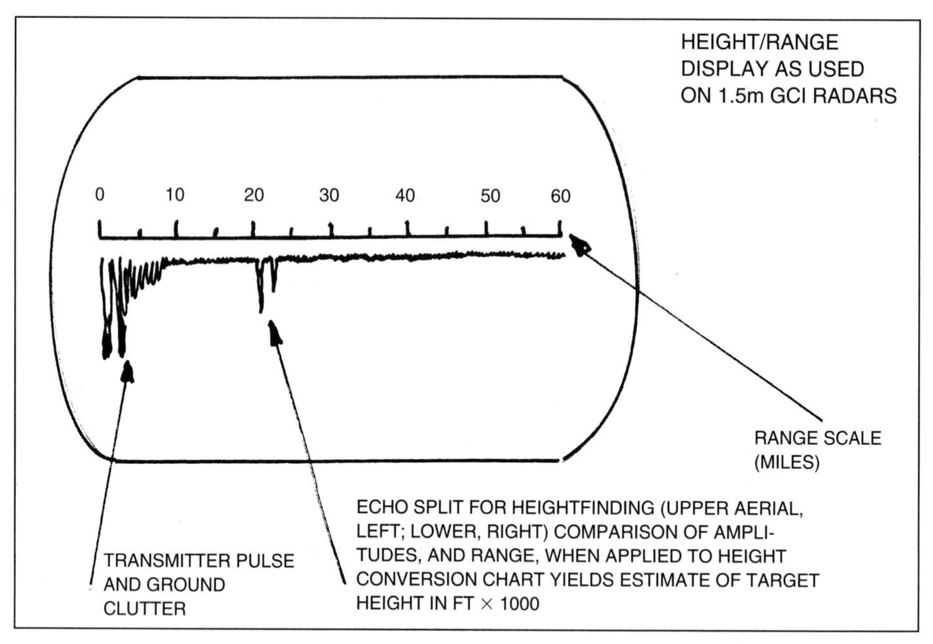

The height/range display as used on 1.5 m GCI radars.

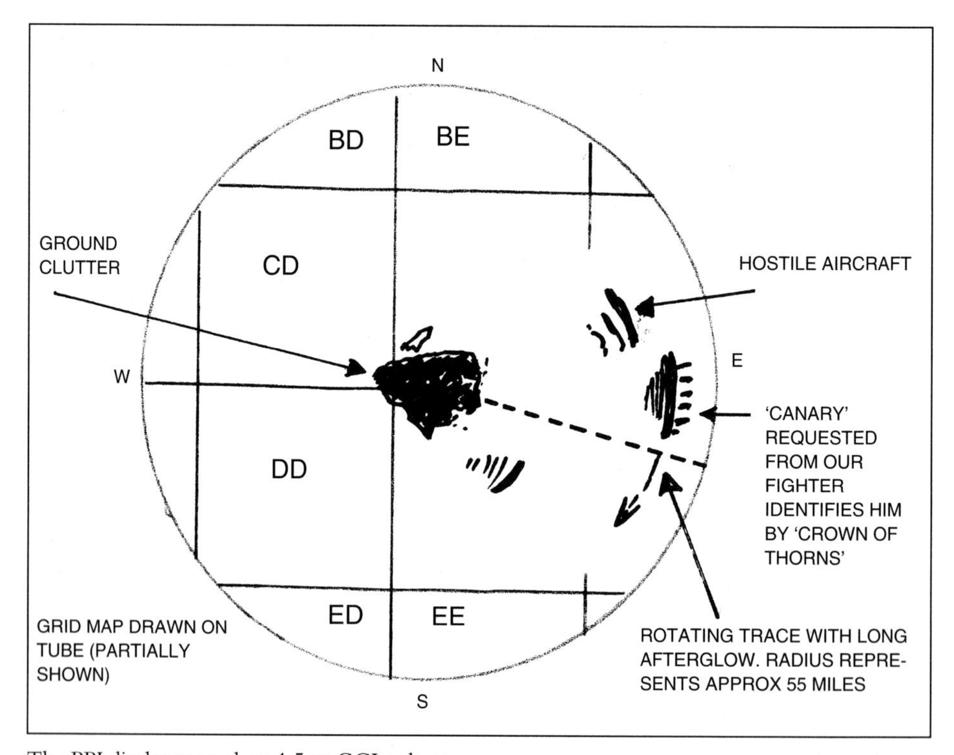

The PPI display as used on 1.5 m GCI radars.

designs capable of far more precise radiation patterns, so that ground reflections became of little significance. For surveillance radars of the '2–D' variety (i.e. providing range and bearing only) it became possible to detect targets such as low-flying intruders, at much lower angles of elevation, while for heightfinding radars the complication of careful siting and the need for height calibration was overcome.

The new aerial designs for microwaves employed various types of reflector to achieve the desired radiation pattern. With a circular, parabolic reflector (like the domestic satellite dishes now so common, but larger) a beam analogous to that of an optical searchlight is formed and this was used in some types of low-looking coast watching and gun-laying radars. However, such a 'pencil beam' was not ideal for all applications, and other shapes of reflectors, often dubbed 'cheeses', were employed (e.g. Type 14 surveillance radars employed a horizontal 'cheese': this gave a beam narrow in azimuth, for discriminating between targets on similar bearings but wide enough in the vertical plane to permit detection at all altitudes).

Cheeses were also employed with advantage for heightfinding, but mounted differently. The need was for a narrow beam in the vertical plane – to enable angle of elevation to be measured – but wider in the horizontal plane to detect targets over a spread of bearings and to aid the observation of fast-flying aircraft whose bearings changed rapidly. The most common early radar in this category was the Type 13. Unlike CHL and systems such as Types 7, 8 and 15, its aerial did not scan or rotate continuously in azimuth, but was slewed – by remote control from the display console – to bearings at which height readings were required. It would then remain stationary in azimuth while the aerial nodded up and down covering all likely angles of target elevation. Both the range and angle of elevation of a target were presented simultaneously on a new form of display enabling height to be read directly (see diagram, p. 67).

Gerald Taylor (who on p. 147 contributes his personal story of a mobile GCI on the Continent soon after D-Day) writes:

> A good example of the high resolution of the Type 13 occurred near Caen in August 1944 at the end of a successful interception. It was noticed on the elevation scan display that two small blips had detached themselves from the strong blip of the German aircraft which was rapidly losing height after being fired on by our Mosquito. The Mosquito pilot, who was following the German down in order to record the crash as evidence of his kill, reported that two of the crew had bailed out in parachutes. It was these that the Type 13 was seeing.

However, centimetric heightfinding did not render 1.5 m heightfinding obsolete. Aerials of the 1.5 m sets rotated continuously, giving the plan positions of all detected targets up to eight times per minute; close cooperation between operators on PPI and height/range displays meant that height could be assessed on plots at all bearings and at a speed hard to equal with a nodding heightfinder unless restricted to a limited arc of azimuth. Each method gave operational advantages in the heat of an interception, and so we see both systems being used throughout the war and into peacetime. The 1.5 m GCI sets, although intrinsically less accurate than centimetric radars, and despite the need for careful calibration, came closer to the ideal of true '3–D' radars – that of providing height on every plot.

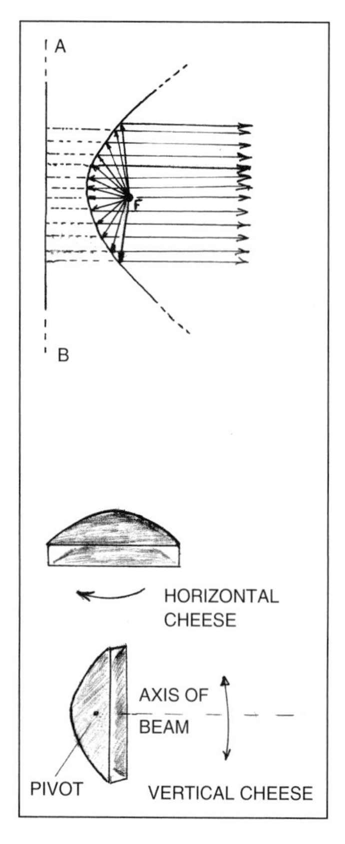

Examples of cheese-type parabolic reflectors, used when a narrow beam-width in one plane was required.
'Parabola': 'Curve traced out by a point which moves so that its distance from a fixed point, the focus, is equal to its distance from a fixed straight line....'
A–B is the straight line and F the focus. If a radiating element (feed) such as a microwave aerial or horn is placed at the focus and arranged to 'look' at the parabolic reflecting surface, a narrow beam is formed. The more the parabolic shape is extended the narrower the beam-width. (The definition of the parabola given above implies that, for a distant receiver, it is as if the radiation were coming from a set of separate sources, all in phase, spread across the line A–B as indicated by the dotted lines.)
Parabolic reflectors work well provided that they are large compared to the wavelength. They are commonly used for microwaves and for optical applications such as searchlights. When parabolic surfaces were first bounded by end plates the structure resembled a cheese and the name stuck. Cheese are used for both transmitting and receiving.
Cheese reflectors (feeds not shown). A horizontally mounted cheese gives a narrow beam in the horizontal plane (ie as seen in plan view) but a much wider spread of radiation vertically. It thus provides good bearing accuracy on targets at different altitudes. Conversely, a vertically mounted cheese capable of being rocked up and down produces a narrow beam in the vertical plane for finding angles of elevation of targets.

A horizontal cheese-type reflector on a mobile Type 14 10cm surveillance radar.

GCI in Action

Starting with the first successful ground-controlled interception in October 1940, improvements in equipment and refinement of procedures continued throughout the war. Gerald Taylor has written of the final GCI system:

> By 1944 the British combination of ground-based GCI and airborne centimetric AI (air interception), with its very high resolution, had been honed into an efficient and very effective nightfighting system. That success was totally reliant on the human element, in the air and on the ground. Teamwork of a high order and absolute competence were vital as even a small mistake could, and sometimes did, end in unwanted fatalities. Much hung on the Controller and his ability to visualize the situation in the cockpit of the fighter. It is not surprising that ex-aircrew usually made the best Controllers.
>
> It was always a privilege to watch a live interception. Undoubtedly it was the most dramatic and exciting demonstration

The vertical cheese-type reflector on a mobile Type 13 10 cm height-finding radar.

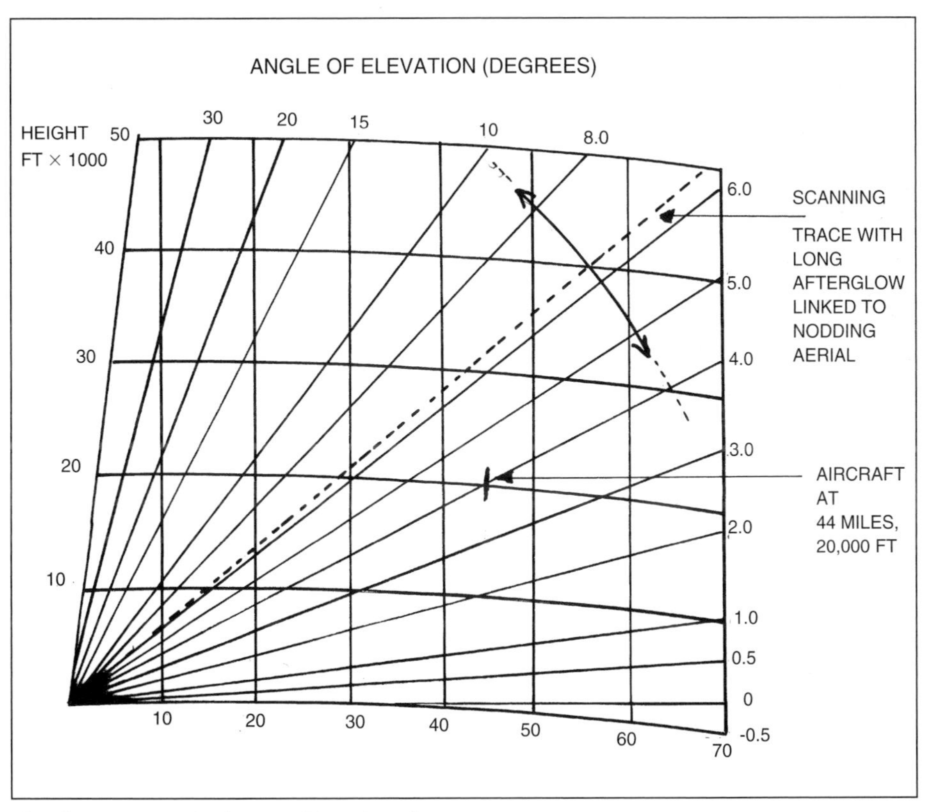

The elevation scan display on a Type 13 radar.

of the power of electric sight. There is a primeval urge in all humans to be roused by the excitement of the chase and a GCI ops room certainly demonstrated this to the full, particularly if the hunt was a difficult one whose outcome was in doubt until the last moment. In true British style, the greater the tension the quieter the room became!

FORMS OF GCI STATION

Many variations appeared within Types 7, 8 and 15:

• *Type 7* – the 'Final GCI' (dubbed 'Happidromes'), were comprehensive, static installations, with multiple displays and plotting facilities, capable of controlling many interceptions at once;
• *Type 8* – early models, in several marks, were transportable and mobile, superseded by Types 7 and 15;
• *Type 15* – in several marks, were transportable or fully mobile versions; many of the latter were sent overseas, often with Type 21 convoys (Type 13 plus Type 14) and with Type 11 (50 cm).

FIGHTER DIRECTION TENDERS (FDT)

A bold programme of work by TRE, RAE, John Brown's shipyards and the RAF, known officially as 'Project Baccy' (unofficially, '60 Group's Navy'), resulted in three complete, floating GCI stations (FDTs), plus an attendant ex-ASR pinnace, being available for the Normandy Invasion of 1944 (completion in some sixteen months, including trials and modifications, illustrates what can be achieved in wartime).

The FDTs, built on heavily-modified LSTs (Landing Ships, Tank), were comprehensively equipped with Type 11 and 15 radars and all associated equipment. Separate rooms were provided for radar transmitters, radar receivers, operation control, cypher work, VHF communications and Y service (monitoring enemy transmissions) as well as an open visual air-plotting post. During their fortnight of intensive, non-stop duty the three FDTs controlled interceptions accounting for some eighty enemy aircraft besides assisting countless rescues. At the end, sadly, FDT No. 216 was sunk and five radar operators lost their lives. FDTs contributed much to the success of the invasion.

So much for the bare background to GCI radar. We have skipped over the auxiliary but essential equipments for IFF and VHF ground-to-air radio, all of which had either to be installed permanently or carried in the mobile convoys, according to the type of station. In total, the range of equipment on a GCI station – including generators and intercom systems – demanded comprehensive knowledge and broadly-based skills on the part of the radar mechanics and technical officers. Their responsibilities matched and supported those of the quick-thinking operational staff. Teamwork was essential.

In the following accounts we read of the exploits of some who worked on GCI at home, in the Middle East and with the invasion forces on the Continent.

GCI AND THE BIGGIN HILL EXPERIMENT

Successful ground-controlled interceptions at night, like the earlier daytime interceptions derived from the coastal early-warning radar chain during the Battle of Britain, owed as much to the efficiency of everyone concerned as to the radars themselves. With least delay, radar data had to be plotted, assessed, converted into flight instructions, transmitted to the fighters and acted upon. The fact that unrelenting practice was needed to achieve this rapidly and smoothly was appreciated by one man above all others: Sir Henry Tizard, aviator of the First World War and a leading scientist.

Having encouraged the early radar workers throughout 1935 in the firm belief that their efforts would soon lead to a viable early-warning system, he realized that no time must be lost in getting the RAF accustomed to the use of intercept information transmitted from ground to air. It was essential to overcome the reluctance of some airmen to accept the idea of relying upon a stream of radioed instructions. Against strong opposition he instigated the series of RAF air exercises of 1936/7 which have gone down in history as the 'Biggin Hill Experiment', after the RAF fighter airfield in Kent where the work was based.

Even before radar had become operational, interception practice was possible with a high-frequency radio direction-finding system which enabled a ground-based fighter controller to monitor the location of his aircraft with fair accuracy. Thus, in exercises, some could act as free 'bandits' and, by direction-finding from several stations, their courses could be plotted. The controller could thus follow their progress and direct his 'intercepting' force against them.

Later, as radar became available, uninvolved civilian airliners could be plotted and 'intercepted'. Step by step, the procedures for ground control of fighters were thus evolved and refined. They became so well practised that when the war started the whole complex defence system with its network of radars, filter rooms, plotters and sector operations centres was ready to swing into action.

THE BIGGIN HILL EXPERIMENT

Air Marshal Sir Arthur McDonald, ***KCB, AFC***:

Sir Arthur McDonald

I served in fighter squadrons and took part in the air exercises in 1925, 1926 and 1927, and after eight years on ground engineering duties, went back to flying in 32 Squadron, Biggin Hill, during 1936 and 1937. I absolutely agree with the importance of what Tizard did through the medium of the Biggin Hill Experiment, and ever since 1940 have held the view that without Tizard we would have lost the Battle of Britain and the war.

Lord Swinton, Secretary of State for Air, visited Biggin Hill to see how we were getting on and said to me in the mess after lunch: 'I hope you young men realize that the whole future of this country depends on what you are doing down here at Biggin Hill.'

Winston Churchill, out of office at the time, drove up from Chartwell and sat for half an hour in the operations room watching the bomber and fighter plots moving across the table during a trial interception. He finally cut short the Station Commander's rather long-winded description of the telephone network with a typically Churchillian remark: 'I see, I see; and I suppose that when your pilots have intercepted the enemy they shoot him down with their Maxim guns.' (The Maxim machine-gun was the first type of machine-gun used by the British Army at the Battle of Omdurman in 1898, in which Churchill took part.)

Swinton and Churchill were civilians: among senior serving officers there was a marked lack of interest. There seems to have been a resentment that a programme of operational research should be under the control of a civilian scientist.

With one exception, no air staff officers from the Air Ministry, Fighter Command or 11 Group visited Biggin Hill or showed any interest. AOC (Air Officer Commanding) 11 Group carried out his annual inspection of Biggin Hill while the interception trials were in progress: he spent some time inspecting the administrative side of the station – cookhouses, barrack-rooms etc. – but went nowhere near the operations room. His only reference to the interception trials was: 'I do hope that Tizard will soon release 32 Squadron from all this ground control nonsense so that they can get on with their proper training.'

Proper training – for what? The next Hendon Air Display?

The only senior serving officer to visit Biggin Hill to find out how the trials were progressing was Dowding himself, who drove down from Bentley Priory (Stanmore) and who clearly did not share his own group commander's opinion that they were a waste of time.

He did make one input to the final result, though not one of sufficient importance, in my view, to justify the description of the resulting system as 'The Dowding System' – a term used by some historians. At the time of his visit we were still using basic English from the controller to give instructions to the pilots. Dowding suggested that in the interests of brevity, clarity and, perhaps, security, we should use some sort of code.

Next afternoon, there being no flying due to weather, I called in one of the flight-commanders and told him Dowding had suggested a code, that I could not think of anything, and would he gather some pilots round a table and concoct some sort of code and come back with the result at 4 p.m. The result was the well-known simple code, some words of which have passed into the English language: e.g. 'scramble' as applied to aircraft, aircrew – 'to take off hurriedly'.

The Biggin Hill Experiment was important because it provided a link between the only type of radar which was available in the opening stages of the Second World War, particularly at the time of the Battle of Britain, and a system of ground control of fighters which the German fighter leader Adolph Galland so much envied and admired.

The link was a fighter fixing system consisting of three HFDF (high-frequency direction-finding) stations in each sector, working from the transmissions of a special HF transmitter, controlled by a time-switch which switched on the transmitter automatically for 14 seconds in each minute, in sequence A, B, C, D. One special transmitter was in one aircraft of each formation, so that four formations could be tracked simultaneously on one frequency. The whole system was code-named 'Pipsqueak'.

How important was the Biggin Hill Experiment? Adolph Galland has been quoted as follows: 'The British had an extraordinary advantage, which we could never overcome throughout the entire war: radar and fighter control.' But the Germans had radar too, so what was the difference? Was it not the fact that we had done the Biggin Hill Experiment, and they had not done any development on similar lines?

Having taken part in it from August 1936 to December 1937, I am convinced that unless a team of people had been collected and kept together for over a year in order to concentrate their efforts on developing an entirely new system of fighter control, then no effective system would have evolved naturally by the outbreak of war in 1939.

No Biggin Hill Experiment – no Pipsqueak – no 'extraordinary advantage' (Galland) – no British victory in the Battle of Britain. As simple as that.

Tizard was absolutely right in 1936. The system could not have been improvised after the outbreak of war.

I think we all owe a lot to Tizard.

Pat Sparks *(née Pattison), LACW Clerk SD, tells the story of the 'Happidrome' at Sopley, Hampshire:*

Note: Most of this account was taken from Pat Sparks's own booklet, entitled *A Brief History of RAF Sopley*, from which she has very kindly given us permission to quote.

Pat Sparks

I was stationed at Sopley from 1942 to 1945. It was a small, free and easy unit from first to last. In the beginning there were no parades (not even pay or sick parades). Discipline was very relaxed – as long as a WAAF's hair was off her collar for inspections, regulations were largely disregarded.

Sopley Mark I was a small caravan which could easily have been towed by a Mini. This housed a couple of PPIs and had sufficient room for three people to plot and phone. There was also a Dennis truck which housed the usual primitive paraphernalia associated with radar screens, and further into the field was the aerial, which rather resembled a flattened birdcage. Inside the cabin at the base of the aerial sat two airmen – the binders – who pedalled a contraption like a static tandem bike. This was the method used to turn the aerial, and was controlled by the CO at the touch of a button, being stopped, reversed, or sent in whatever direction the controller wished. Later on, these aerials were power-driven.

A mobile GCI unit at Sopley in 1940, showing the separate transmitting and receiving aerial cabins which had to be kept 'in step' by the binders.

The work of a GCI station was to control the fighters from the ground until they had contact on their own AI radar.

In the centre of the control desk there was a large cathode ray tube on which had been painted the coastline of our area. On the tube, all aircraft coming within range produced a small blip which marked their position on the map. The crew gave readings in brisk tones to others at the far end of the caravan, who in turn were plotting the tracks of the aircraft, juggling nimbly with navigation computers and working out courses and speeds. Other crew members sat in front of another CRT working out the heights. The controller could identify friendly aircraft by asking the pilot to 'make your cockerel crow' (activate their IFF).

By the spring of 1941 Sopley could not serve the customers fast enough, and another radar beacon was set up near the GCI to act as a holding point so that the pilots could keep themselves in position until wanted. As soon as the first fighter was brought into contact with a 'bandit', the GCI had only to call up the next in line from the 'taxi rank' and so keep the flow going.

On 7 May 1941, the King visited Middle Wallop and then Sopley. When he arrived, the controller had a contact with a bandit well out to sea, giving him plenty of time to arrange a 'Command Performance' for His Majesty. The bandit was chased towards the coast and towards Sopley itself, and in due course the controller invited the royal party to view the aerial battle from outside the ops room. They soon spotted the Heinkel with John Cunningham on its tail, and were able to watch the kill for themselves as the enemy aircraft plunged to the earth in flames.

In due course the caravanserai was replaced by Sopley Mark II (the 'Intermediate') – a hutted mobile; this was fitted with increased power, the PPIs were improved, and the height system grew better as operators improved their technique.

Then came the 'Final' – or 'Happidrome' as it was called. This was a permanent building designed for the purpose, with cabins for interception purposes, proper height-reading areas, and a large room housing a table showing the whole area we covered, which was divided into grid squares.

Plots were passed down the line of command, and from these given positions we placed a metal arrow on the table, giving the fix and direction of a flight. We used metal rods with a magnetic tip, and kept track of several flights at a time by moving arrows coloured according to the 'colour change clock'. Each five-minute period was divided into red, yellow and blue sections, which distinguished any old plots not yet removed.

On busy days we had a monitor who would watch out for these and also make up metal plaques which gave the number of the flight, with 'H' for 'Hostile' or 'F' for 'Friendly'. The detail of each flight was also put up on a 'tote' which showed the height, number of aircraft, etc. Above the ops room table was a gallery where the controller sat watching all movements.

We also had cabins where radar screens were operated and our fighter aircraft were controlled from plots on the screen until the navigator/radar op. in the plane could see contact on his AI.

The site now acquired guardrooms, rest rooms, a canteen and controller's rest room plus a PBX telephone exchange and an apparatus room with complete telecommunications.

We worked closely with 604 Squadron at Middle Wallop, which included famous pilots such as John ('Cats-Eyes') Cunningham and Jeremy Howard-Williams. We worked with many other squadrons as well as 604: 406 Canadian Squadron, 465, 151 and 125 Squadrons all worked with Sopley, some operating from Hurn.

Sopley's first 'kill' was on 4 March 1941 (although 'damaged' had been claimed before that date). In total, Sopley was responsible for over 100 enemy planes shot down between 1941 and 1945.

Air-sea rescue work was also carried out, and many nights were spent with planes stooging around up and down the Channel looking for crew who had ditched in the area.

D-Day at Sopley

On 5 June 1944 I had already been on the 8–1 watch, and most of my friends had gone into Christchurch, when I met the CO in the hallway at our billet. I received instant promotion – unpaid and very temporary – to NCO (non-commissioned officer) until I could hand over to whichever NCO returned first. I was to forbid anyone from leaving the station, and anyone who returned was not to go out again. We were to go on duty an hour early, at 2200 hours.

As soon as we'd been bussed to ops, the CO told us – as if we hadn't guessed – that this was the day we had all been waiting for.

My first job was behind the 'tote', the board on which was displayed all available information regarding aircraft – number, height, designation, etc. It became very hectic as information was passed continuously, changing frequently. We were given details of shipping, and the Channel marked on our tables was soon covered in model ships. Plots were coming through as fast as tellers could talk, and eventually I got my first relief, at about 5 a.m. I dashed to the canteen, where everything that night was self-service. If lucky, there might be a cup of tea; if not, you put the kettle on for the next person. A quick dash to the loo, then back to take over another position.

At dawn we were allowed a break to go up on the roof, from where we could see the gun flashes across the channel. We were told it was probably HMS *Belfast*. It was a horrendous sight.

All night we were thinking of our many friends who were taking part, either in the air or on the sea. Some 6,000 ships of various sizes, 13,000 aircraft and a quarter of a million men were out there – many prayers were said, in silence, even while our heads were full of grid references.

0800 hours came at last and we stumbled out of ops for the waiting bus. We were all exhausted and wanted only a cup of tea and bed and quickly to sleep, for we were on watch again at 5 p.m. No sooner had we got to sleep than we were woken by the cooks to tell us the joyful news that the invasion had started!

Next day, all our watch were given a copy of the letter from Eisenhower which had been given to all who took part in D-Day. I treasure that letter more than my medals – everyone got those too, but not many WAAFs have the Supreme Commander's letter.

Group Captain John Cunningham, CBE, DSO, DFC, *nightfighter pilot, describes the early days of using GCI/AI radar*:

John Cunningham

At the beginning of 1940 I was in 604 Squadron, which was a nightfighter squadron equipped with Blenheims. One day, a Blenheim appeared from Martlesham – one of the first of these aircraft to be equipped with a radar set – and it was so secret that we at North Weald, who had Blenheims with no radar, were only allowed to have a look at this aircraft. We were told that in due course it would be developed and make our job possible at night.

Up until that time we had had to rely solely on searchlights for nightfighting, which were pretty useless; but in that winter of 1939/40 there was no German activity at night over Britain, which was fortunate because, until we got radar fitted into the Blenheims in July 1940, we were really quite ineffective at night.

The Blenheim, though a nice aeroplane to fly, was useless as a nightfighter, having neither the armament nor the radar, and it was soon replaced by the

Beaufighter, which appeared in September 1940. My squadron at that time was based at Middle Wallop, and our area of activity was roughly between the Isle of Wight and Lyme Bay – an area covering a large amount of German activity when the bombers were heading for the Midlands.

It wasn't until early 1941 that we got our first GCI station, at Sopley, near Christchurch, using radar to direct us into a position to within three or four miles of the aircraft we were trying to intercept.

My first two successful night combats actually took place before Sopley was operational. We used to patrol up and down the Channel across the path of incoming bombers, and on the first of these occasions we were just inland when the searchlights indicated that there was an intruder crossing the Channel heading inland towards the Midlands. I could see these searchlights on cloud, and my radar operator fortunately picked the plane up on his screen (we were equipped with our own AI radar). He managed to hold on to this contact and direct me in until I had a visual on it myself, and we successfully shot it down. It was a Ju88, and it finished up on the ground near West Wittering. That was the first night bomber shot down in Britain during the war.

It is a sad fact, but never during the whole war were we able to rely on IFF. We had to rely on our own eyes, so that any interception could take place only after we had established a radar contact and closed in to a position from which we could positively identify what it was. So one of the problems of nightfighting was that you had to close in and position yourself beneath the aircraft you were following in order to study the outline. If you were beneath it, there was always some light from the stars above it, and if above it, there was light reflected from the water below, so you could see its silhouette and make your identification. In 1941/2 most of the bombers coming over were Heinkel 111s, which were very distinctive.

But once we had the system going properly, with the combination of ground control and air interception, our lives changed dramatically. We were lucky: our controller at Sopley was quite exceptional – a marvellous chap (Squadron Leader Brown), running a very happy and successful GCI station. He had been a pilot before the war, and later on some of our own pilots, when they'd done a tour of operations, would take over as controllers on GCI stations, and naturally, they were ideal for the job.

We had total faith in 'Brownie' and it wasn't until people became more experienced in the use of radar that we began to perfect what was called a 'freelance' contact, when the radar operator in the plane suddenly got a contact with no information from the ground about which way it was going. This needed a high degree of skill and was a tremendous asset, because the ground controller could only deal with, perhaps, two nightfighters at a time, so if there were more than that in the air in our sector it was very useful if the spare ones which were waiting to be taken over could make use of any radar contact, without knowing whether it was hostile or friendly until they closed in and identified it.

The Day the King Came Down

The King had wanted to visit a nightfighter squadron, and in May 1941 it was arranged by Fighter Command that he should visit 604 Squadron, based at Middle Wallop. He came down in the late afternoon to meet and talk to the aircrew. When he stopped in front of Jimmy Rawnsley, my radar operator, he asked him what his score was so far. A bit abashed, Jimmy replied: 'Nine, Sir.'

'Nine, eh?' said His Majesty, 'Well, will you get another one for me tonight?'

This was a tall order. A Command Performance!

We climbed into our aircraft, and while we were getting airborne, the King was being driven down to Sopley so that he could watch what would happen that night. By the time he got there it was getting dark – the time when any enemy activity would be likely to happen.

We were patrolling somewhere in mid-Channel when Brown at Sopley suddenly said to us: 'We have a customer coming in,' and directed me to a position approximately two or three miles behind it. Presently, Jimmy said, 'I have a contact.' He would only ever say this when he felt absolutely confident that he had a contact, and that was the moment when we told Sopley and switched off contact with them (it was vital at this point that I should have only Jimmy talking to me, who was in the back of the Beaufighter interpreting his radar picture).

He passed me the range, elevation and azimuth of this aircraft and brought me in

King George VI visited Middle Wallop on 7 May 1941. He is shown talking to Squadron Leader John ('Cats Eyes') Cunningham; behind the King is Air Chief Marshal Sir Sholto Douglas.

to a point well below and behind it. Because we were coming in across the Channel, we waited before closing in on him until we got over land, because the contact's tail gunner would be watching out and we didn't want to be silhouetted against the sea.

So it was not until we were well over land that we closed in on him, got underneath him and I visually identified it as a Heinkel 111. But at this point I always asked Jimmy to leave his radar set, turn round and look out above and see what he thought it was, without telling him my opinion until he confirmed it. On this occasion he agreed with me, and we started to get into position for firing. Being below it for identification purposes, I had to move slowly in formation with it and come up gradually to its height, because our cannon (we had four fixed cannon, forward under our feet) had to be at the same level as the target to hit it effectively. This was always a slow business, climbing to the correct level.

We were successful, and our target burst into flames. I moved into a position alongside it and watched; it continued for a while, then dived down and went straight into the ground with a great flash and bang. It crashed somewhere to the west of Sopley, and the King had his Royal Command Performance. We heard later that he was very impressed.

At the end of 1942 I went to No. 85 Squadron, near Ware, where we had Mosquitoes, which were a delight to fly. The Beaufighter had not been fast enough for the job; the Mosquito was 100 m.p.h. faster. Our squadron was moved to West Malling in Kent in May 1943, and our higher speed enabled us to shoot down FW190s at night.

There is no doubt that anyone who ever did any nightfighting would confirm that the advent of GCI/AI radar was the turning point in our operations. The press inflicted upon me the unwelcome nickname of 'Cats-Eyes' – little did they know that the real cats' eyes were our highly-secret and very successful radar sets!

CHAPTER FIVE

Calibration of Radar Stations

G.D. Speake, OBE, *Technical Officer, 60 Group RAF*:

G.D. Speake

Calibration of both CH and GCI stations was organized by a small team based at 60 Group Headquarters at Leighton Buzzard. They issued guidance notes, arranged courses, maintained central records and carried out other functions which one would expect from a central organization. For example, one such activity was to prepare and circulate charts from which one could read off true height of aircraft above the curved earth surface from a measured range and angle of elevation.

However, the practical work of calibration was delegated to Wing Headquarters, where specialist sections were set up for the purpose (in the early part of the war they were composed largely of civilians, but by late 1942 all had been absorbed into the RAF).

Preparation

As and when a station became due for calibration, one, or sometimes two, members of the section would be assigned to the job. On arrival at the station, one of the first tasks would be to ensure, with the cooperation of the resident technical staff and possibly also of a quarterly overhaul party, that it was in a fully operational state. For example, it was vital to ensure that the signals from the two components of each of the crossed dipoles used for direction-finding were in phase.

One of the more daunting tasks facing the calibrator was to climb the receiver mast with an avometer to check continuity of the feeders, and to ensure that the reflector dipole, used to determine whether a target was in front of or behind the station, was being brought into operation when needed.

CH

For azimuth calibration of east coast stations, autogiros were used, but since – unlike helicopters – they could not hover without some forward movement, they flew in as tight a circle as possible over a selected point, and the measured bearings from the station were averaged and compared with the known bearing of that point. For west coast stations, the autogiro was replaced by a Hornet Moth fixed-wing aircraft.

The aircraft, which was equipped with a squegging oscillator tuned to the station frequency, was flown directly over the station on designated bearings, and was tracked by a theodolite until it was no longer visible. The pilot was then called on the R/T and requested to return on the reciprocal bearing, again being tracked by the theodolite as soon as the aircraft came into view. A landline telephone connection between the theodolite observer and operations room ensured that the theodolite readings and goniometer observations were correlated in time so that minor variations of the aircraft from the planned course were not critical.

The advantage of this method over the alternative, whereby an aircraft circled over known landmarks, was that it was only necessary to know the map coordinates of the station and one other landmark, such as a church, in order to set up the theodolite. Thereafter, it was possible to take measurements on any desired bearing, which was particularly important when the station was right on the shoreline and the main area of interest was out to sea.

Charts and/or tables showing measured vs. true bearing were produced on site and, in the fixed stations, were used as the basis for setting up the electrical calculator employed as a plotting aid. On the transportable (ACH) stations, the calibrator used this information to produce what was called a 'distorted rose', which was a circular scale on which the bearing marks had been displaced from the usual position to the extent that an operator using them with goniometer readings and a measured range obtained a true plot. This was overlaid on the plotting table.

During the calibration exercise, the people primarily involved were: the operator at the tracking console; the theodolite observer; a person to note theodolite readings at regular intervals (it was generally impracticable for one person to be responsible for tracking the aircraft and to break off frequently to take a reading); a recorder in the ops room to note down both goniometer and theodolite readings, and an operator to maintain R/T contact with the pilot of the aircraft. The calibration officer normally acted either as goniometer operator or as theodolite tracker, depending on the skills of the other people present, and the other tasks were carried out by station personnel.

For height calibration – i.e. the correlation of a goniometer reading obtained by comparison of signals from two dipoles at different heights and the angle of elevation of a target giving rise to them – it was necessary to use an aircraft capable of flying at similar heights to those expected from potential enemy targets.

Typically, a Blenheim – equipped with a repeater which received a signal from the ground transmitter and re-transmitted an enhanced one on the same frequency – was used. The calibrating officer normally contacted the local met. office prior to a flight and asked what would be the altimeter reading for a prescribed height (say, 5,000 ft). He passed this information in code form to the pilot, who then carried out a series of flights on radial bearings from the station. To obtain information relating to higher angles of elevation, a similar procedure would be carried out with the aircraft at, say, 18,000 ft.

Since the relationship between the range and the angle of elevation of a target above a curved surface in an atmosphere which refracts radio waves is not a simple trigonometrical one, charts prepared by the headquarters team at 60 Group were used to derive angles of elevation from the known height and measured range, and the results were used to provide the necessary data for the station's Electrical Calculator. On some sites, particularly those where the land sloped sharply towards the sea, the conversion between goniometer reading and angle of elevation varied sharply with azimuth, and it was important that flights were taken on a sufficient number of bearings to take that into account.

It will be apparent that calibration, either azimuth or height, was not intrinsically a lengthy procedure, but was almost always prolonged because the flying conditions had to be favourable, and in particular, a Hornet Moth had to be in visible range for some miles from the station. (It is fair to say also that a pilot could not be expected to take the same risks with his aircraft that he might have done in carrying out an operation against the enemy.) Therefore, it was not unusual for a calibration officer to be on a station for two weeks or more before a satisfactory outcome was achieved, but throughout this period the station was maintained in a fully operational state.

GCI

The procedures for calibrating a GCI station were simpler than those for a CH because no appreciable azimuth errors were likely to occur, the stations being on flat sites inland. Moreover, even had such errors been present, they would be applicable equally to the target and to the intercepting fighter. It was therefore only necessary to determine from flight results the relationship between angle of elevation of a target and the ratio of the signals received from the two aerials at different mean heights which formed the basis of the system.

As with the CH system, an aircraft was flown out at a constant height from a position over the station, and simultaneous readings of range and ratio of signals were taken. The larger signal was assigned 10 units, and at any given range the calibrator would assess the smaller signal to as close an accuracy as he regarded practicable: he might, for example, call out '10 to 5½' or '3¾ to 10'. The results from outward and return runs would be plotted, and on a good site, an experienced calibrator would get a consistency between outward and inward observations of a few per cent.

One significant difference between flights carried out for CH and GCI calibration was that in the former case the aircraft was entirely under the pilot's control but carrying out a series of operations agreed in advance, or during the flight, with the calibration team, whereas in the case of the GCI the aircraft was subject to the instructions of a ground control officer.

Another difference was that while it was possible by theoretical means to get a reasonably close approximation to the results of a height calibration of a GCI where the mean heights of the antennae were known and the site was level, it was virtually impossible to do so on a typical CH.

K.S. Platt, *Radio Mechanic (Air) describes calibration duties*:

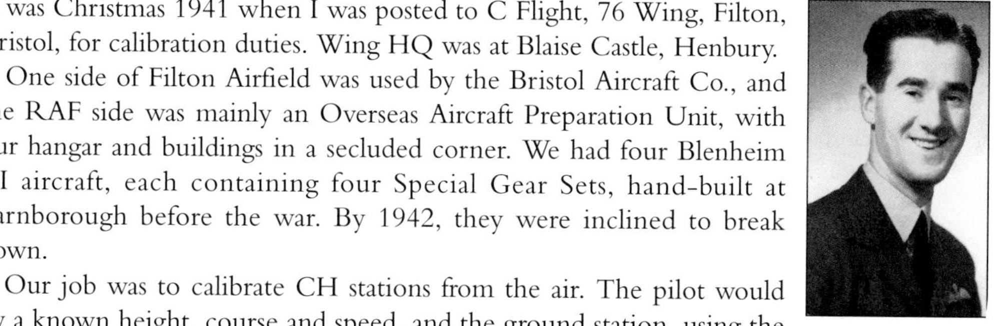
K.S. Platt

It was Christmas 1941 when I was posted to C Flight, 76 Wing, Filton, Bristol, for calibration duties. Wing HQ was at Blaise Castle, Henbury.

One side of Filton Airfield was used by the Bristol Aircraft Co., and the RAF side was mainly an Overseas Aircraft Preparation Unit, with our hangar and buildings in a secluded corner. We had four Blenheim VI aircraft, each containing four Special Gear Sets, hand-built at Farnborough before the war. By 1942, they were inclined to break down.

Our job was to calibrate CH stations from the air. The pilot would fly a known height, course and speed, and the ground station, using the specific 'blip' created by our Special Gear, would adjust their controls to show our particular aircraft following the known course and at the prescribed height and speed.

When we first joined the flight, the Special Gear, housed in the aircraft floor near the bomb bay, was operated by the air gunner. He had to come out of his turret, plug into the gear and thus lose intercom contact with the pilot, leaving the aircraft unprotected. By February 1942 the order came that in future the radar mechanic would fly with the gear, leaving the airgunner to do his proper job.

Thus began over 200 hours' flying, recorded in my log book as 'SD' (Special Duty), doubtless for security purposes. We covered the area approximately between Southampton and Lyme Bay. The south-western peninsular was covered by a flight based, I believe, at what is now Exeter Airport. Then we began again on the Welsh coast from Pembroke to Aberporth. Sometimes we calibrated direct from home, but on some occasions we landed at other airfields such as Warmwell, Colerne, Carew, Cheriton and Aberporth.

The sets were old and frequently unserviceable, so at one time we successfully converted an IFF set to provide an identifiable blip to a ground station. But eventually we received, to our delight, four new 'factory-built' sets, supplied, I believe, by Ferranti. They looked quite splendid, complete with coloured knobs. But alas, they didn't work! They gave a blip on the screen about 6 in long. However, after much research, we identified the offending component and were able to get them working properly.

I worked on calibration for about seventeen months before leaving the flight to train as a pilot.

Valerie Sullivan *(née La Niece), CH Radar Operator:*

I remember the Calibration Flight coming to Bride, Isle of Man, in late spring or early summer 1943. The plane was piloted by a Flight-Lieutenant Cohen, based at Speke Airport, Liverpool. He flew around the radar site at various heights, ranges and vectors as requested by his team on the ground or up the tower with their theodolite. The tricky part for the radar operators on duty was communication – liaising between pilot and calibration party via an R/T set in the R-block, which was rarely used at other times. Getting tuned in was slow work – the pilot became frustrated trying to maintain contact and having to shout above the noise of his engine. Not a good afternoon at all, as I recall.

A few days later, a notice appeared to the effect that Flt. Lt. Cohen would like two operators from each station in the wing to go on a short course at Liverpool to learn how to operate the R/T correctly so that they could gain first-hand experience of his difficulty in hearing instructions from the ground. Almost every radar op. at Bride volunteered.

At the same time, volunteers were sought for a W/T (wireless telegraphy) course. This was in case of invasion and the landlines being cut, so that information could be passed to filter room by W/T. Two names only appeared on that list – mine and Penny Young's. (Well, we'd been Girl Guides and knew our Morse Code!).

Imagine our surprise and delight when the WAAF officer called us into her office and told us that we could go on the R/T course at Speke. She had intended drawing lots, but as we were the only ones willing to go on the WT course, she was offering us the places on the R/T course as well. (Who says 'never volunteer'!)

We went to Speke for two or three days and were given instruction on operating the R/T set correctly both on the ground and in the air. Half of the course members went up in the Dominie[1] and operated a set within the plane, while the others manned another set on the ground. After twenty minutes or so the plane landed and the operators changed places. Thus as well as learning how to operate the R/T set, we learned to appreciate the pilot's difficulties.

The following is reproduced from the Proceedings of the Symposium of 'Fifty Years of the Cavity Magnetron', 21 February 1990, the School of Physics and Space Research, University of Birmingham (part of a paper given by J.R. Atkinson, who had worked with Watson Watt):

From: Air Ministry, Director of Radar
To: C. in C. Fighter Command.
Subject: Interference to Church services by experiments conducted with an autogyro.

In view of possible repercussions from the Church and the Press, you may wish to be advised of the regrettable and unusual results of an experiment conducted under the direction of TRE, Worth Matravers.

[1] Dominie – RAF name for the De Havilland Rapide. Many of these biplanes were in use at the airfield near Yatesbury as 'flying classrooms' for wireless operators being trained there.

J.R. Atkinson

The facts, as far as we have been able to ascertain them, are as follows:-

On a Sunday morning recently, the Scientific Officer in charge of tests instructed the pilot of an autogyro to proceed to the village of Kimmeridge, Dorset, and hover over the church steeple, which afforded an admirable fixed point for calibration purposes.

It would appear that, in their observation of this vital aspect of the national effort, all concerned had momentarily forgotten the day of the week and the fact that Matins would be in progress.

In accordance with his instructions therefore, the pilot brought his autogryo into position, at a low altitude over the steeple, and hovered during the entire proceedings of the Service, thereby, it is feared, making devotions difficult, and the sermon inaudible.

The pilot observed the congregation leaving the church, and regarding the autogyro with expressions of annoyance and distaste, but continued hovering in accordance with instructions.

Shortly afterwards he was startled by two loud explosions and, looking down to ascertain the cause, was surprised to see the Vicar standing in the graveyard with a smoking shotgun with which, the pilot deduced, he had just attempted to secure a left and right at the autogyro.

Considering that the interest of science would best be served by withdrawing from the danger area, before the Vicar had time to reload, the pilot returned to his base at Worth Matravers.

The Scientific Officer, however, was of the opinion that he was fully justified in ordering the pilot to risk further salvoes of AA from the Vicar, in view of the urgent importance of completing tests.

The pilot, to whose intrepid 'sangfroid' you may wish to draw the attention of the appropriate authorities, resumed his station over the steeple during the late afternoon and evening, a period which unfortunately coincided with Evensong, which the Scientific Officer – doubtless by sheer inadvertence – had overlooked.

No further AA fire was encountered, but signs of alarm and despondency among the parishioners were not lacking, and the Vicar was observed marshalling his flock and giving them urgent instructions.

There was much coming and going from the vicarage and the village. The pilot observed that the parishioners were laying out white objects among the graves in the churchyard. Slightly reducing his altitude, he was able to identify these objects as bed linen, sheets, pants, vests, nightshirts and so forth, but it is understood that these articles were specifically brought from the vicarage and neighbouring cottages and that any reports that may be received to the effect that the parishioners were disrobing in the churchyard under the Vicar's instructions, should be treated with reserve.

Eventually, this assortment of linen and underclothes was seen to take the form of huge letters spread across the churchyard, which the pilot was able to identify without difficulty as a message clearly intended for himself:

The message read: '*In the name of God – GO.*'

In our view, the pilot was correct in interpreting this as a sign that his presence was unwelcome to the civilian population, and not desirous of unnecessarily hazarding his aircraft by further AA fire, he decided, no doubt wisely, to terminate the test and landed safely at Worth Matravers.

It is not unreasonable to anticipate the possibility of unfavourable criticism being directed against this branch of the Service through the usual channels, and you may wish to be apprised of the facts in order to consider appropriate action.

(Sgd.) Group Captain . . . .
Signals 4.

CHAPTER SIX

Radionavigational Aids

The equipments considered elsewhere in this book fall firmly into the category of radar – they were designed to locate the position in space of a remote target without its active cooperation. In other words, they did so without transmission from the target, relying entirely upon the passive reflection of radio waves from its structure.

None of the equipments in this chapter, classified as 'navaids', relied upon the reflection of radio waves. Thus, unlike radar, they did not suffer the same severe reduction of signal strength with increasing range. (See the Appendix: when range doubles, radar signal strength falls to one-sixteenth; but for radio communication, only to a quarter.)

We have included these non-radar navaids (such as Gee, Gee-H, Oboe and Loran) because their technology is so closely related to radar and because many of our contributors were involved with them. They were developed by radar scientists and engineers, maintained and operated by radar personnel and often sited with radar equipments. They used pulse and precision-timing techniques to levels of sophistication frequently exceeding those of normal radar, and they required the highest skills in those concerned with them.

When Gee (AMES Type 7000) and Oboe (AMES Type 9000) ground stations were installed, the secrecy surrounding them exceeded even the high level accorded to radar. Where these equipments shared sites with existing radar stations, access was normally withheld from 'ordinary' radar personnel and could lead to curiosity, speculation and possibly envy among those not 'in the know'. Sometimes an operator or a mechanic would disappear from normal radar duties without prior warning; when friends asked what had happened, all they could be told was 'gone on 7K' or 'posted to 9K', and the mystery deepened – until one day it happened to you!

GEE (7000 or 7K)

Gee was the most widely-used radionavigational aid of the war. Thousands of Allied aircraft and many vessels of the Royal Navy were suitably equipped. It possessed two great attractions. First, no transmission was required from the user, and so radio silence could be maintained at all times – an especially valuable point when over or near enemy territory. Second, as a consequence of the first, it could not be saturated by the number of simultaneous users (D-Day, when it was used to a truly vast extent, has been dubbed 'Gee-Day').

Credit for the concept is due to R.J. Dippy of Bawdsey Research Station. Although the idea was considered shortly before the war, it was not followed up then due to the pressure of essential early-warning radar work. However, when it became painfully clear that Bomber Command desperately needed a significant improvement over its traditional methods of astral navigation and dead-reckoning, it was developed as a high-priority project. Service trials began in the early part of 1941, and it was used extensively on operations from the spring of 1942 onwards, despite some eventual German jamming.

The range at which Gee could be used operationally, measured from ground stations in the UK, depended upon aircraft height and reception conditions. In general, a maximum figure of around 350 miles seems to be typical for aircraft flying high in the absence of jamming or other interference. At such long ranges, accuracy of a navigational fix was in the region of a few miles. Gee was extensively used as a means for bombers to approach target areas before switching over to more precise systems (inevitably breaking radio silence) for the final run-in. It was particularly valuable as a reliable means of navigating back to base after a raid, its accuracy increasing and the possibility of enemy jamming reducing as the range decreased. Returning aircrew owed much to Gee.

Gee was the first of several successful radionavigational systems based on a grid (hence the name 'Gee') of hyperbolic lattice lines drawn on a map of the territory. Others were Loran (an American system of much longer range but initially somewhat lower accuracy), and Decca (an accurate system, employing the phase difference of continuous waves rather than the time difference of pulses) was used by minesweepers for the D-Day invasion. (Loran – now much improved – and Decca systems have survived to this day, even with the advent of satellite navigational aids.)

HOW GEE WORKED

The principle of Gee is superbly elegant and easy to understand if approached step by step: we hope readers already conversant with the subject will bear with the following such explanation in twelve steps. Unfortunately, brief descriptions sometimes tend to omit vital points, leading to confusion. Even as great a writer and superb historian as Sir Winston Churchill, in a statement entirely sufficient in its context, can put the enquiring reader on the wrong track when he writes: ' . . . a device called 'Gee', by which radio pulses were sent out simultaneously from three stations . . . '.[1] As seen opposite, the radiated pulses, while on the same radio frequency and synchronized, are not simultaneous, but *sequential.*

1 Fig. (a) represents the plan view of a pair of radio stations. Station A radiates a series of short pulses in all directions.

2 Station B has a receiver tuned to Station A so that, after a delay due to the travel-time of the radio wave from A to B, it receives the A pulse. Station B also has a transmitter, similar to that at A, but only after it has received the A pulse does it transmit a pulse of its own. Thus, because A commands B to transmit,

[1] A fine summary of navaids can be found in W.S. Churchill, *The Second World War*, Vol. IV, Ch. XVI, Cassell & Co. Ltd, London, 1951.

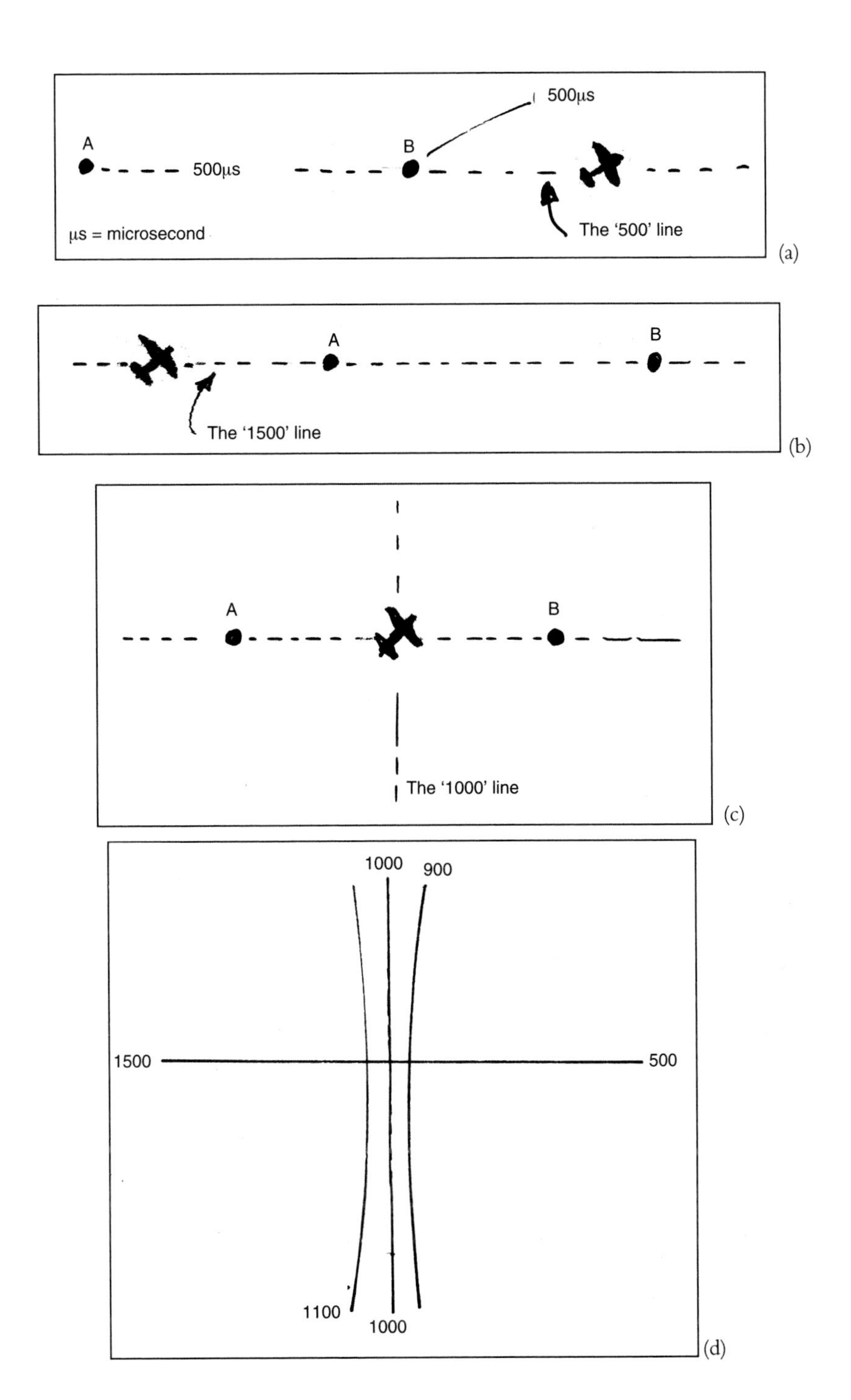
500μs
A
B
500μs
μs = microsecond
The '500' line
(a)
A
B
The '1500' line
(b)
A
B
The '1000' line
(c)
1000
900
1500
500
1100
1000
(d)

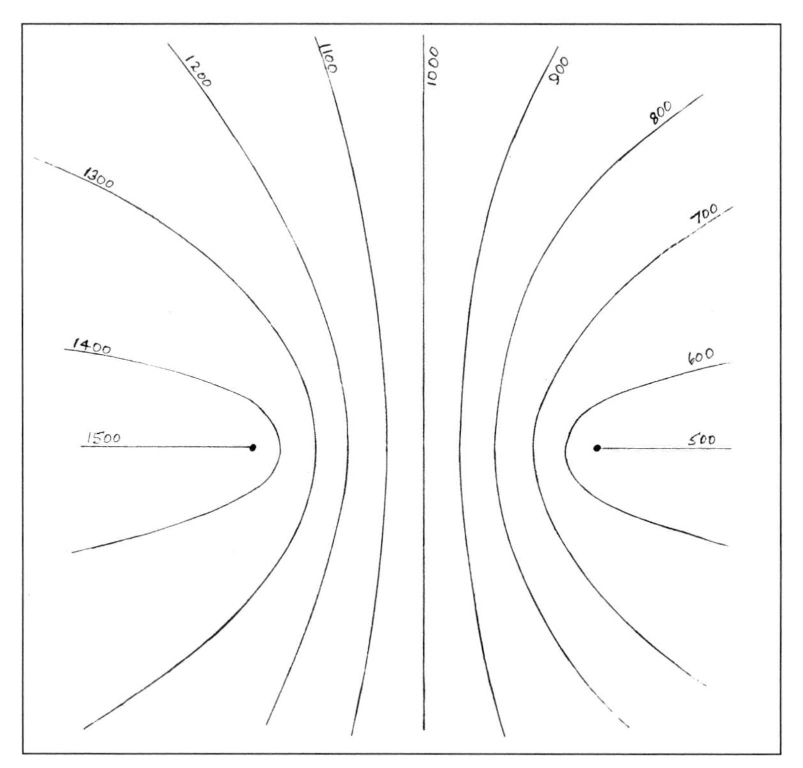

(e) The basic grid of constant time differences produced by master and slave.

they are known, respectively, as 'master' and 'slave'. The two stations are separated by many miles – in practice, perhaps a hundred – and an aircraft flying within the coverage of both would receive the A and the B pulses.

3 Let us suppose that the transit time of a radio wave from A to B is a nice, round figure of 500 microseconds. This is not untypical, since it represents a distance of just over 93 miles. Within the slave station, some inevitable delay must occur between reception and transmission, and in order that this shall be constant, unaffected by drift in the circuits, some additional, adjustable delay is deliberately added. Operators, who tediously monitored the total delay between reception and transmission, continually made corrections to maintain a constant overall delay. Let us suppose that the total delay within the slave is also 500 microseconds and look at the result for aircraft in different positions.

4 Consider first an aircraft at a point dead in line with both stations to the right of B. It will receive first the A pulse and then, 500 microseconds later, the B pulse; the 500-microsecond time difference being the 'wake-up' time of the slave as the A pulse passes by. Note that *anywhere along that line*, providing the receiver is within range of both stations, the observed time difference is *always* 500 microseconds. So we can label that line '500'.

5 Fig. (b). Now consider an aircraft at a point dead in line with both stations, but on the other side. As before, A and B pulses will be received, but the time difference

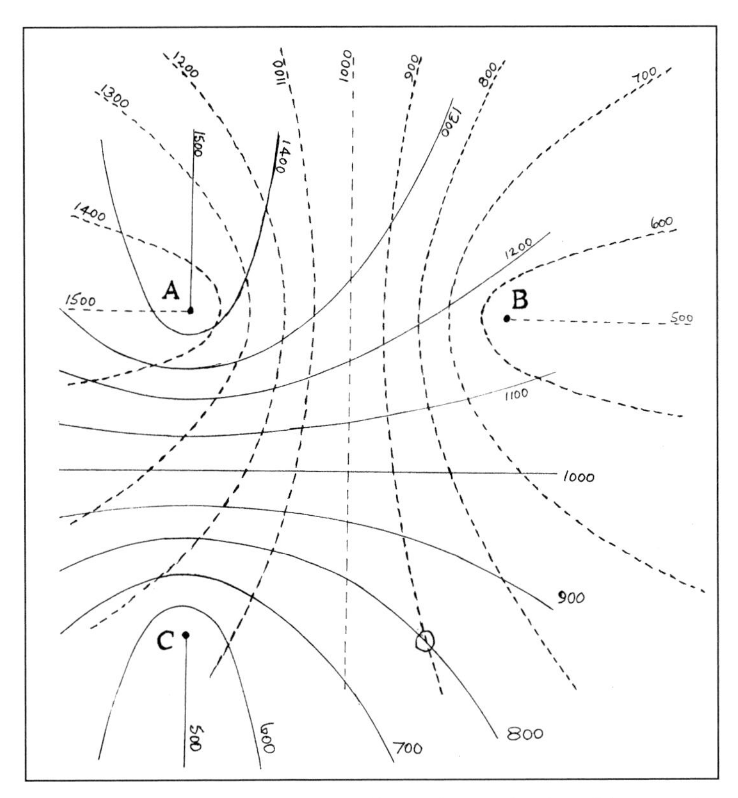

(f) How a lattice chart is produced by a master and two slaves. The dotted lines are due to A and B stations; the solid lines to A and C. The circle at bottom right indicates a fix due to a time difference of 900 microseconds between A and B pulses, and 800 between A and C pulses. Here, for simplicity, the time differences are given in microseconds. In practice, Gee maps were superimposed on maps of a given area and calibrated in Gee-units. Intermediate lines were included for finer resolution. Sets of lines were printed in different colours according to the slave producing them (for example, B slave produced red lines, C slave green).

between them will be greater. The A pulse travels directly to the aircraft, but the slave pulse is now delayed by 1,500 microseconds (500 for the A pulse to reach B, plus 500 delay within the slave station, plus another 500 for the return journey to the master station which, having no receiver, ignores it while it passes by to the aircraft). Note again that at any point along this straight line to the left of the master station (within range of both stations of course) the time difference between the pulses will always be 1,500 microseconds. We label it accordingly.

6 Fig. (c). Now consider the case of an aircraft sited exactly midway between the master and slave stations. Clearly, the time of travel from each is the same, so the time difference will be 1,000 microseconds (500 for the A pulse to reach B, plus 500 delay within the slave). And the same is true anywhere on a line drawn through this centre point and perpendicular to the baseline between A and B. So we can label this line '1,000'.

7 Fig. (d). Putting together the results so far, we have an embryo navigational

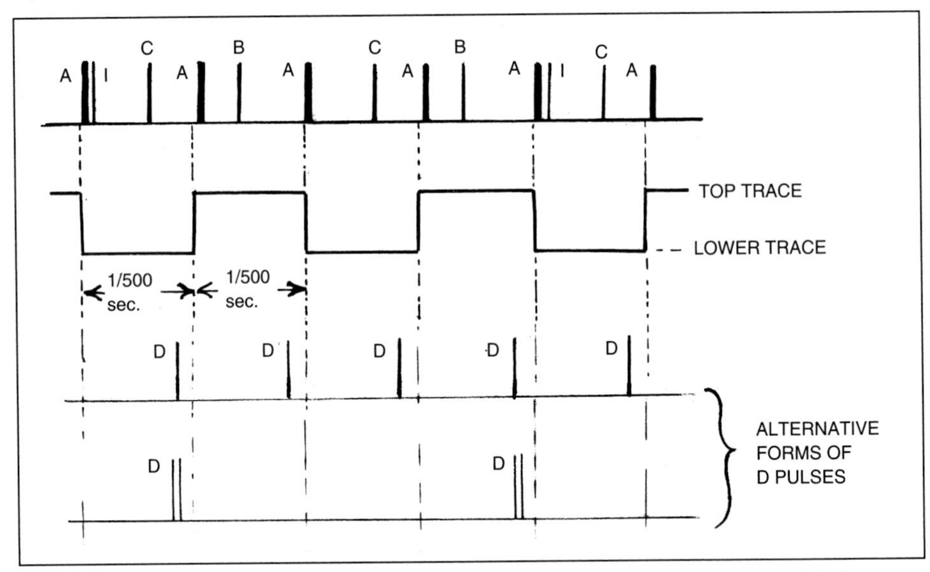

(g) The sequence of Gee pulses. The D slave may transmit single pulses, one per 1/500 second period, or double pulses every third period. In either case it appears on both upper and lower traces of a Gee display and is identifiable.

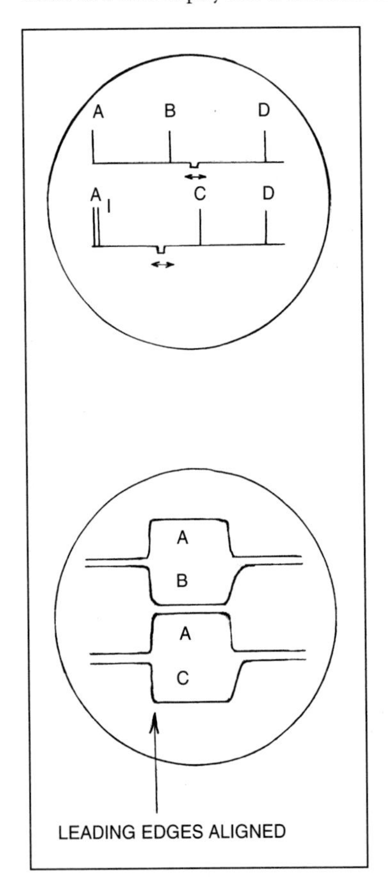

(h) Above: Full form of display on Gee indicator in the aircraft. Four strobes (expanded time base areas) are provided, one under each A pulse and one in each of the little moveable buckets.
Below: The strobe display for accurate fixing. This is obtained by putting slave pulses in buckets and adjusting strobes until the leading edges line up. Then calibration pips (not shown) could be used to measure the time differences accurately, for application to the lattice chart.

grid. Measurement in the aircraft of the differences in arrival time of the A and B pulses is beginning to give a clue to its position – simple enough if the difference is 500, 1,000 or 1,500 microseconds, but what if other time differences are indicated? For example, suppose it were 1,100 – where might the aircraft be? The answer is somewhere on a curved line just to the left of the straight '1,000' line. And we could also construct a '900' line, curving the other way, just to the right of the '1,000' line. With patience, a complete series of constant-time-difference lines may be drawn to fill in the gaps from 500 to 900 and from 1,100 to 1,500. (Each of these lines takes the form of a hyperbola.) (e)

8 So far, if our aircraft can measure the difference in arrival time of the pulses, it can tell on which line (or between which lines) it is located. All that is necessary to get a fix is to have two such sets of lines overlaid on the same map, and to find the time difference for each: the intersection of the lines will fix the position. This can be done by giving the master another slave, located elsewhere (Fig. (f)). Constant time-difference lines of A and B pulses were RED; A and C, GREEN.

9 We now have the basic elements of a Gee chain. Since all the transmitters work on the same radio frequency, they are all tuned in at once on the aircraft receiver; so how can the navigator (happily provided with maps, complete with red and green Gee lattice lines) tell which pulse belongs to which station? The answer is fourfold: it lies in the pulse repetition rates; an identification pulse added to A pulses; the sequence of the pulses, and the particular form of the Gee display.

10 All Gee pulses are quite short – just a few microseconds – and are similar to radar pulses, except that they are more carefully shaped and controlled. The A master station transmits 500 pulses per second, with an extra 'ident' pulse after every fourth. B and C slaves work alternately, each transmitting 250 pulses per second. The sequence of pulses is: A+Ident-C; A-B; A-C; A-B; A+Ident-C . . . (see Fig. (g)).

11 Fig. (h). The Gee display in the aircraft has 500 horizontal traces per second, alternately displaced vertically. In consequence, A pulses appear on both traces, and each slave's pulses appear on one trace only. The navigator can therefore measure the A-B and A-C delays and apply the results to the map to obtain a fix. To ensure accurate measurement, the display can be switched to an alternative 'strobe' presentation with expanded timebases. A clever system of calibration markers enables accurate readings to be taken to obtain a fix; alternatively, the strobe display can be set up so that pulses become aligned when a predetermined position is reached.

12 On some Gee maps, red and green lattice lines could cross at more than one point, thereby causing a fix to be uncertain. Often, the correct and false positions were obvious if the aircraft's immediately previous track was known. However, to resolve positively any such ambiguity and to extend the coverage of a Gee chain, a third slave – D was sometimes added. Either of two possible schemes ensured identification of the D slave. It could transmit 500 pulses per second, responding to every master pulse, and thus appear at the same point on both traces of the display (but would not have an ident pulse, to avoid being

mistaken for a master station); alternatively, it could produce a double pulse in response to every third master pulse. In this case, as will be seen from Fig. (g), it also appears on both traces by hopping from one to the other. Lattice lines for A-D time differences were marked in purple on the maps.

In the above description of Gee principles, it was convenient to assume time delays in round numbers of microseconds. In practice, because of the way the

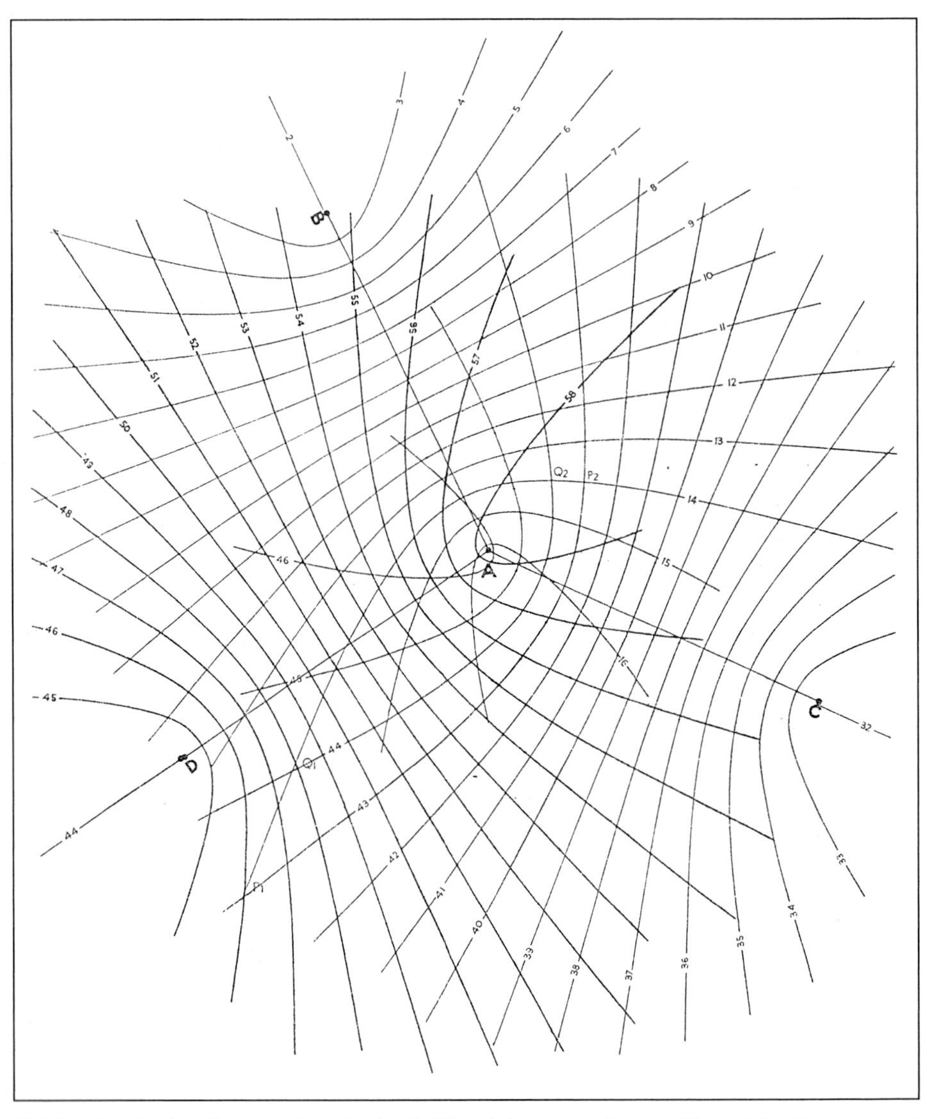

(i) The Gee Lattice diagram given in the RAF training manual was calibrated in Gee-units and showed a third (D) slave. In the original the lines were shown in different colours. (Courtesy of the Communications and Electronics Museum Trust.)

pulse repetition rates were derived by frequency dividers locked to a stable crystal oscillator, it was more useful to calibrate both the Gee displays and the lattice maps in a specially-invented unit of time known as the 'Gee Unit' (GU). 1 GU = 66.67 microseconds. Accurate calibration pips were provided at 0.1 GU intervals (6.67 microseconds), and fractions thereof could be estimated with adequate precision (Fig. (i)).

For radio enthusiasts who had become RAF mechanics and were already impressed with the technique of RDF, new technical insight gained into the workings of the Gee circuits often came as a series of further thrilling revelations. The precision of the timing circuits set new standards by various means – e.g. 'anode-catching diodes' positively determined the excursions of pulse-shaping stages; some of the normal radar circuits – once admired – now seemed comparatively sloppy!

Since, in Gee, the essential measurements of time-difference were taken from the leading edges of pulses, it was desirable for transmitted pulses to be as steep-fronted and stable as possible. The fixed ground stations used specially-modified versions of the reliable west coast MB2 transmitter, and one unit in particular – the 'sniffer' – contributed greatly in this respect. In the standard MB2 the radio frequency pulse was produced, before power amplification, by a push-pull pair of triode valves which oscillated when a hold-off bias was removed from their grids. The onset of oscillation, entirely satisfactory for radar purposes, was somewhat ragged, and jittered slightly from pulse to pulse.

The sniffer was a comparatively low-power valve oscillator (Type 807, a favourite of radio hams) placed in the main oscillator compartment. It was pulsed a few microseconds ahead of the main transmitter, and injected, by its proximity and inductive coupling, a signal into the main oscillator's grid coils. It was instructive to examine the transmitter output pulse while tuning the sniffer and to see the dramatic improvement in steepness and stability when resonance was reached. A ragged and jittery pulse would suddenly become smart and shapely; it was like an airman, standing at ease, hearing the shouted command 'Attention!'

With such technical delights and the ever-present thought that countless unseen users might, at any moment, be relying desperately on the Gee chain, a mechanic's job not only held much interest but presented a great and worthwhile challenge. Many became highly skilled in super-fast restoration of service if, for example, a transmitter tripped. And they were aided in this by the provision of more backup equipment than was usual on radar stations. Whereas a radar station might have main and standby transmitters, a fixed Gee station was typically equipped with five.

But if life was sweet for mechanics, it was hardly so for operators. Taken from radar chain stations, where the activity of radar traffic was obvious, intense and sometimes thrilling, it was relatively boring to sit in front of a display of pulses and merely ensure their correct phasing. Of course, it was a vital job, since maintenance of a slave's correct delay was essential for the accuracy of the system. But it lacked excitement.

In summary, a Gee chain comprised a master station and up to three slaves, plus a monitor station where operators continually checked the transmissions of all stations and the essential time delays of the system.

Note: For siting of Gee stations, see the map on p. 223.

Jeremy Howard-Williams, DFC *(died September 1995), Mosquito pilot, recalled his personal experience of Gee:*

Jeremy Howard-Williams

There is no doubt that Gee was an excellent navigation aid within its limitations. Initially, it enabled a fumbling Bomber Command (over half of whom never found their target, and then half again failed to bomb within 5 miles) to locate targets which would otherwise have been beyond them, thus paving the way for the Pathfinders and a greater general accuracy. But it has to be said that once the Germans started to jam it, the effect was dramatic; fixes which had been easy and reliable up to the enemy coastline suddenly became indistinguishable in the interference as the coast was crossed. The cut-off was quite abrupt; so much so that it was possible to determine exactly when the coast had been crossed.

Nevertheless, it enabled an accurate track to be maintained over the North Sea, with attendant ability to compute the true wind (not always the same thing as that which had been forecast). This produced more accurate navigational data, so that courses over enemy territory could be re-worked with confidence. Gee was also, of course, most welcome when returning to base, possibly uncertain of position until one crossed the enemy coast and the blips became discernible again.

Gee, of course, had the additional advantage that it was a 'passive' navaid, in that it only needed a receiver, not a transmitter; aircraft using it therefore did not run the risk of giving away their position.

We used it *every* time we flew offensive operations (and very glad of it we were). Also, of course, the brilliant deception put up by 218 and 617 Squadrons on D-Day, where they simulated a dummy invasion convoy in the Channel with the aid of 'window' on the night of 5/6 June 1944, was entirely made possible in the case of 617 Squadron by the use of Gee. 218 Squadron used Gee-H. (See p. 137.)

Thomas R. Dolezal, *Group Radar Officer, 322nd Bomb Group, 9th US Air Force*:

In 1942 I was assigned as an officer student to No. 7 Radio School, RAF, in South Kensington (at the Royal College of Arts!). In a three-month course we covered all airborne radar equipment in service in the RAF. Our school training was augmented by assignments to RAF Fighter Command, Bomber Command and Coastal Command.

In November 1943 I was assigned to the 322nd Bomb Group (Medium), 9th US Air Force. This group was flying the Martin Aircraft Company's B-26, called

Thomas R. Dolezal

the Marauder, also known as the 'Flying Whore from Baltimore' because of its very short wingspan (no visible means of support). Later models had a 6 ft greater wingspan, but the name stuck.

I was assigned as Group Radar Officer to the 322nd, which had been designated to receive the first four Gee sets to be installed in the B-26. My mission was to organize the Group Radar Section, convert some radio repairmen to service the Gee equipment, and train the group and squadron navigators on the operation of Gee.

The repairmen were no problem as they had the basics of radio theory and how to read circuit diagrams. The navigators were a slight problem: they expressed some scepticism after I had briefed them on what use Gee would be to them as a navigational aid, and in some cases a blind-bombing aid.

I realized that the only thing to do was to hold a live flying demonstration, with me serving as the Gee operator and navigator. They agreed to this, and the group navigator and two of the four squadron navigators and I took off in a Gee-equipped B-26.

I suggested that they have the pilot fly any type of erratic course he chose, and I would not look at the compass. We flew about for a while, and then I turned on the Gee set and gave a course for base. This was easy, since I knew the Gee grid intersection for the base; consequently, I had the pilot fly down one grid and I preset the second for intersection over base. At the appropriate moment I told the pilot he should enter the final approach pattern.

That convinced the navigators that Gee really was everything I had claimed. After a few weeks of further training and use on bombing missions by several of the lead navigators, Gee became a 'must have' item. Squadron commanders were calling me and demanding that I get Gee into their aircraft. This was done as quickly as the depot could do the installations, and eventually all eight of the B-26 bomb groups of IX Bomber Command were equipped with Gee.

In mid-1944 the 1st Pathfinder Squadron (Provisional) was established. Its B-26s, in addition to being equipped with Gee, were also equipped with Oboe. They served as the lead aircraft for a bomb group involved in a blind-bombing mission. All aircraft following the Pathfinder dropped their bombs where he dropped his.

CL CONTINUES: OBOE AND GEE-H

While UK-based Gee chains were a tremendous boon for general navigation around the British Isles and much of the Continent, they were not accurate enough for precise blind-bombing over enemy territory. As distance increased, so the lattice lines, from which fixes were obtained, intersected at shallower and shallower angles, and accuracy suffered. If such map lines could be made to cut more steeply, accuracy would be increased. This was achieved, in both Oboe

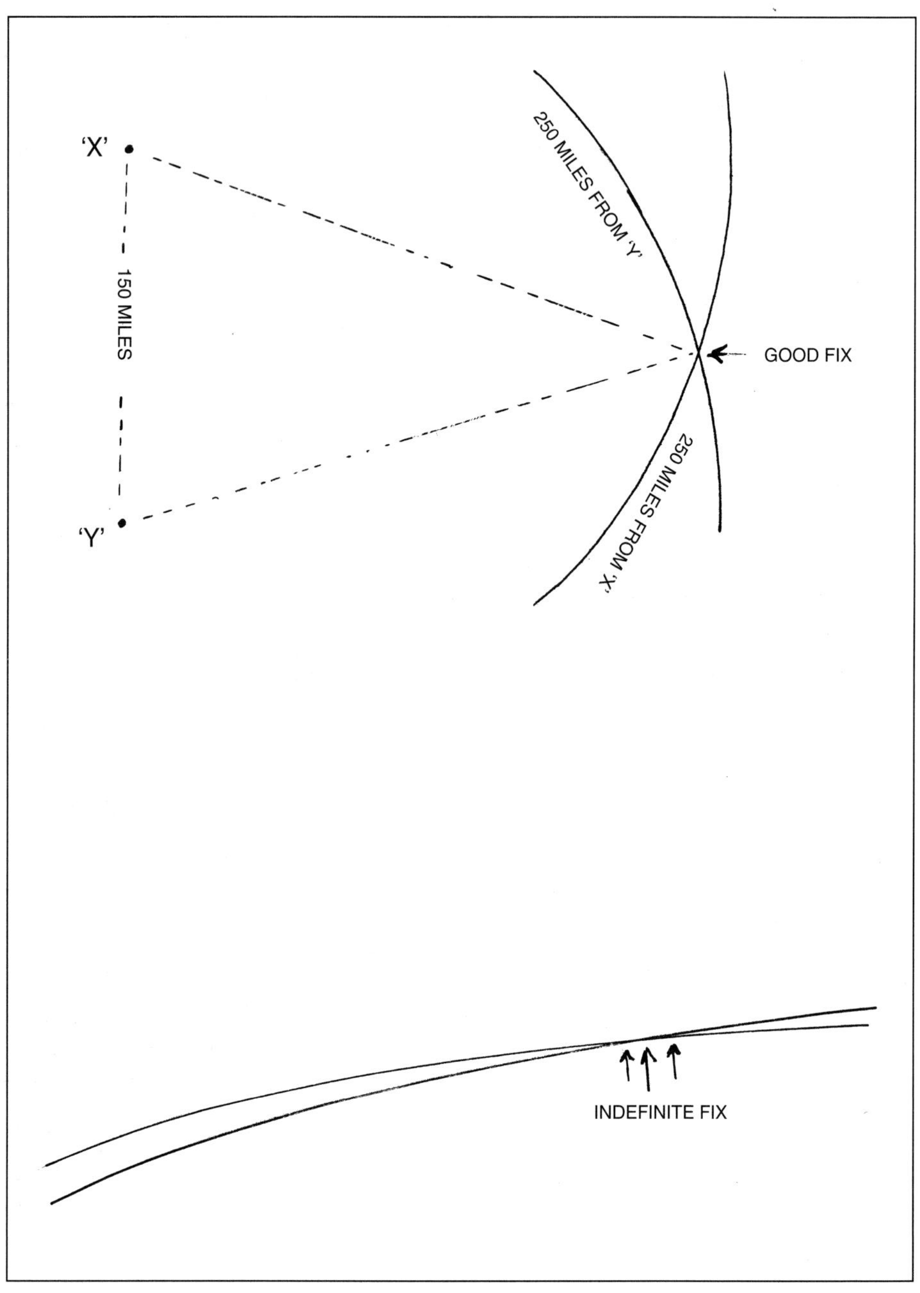

Comparisons of accuracy. (Above) the fix from the intersection of range circles from beacons 150 miles apart is distinct at 250 miles; (below) the Gee lattice lines at similar range cut less sharply.

and Gee-H, by measuring, with precise timing circuits, the distance of the bomber from a pair of widely separated, fixed ground stations (see figure, p. 96 for comparison with Gee). Oboe and Gee-H achieved the same aim by different means, each having advantages and disadvantages.

First, though, it may be wondered why it was not feasible for a pair of radar stations to track a bomber, each measuring its range, and for a signal to be sent when the range from each indicated the bombing point. The answer is that at the long ranges of interest – usually greater than two hundred miles – the radar echoes, if receivable at all, would be so weak and inconsistent and masked by noise that precise measurement would be out of the question. (Radar signal strength diminishes as the fourth power of the distance – see the Appendix). For a precise blind bombing system, it was essential to work with reliable, clearly defined pulses, and this could only be achieved by re-transmission rather than mere reflection. Thus, for Oboe and Gee-H, it was necessary for the aircraft to carry a transmitter and to break radio silence during the final bombing run. This was limited to as short a period as possible by navigating into the general area by means of Gee.

OBOE

The following brief explanation of a highly sophisticated system includes, by kind permission of Marconi Radar Systems, extracts from their published articles written by the late Bruce Neale. His wartime RAF service as a radar mechanic (LAC to Warrant Officer) included work on CH, CHL, and Oboe before he became a distinguished postwar designer of radar equipment. He writes:

> The inaccuracy of our all-weather bombing, especially at night, had been recognized for some time; something had to be done.
>
> Oboe was the brainchild of Alec Reeves, the PCM (pulse code modulation) wizard of Standard Telephones and Cables Ltd, who along with Frank Jones of TRE, developed an idea from the back of an envelope to a potent instrument of war. The basic principle of Oboe is really very simple, it was the inspired engineering and operational concept that was the key to its success.
>
> The range of a target, say the Krupps armament works in Essen, measured from two widely spaced ground stations in the UK, was derived from pre-war ordnance survey maps and aerial photographs [see p. 99, top]. One ground station, code-named CAT, controlled the track of the marker aircraft (usually a Mosquito) by interrogating an on-board transponder.[1] The returned pulse was displayed on a cathode ray tube with a delayed, magnified time-base (one mile filled the whole 12 in screen). The precise range of the target from the CAT station was set up on the tube by a strobe marker.[2]
>
> The Mosquito flies on a circular arc centred on the station at a radius equal to the target range, appearing stationary on the tube face, i.e. zero radial velocity.
>
> The purpose of the CAT was to keep the returned pulse exactly in line with the target marker strobe by automatically signalling dots or dashes; dots if the Mosquito range was less than the target range, dashes if it was greater. The dots and dashes merged into a continuous or 'equi-signal' note when the Mosquito range

[1] Transponder: a unit which, on receiving a specific radio pulse, transmits another in reply, usually on a slightly different frequency.

[2] Strobe/strobe marker: portion(s) of a display expanded or specially marked to permit detailed examination.

and target range coincided, i.e. it was precisely on track.[3] The dot/dash signal was transmitted by width-modulation of the primary interrogating pulse.

The sensitivity of the system was such that a deviation of plus or minus 17 yards from the circular arc would cause either dots or dashes to be sent, thereby enabling the pilot to steer along an invisible track some 35 yards wide in the sky above the target; there was no beam as such [see p. 99, bottom].

The other ground station, code-named MOUSE, signalled the Mosquito as it passed a number of 'milestones' along the arc until it reached the release point – the intersection of the Cat and Mouse ranges – when the bomb release signal (five dots and a dash) was given automatically. Like the Cat station, the target was set by a strobe on a CRT with a delayed, magnified time base. Unlike the Cat, the returned pulse moved along the trace as the Mosquito approached the target region.

The precise release point was influenced by many factors e.g. time of bomb fall, trail distance[4] (a function of bomb ballistics and airspeed), meteorological data, the velocity and heading of the Mosquito just prior to release plus instrumental corrections.[5] These were taken into account by the Mouse computer (aptly named the Micestro!), the release point being continuously and automatically corrected to ensure that the predicted impact point of the bomb (or Target Indicator) was within the target zone.

There were several Oboe stations around the east and south coasts of England (from Cleadon in Durham to Sennen in Cornwall), any of which could be nominated to perform a Cat or Mouse function depending on the target location. Early stations (MkI) used modified CHL equipment working on 200 MHz using pulse space modulation for signalling. Later stations (MkIII) worked in S-band (10cm wavelength) and used pulse width modulation as already stated.

It is easy to understand Bruce Neal's fascination for Oboe, because the elegance of its principles plus the ingenuity and precision of its circuits reflected perfectly his own passion for first-rate electronic design.

Oboe, perhaps to a greater extent even than Gee, advanced the techniques of stable and cunning electronic timing circuits. To give just one example, at Mouse stations, the Micestro's 'walking strobe' monitored and measured the controlled aircraft's velocity to within half a mile per hour. Another step towards system accuracy was serious consideration of the tiny variation in the velocity of radio waves at different altitudes. It was concluded that a mean figure of 186,234 miles per second was appropriate for the path between a ground station and an aircraft flying at 30,000 ft (186,240 miles per second is generally assumed for ordinary radar work).

In retrospect, wartime Oboe operations, in which solitary aircraft were carefully guided to a precise point in the sky up to 300 miles away by a dedicated ground-based team, may be viewed as a portent of things to come in the space age. Houston's control of the Apollo moon missions was on a vastly greater scale, but parallels are not hard to see.

To achieve a precise bombing run, a single aircraft needed to be under Oboe control for ten minutes, and thus the absolute theoretical maximum number of runs per hour, from any given pair of Oboe stations, was six. In practice, a

[3] Not to be confused with the dot/dash signals of the Lorenz blind-approach system developed in Germany and widely used by airlines before the war. Indication was similar, but meaning, principles and purpose quite different.

[4] Trail distance: at the moment of release, aircraft and bomb are travelling together, but the bomb, as it falls, is retarded by air resistance.

[5] All factors contributing to bombing accuracy were embraced by the work of AWAS – the Air Warfare Analysis Section of the Air Ministry.

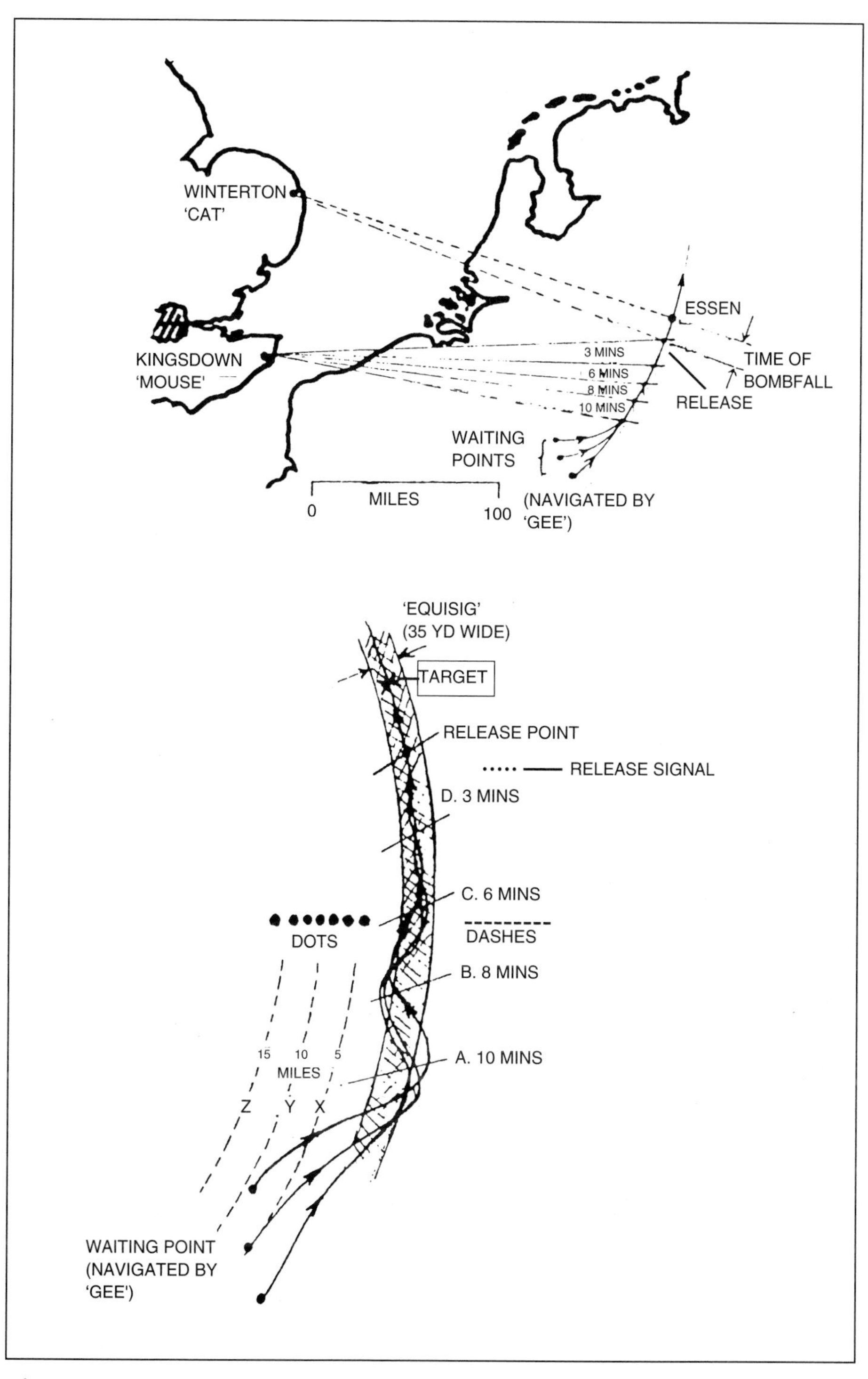

Oboe principle (top) and Oboe track (bottom).

smaller number was more realistic: consequently, Oboe was used for special bombing strikes on specific targets or, when a greater effect was required, for use by target-marking Pathfinders who led in the main force.

In a further article, Bruce Neale refers to the elimination of Hitler's guided weapon sites by Oboe-aided bombers, and continues:

> If the destruction of these sites was Oboe's only success, it would have been worth while in terms of lives saved from the flying bomb. As it was, Oboe (along with H2S, Gee, Gee-H) played a decisive part in the total bomber offensive against Germany. But one must never forget the courage, skill and dedication of the pilots and navigators of the Pathfinder Force and, of course, the superlative qualities of the ubiquitous Mosquito! Towards the end of the war in Europe, food 'bombs' were dropped on Holland for the starving Dutch people. By pre-arrangement with the Dutch Resistance, a site was chosen well away from the German security forces for a 'drop'. The precise aiming point was signalled to London and the CAT/MOUSE ranges calculated. At a pre-arranged time Oboe Mosquitoes carrying food cannisters set out to rendezvous with the Resistance and the cannisters were dropped to within 30 yards of the aiming point where eager hands rapidly distributed the contents.

Bruce then recalls a visit to The Hague in 1976, where he 'had the good fortune to meet Professor Eric Goldbohm who was a member of the Dutch Resistance and was present at the receiving end of one of these operations. He remarked on the accuracy of the drop; in fact he was very nearly clobbered by one of the cannisters. He said how truly grateful the Dutch people were and bought me a pint!'

Note: For full technical details of Oboe, see F.E. Jones, 'Oboe: A Precision Ground-based Blind-bombing System'; *Journal IEE*, Vol. 93, Pt. IIIA, No. 2, 1946.

Group Captain Keith ('Slim') Somerville, DSO, DFC, AFC, *Pathfinder Mosquito Pilot and Pioneer on Oboe*:

Keith Somerville

I joined the RAF in 1938 at the age of 18, straight from school. I did my flying training at Brize Norton, on Airspeed Oxfords, and by the time war broke out I had also flown Whitleys. In early 1940 I found myself with 10 Squadron at RAF Leeming. This squadron was known as 'Shiny Ten' on account of its much-decorated members; I myself received a DFC after completing 35 trips.

The commander at Leeming was Wing Commander Syd Bufton, who sent for me one day and said: 'I've just had a phone call from my brother who's stationed at Boscombe Down. He asked if there was anyone here who'd like to go to Boscombe Down, to be in at the beginning of something brand new and very hush-hush.'

And that was how I came to be involved in the very early days of the highly-secret bombing device known as Oboe. The squadron I joined at Boscombe Down was known as 'WIDU' (Wireless Intelligence Development Unit) when I first arrived, though two months later, in January of 1941, it became 109 Squadron. It was an intensely secret squadron.

It was 1941, and the first thing we did was to play 'Hunt the Knickebein' ('crooked leg'). This was the German radio system which they were using very successfully for their bombing, and it was vital that our scientists located it and interfered with it as quickly as possible. Fortunately, we were successful in this; so successful, in fact, that in due course we worked out an amusing little ploy whereby we ourselves used the Knickebein beam and flew straight down it in the opposite direction, in our Wellingtons, and dropped our bombs supposedly on the beam transmitter, but to no effect. We turned to TRE, with whom we already had contact, to elicit their help in measuring range and ground speed. Their assistance with ill-adapted equipment was equally non-effective, but the work came to the notice of Alec Reeves, who bent his mind to the problem of accurate blind bombing. A team was formed in May 1941 under Dr F.E. Jones, when the principles of what became Oboe were developed, for which we carried out all the experimental flying and bombing trials.

Thus we started to learn about the miraculous Oboe. This was to be our own device for precision bombing, with an unbelievable accuracy. There were only three of us, flying Ansons, and working in close collaboration with the boffins, Frank Jones and Alec Reeves. In July 1942 we were sent Mosquitoes, and from then on these were the planes chosen to fly with Oboe on board.

Oboe worked by means of signals sent from two ground stations. One station, codenamed the 'Cat', sent dots or dashes, and you flew to the target at constant range from the ground station. The Mosquito was so beautifully manoeuvrable that with the slightest touch on the rudder you could keep straight down the narrow line between the signals, which was actually narrower than the width of the plane. The pilot, not the navigator, listened to this signal, so that he could weave gently from side to side until he got the continuous note and knew he was bang on course.

As he approached the target (10 minutes, or approximately 50 miles from it), the navigator received a signal consisting of four Morse Code 'A's. This then changed to four 'B's 8 minutes from target, followed by four 'C's 6 minutes from target and four 'D's 3 minutes from target. Throughout this run-up time, the plane had to be flown at constant airspeed and height. At approximately 2¼ minutes after the 'D's, the release signal was received, consisting of five ½-second dots and a 2½-second dash, then silence. In this silence, the navigator pressed the bomb release button and switched off the transmitter. The other ground station (codenamed 'Mouse') had calculated the exact release point and sent the release signal direct to the navigator.

Our training was going well, and the accuracy of the bombing was something no one had dared to hope for. Then, in December 1941, we had to stop testing Oboe at the request of the Royal Navy, who wanted assistance in bombing the *Scharnhorst* and the *Gneisenau* at Brest. Churchill's staff suggested that three or four pilots of 109 Squadron should be selected to see whether they could bomb the ships – using Stirlings, which had recently come on the scene – with the aid of radio beams directed from the south coast to Brest.

Fortunately, the boffins had already perfected the technique sufficiently to be able to put the radar release signal into the Sterlings. So we bombed the *Scharnhorst* and the *Gneisenau* using the very narrow Lorenz *radio* beam to fly on,[1] with its dots and dashes, while the wireless operators listened to the very first Oboe release signals. An interesting combination of technology which worked well.

Our first two ground stations were at Trimingham, near Cromer, and Hawkshill Down, near Walmer. The two squadrons which learned to fly on Oboe were 109 and 105, and they remained the only Oboe squadrons throughout the war. 109 came first, and then, on the instructions of Bomber Command, 105 proceeded to Marham, where they learned how to fly on Oboe.

When the technique for deploying Oboe was finally perfected, it worked like this. The Mosquito set off for the target ahead of the main force and ahead of the Pathfinder Force. (The Pathfinder Force had been created at Wyton in August 1942.) With pinpoint accuracy (flying at 30,000 ft), the Mosquito arrived over the target and dropped a pyrotechnic bomb as a marker. This bomb had to be dropped at precisely the right height and precisely the right second (timing was vital). The marker bomb burst at 600 ft into bright red or green brilliance which could be seen very clearly by the Pathfinders, who were stooging around waiting for it. Finally, the main force came in and finished off the job.

So, you might say that the Mosquitoes with their Oboe on board acted as the Pathfinders for the Pathfinders. And a highly successful recipe it proved!

The first successful raid took place on 20 December 1942 and was shortly afterwards followed by a raid on a carefully-chosen target at Florennes, in Belgium. Six Mosquitoes took part, of which mine was one. Agents on the ground were told beforehand to expect a special raid and were asked if they would go and wait to see if they could spot the bomb bursts. We wanted to know where the bombs fell so that we could determine the accuracy with which British and Continental maps coincided.

Within thirty-six hours we got information back from the Resistance as to where some of these bombs had dropped, and our maps had been accurate down to 17 yards!

Culmination of our success was achieved on 5 March 1943 with the bombing of Essen. On this occasion, eight Mosquitoes (of which mine was one) dropped marker bombs over a thirty-minute period, one after another. And after the

[1] This was a beam of the Lorenz type, generated by a transmitting station in Cornwall, set up to direct our bombers over Brest. A CHL station, also in Cornwall, was specially equipped to measure accurately the bombers' ground speed and range so that the bomb-release point could be determined. Many sorties were made, and although this 'semi-Oboe' phase delayed the main Oboe development programme, it helped to convince those who doubted the possibilities.

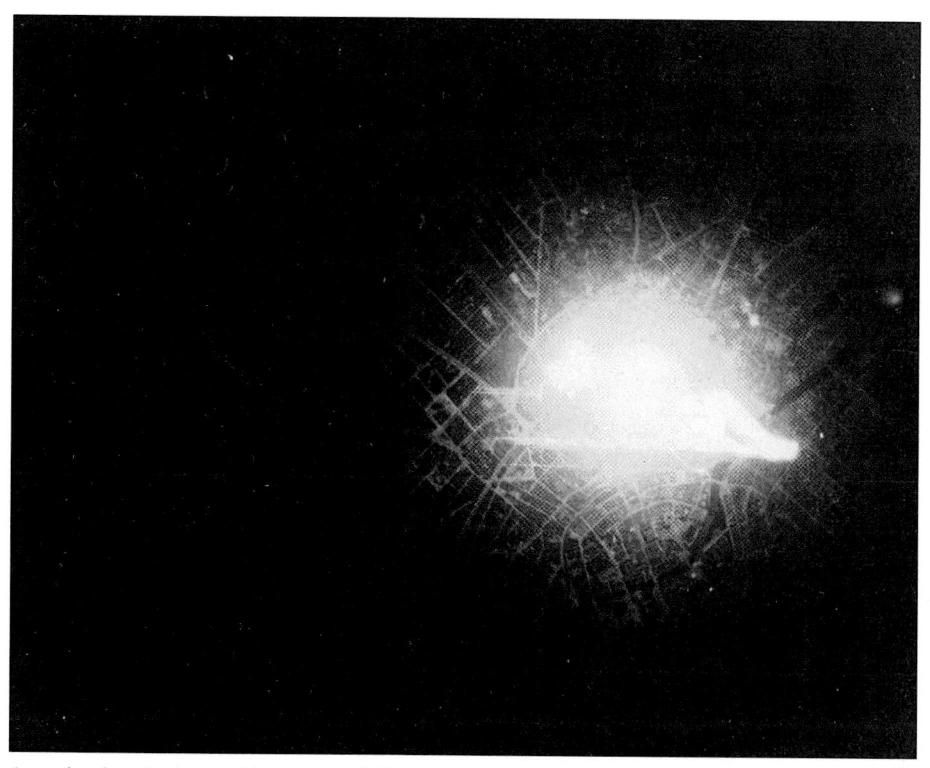

A marker bomb, dropped by means of Oboe, exploding over Berlin. (via Authors)

Pathfinders, 400 Lancaster bombers came in their wake. Half of the Krupps works was destroyed that night.

Oboe proved to be the most successful aid to bombing devised in the war. Although we flew at 30,000 ft – almost above the defences – it nevertheless required the most intense concentration to keep the plane precisely level, to listen to the vital signals coming from the ground station, maintain exact speed and height ignoring all distractions, and release our marker bomb exactly when and where it was required.

The limit of range for Oboe was the Ruhr, which was 300 miles from our ground stations. The accuracy of the pyrotechnic bomb was to within 100 yards (dropped from 30,000 ft). No wonder we thought the world of those boffins at TRE who led the scientific teams – F.E. Jones and John Hooper. And no wonder I was glad to have been in on the project right from the very start. In fact, I was privileged to fly one of the first Mosquitoes which dropped the first marker bomb with the aid of Oboe.

Between 1943 and June 1944, 105 and 109 Squadrons carried out hundreds and hundreds of Oboe raids on the Ruhr. These two squadrons flew over 750 sorties for the loss of only three aircraft.

Then, in June 1944, the Chief of Staff requested the two squadrons to begin to work up their act for what was probably the most important raid for Oboe. D-Day was approaching, and the COs were told that we were required to bomb – with the help of the Pathfinders and over a thousand Lancasters – the ten heavy gun emplacements strung along the coast of Normandy. Because of secrecy, the aircrew had only six hours' advance warning of their targets. Out of the ten gun emplacements positioned right across the invasion beaches, nine were put out of action on that raid, and the tenth could fire only one gun. Out of action for at least twenty-four hours – the vital twenty-four hours!

After D-Day, the vital work of Oboe marking continued, the first task of which was just outside Caen, where both squadrons were used to mark just a few hundred yards in front of our troops (from 25,000 ft) – a very hairy job!

After that, we had to wait for the Army to break out of Normandy, and then we started to set up our ground stations on the Continent. We had a maximum range of 300 miles, and as our armies advanced, so did we with our ground stations. During that time we also accurately marked the V2 and V1 sites around Calais for the main forces. And we also marked at the German town of Wesel, which was the point at which the Canadian forces made the first breakthrough across the Rhine out on to the plains of Germany. We received a personal signal from the officer commanding this Rhine crossing, congratulating us on our efforts because their losses had been so very much lower than expected.

Then, at long last, we managed to get two ground stations on German soil, which enabled us, with Oboe, to bomb Berlin, which we had been unable to do until the last few months of the war.

And so the war ended. The Oboe squadrons had one last task – to mark the dropping zones for the food so badly needed by the Dutch. A fitting end to Oboe in Europe.

Wing Commander Frank Metcalfe, CBE, *Pilot and Senior Oboe Controller, tells what happened on the ground*:

Frank Metcalfe

A typical night operation went like this. In the morning, details were signalled (to home stations by scrambled telephone, to overseas convoys by coded W/T) from Pathfinder Headquarters, of target and position, size of attacking force, aircraft airspeed and direction, bomb load and ballistics and timing of the raid. Thereon, controllers of both 'Cat' and 'Mouse' stations started the calculations necessary to determine the precise settings needed for each piece of equipment to meet these criteria.

All controllers were former aircrew who had completed their operational tours or were disabled from wounds, and who received intensive training for this new work.

The equipment set-up was something like this. When the raid began, the aerial was turned to direct the ground transmission to the target area, and the first aircraft to attack was called by modulating the pulses of the transmission. The aircraft navigator now switched on his transmitter when its pulses appeared on the CRTs of both stations as a vertical line about 2 in long on the time trace.

At the 'Cat' station, the transmission was pulsed dot or dash to direct the pilot to the required range, which was identified as a continuous note. The pilot set course, guided by this note, to the target.

At the 'Mouse', the operation was more elaborate. As the pilot approached the aiming point along the 'Cat' track, his navigator was given warning of his proximity to the target by signals sent manually by progressively modulating the 'Mouse' transmission with the morse letters 'A', 'B', 'C' and 'D'. After point 'D', the display was magnified, the ground speed measurement and release signal were introduced and the bombs were released by the navigator. This signal could have been arranged to release the bombs, but reasonably enough, the navigator, having done the hard work, insisted on pressing the bomb release, which incidentally switched off the airborne transmitting equipment.

WAAFs setting up the target and time of bombfall in a UK Oboe station in 1943. In the background is radar mechanic Warrant Officer Bruce Neale. He later married the WAAF Sergeant standing near him, June Vince. There were many successful RAF/WAAF marriages at this period.

The aircraft were Mosquitoes, flying at over 25,000 ft at about 300 m.p.h. Several such aircraft in turn led forces of hundreds of bombers against targets by delivering frequent coloured target indicators at the aiming point with an accuracy averaging 100 yards.

This astounding accuracy was well illustrated when, as D-Day approached, an area of some 60 miles radius around the beaches was immobilized by the destruction of railheads, road junctions, flying-bomb sites and enemy supply concentrations. On D-Night itself, nine out of ten protecting coastal batteries were rendered useless by an attack which surely saved thousands of lives of the invading armies.

Nigel Ellis-Robinson, OBE, *Radar Operator/Mechanic attached to TRE*:

Calibration of Blind-Bombing Systems

Nigel Ellis-Robinson

The Oboe blind-bombing system operated on the same basic principles as radar, in so far as it determined range by measuring the time interval between the transmission of radio-frequency pulses and their amplified return sent back from the aircraft under control.

However, in view of the fact that the objective of the system required that the range of the aircraft be measured to an accuracy of a few yards, it was of paramount importance that details of all aspects contributing to the time interval were established with considerable precision.

The Pathfinder aircraft which were to be controlled by the Oboe system had to fly at a height which ensured that there was direct radio-wave propagation between it and the two ground stations involved in its control. To achieve this at ranges between 200 and 300 miles, the aircraft needed to fly between 28,000 and 32,000 ft (or just at the top of the troposphere), when over the target area – which was no mean feat for any aircraft in 1942/3.

In late 1942, when the Oboe system was under development, it became apparent that there was not enough known of the speed of electromagnetic wave propagation within the atmosphere, although above it, in a vacuum, the figure of 186,400 statute miles per second was quite accurate enough for all existing applications. However, in the atmosphere, the temperature, the partial pressure of the dry air and the water vapour content normally decrease with increasing altitude, and therefore the index of refraction decreases with altitude. The velocity of propagation of electromagnetic waves varies inversely with the index of refraction of the medium; hence, the radio waves move slightly less rapidly in the lower atmosphere than in space or the upper atmosphere.

The Oboe propagation link to the aircraft spanned these variations, and therefore detailed knowledge was vital since, for the system to achieve its objective, the measurement of range was required to an accuracy of better than 1 part in 5,000.

To this end, in the spring of 1943, a special mobile calibration unit (MCU) was set up specifically to establish the actual variations and the operational corrections necessary. At the outset, the MCU, equipped with optical sights and the best Army gun-laying equipments available, was set up on the high ground overlooking Margam Sands, just off the coast of South Wales. The object was to track Oboe-controlled aircraft and their bomb falls as accurately as possible on practice bombing runs over the Margam bombing range.

In the beginning, the accuracy of the track flown and the timing of bomb release was poor and the resultant impact errors were considerable. However, as the propagation velocity corrections (up to 1 part in 1,000) were established and a number of other errors corrected, the bomb impact point was usually within yards of the intended target. From the measurements by the MCU of aircraft altitude, speed and track together with exact time of bomb release, it became possible to predict the impact point within a few yards and, as a result, the dropping of dummy bombs became unnecessary.

It may sound as though this was an easy task which should have been accomplished within a few days. However, it must be remembered that in early 1943 there was only the Mosquito bomber which could fly at 32,000 ft and, even when stripped of all weapons would take forty minutes to climb to this altitude, and then only when its engines were in very good heart. Having got up there, it only had short endurance and therefore could only do a small number of bombing runs before fuel shortage meant it had to return to base. The weather and lack of good visibility certainly did not help.

Having established the necessary system and equipment accuracies plus the overall measurement technique, the MCU moved to various alternative sites so that checks on operational equipment and practice with it could be carried out without the need to drop dummy bombs.

Eventually, the MCU moved to a site near Islip, from where it was possible to monitor runs over both Ot Moor bombing range and the City of Oxford. At this location it was possible to drop dummy bombs on the range and use selected buildings in and around Oxford as aiming points and then predict impact points for the drops.

The technical advisers of the US 8th Air Force became aware of the special capabilities of the MCU and requested their help in checking the performance of the American X-band airborne radar used for blind bombing by the B–29s. As a result, some thousands of high-level bombing runs were flown over Oxford by the American Superfortresses, and their performance was predicted by the MCU.

Not surprisingly, the MCU was disbanded shortly after VE Day.

GEE-H

As its name implies, this was a marriage of two systems, using airborne Gee Indicators, slightly modified and with a small amount of extra equipment, to obtain fixes – or to fly to predetermined positions – by means of the H navigational system.

Like Oboe, the H system gained in accuracy over Gee by using a pair of widely-spaced ground stations from which ranges were measured. However, the procedure was reversed: whereas Oboe ground stations sent pulses to interrogate the aircraft, it was now the aircraft that interrogated the ground stations. And whereas, with Oboe, the entire process of careful tracking was done on the ground, this now became the navigator's task, using the extra facility added to his modified Gee Indicator.

Although the Gee Indicator was an instrument of excellent stability, it did not embody the refinements of the Oboe ground equipment; furthermore, even the best of navigators, flying over hostile territory, could hardly be expected to perform the task of precise pulse alignment with the same concentration as a ground-based operator working quietly in near-laboratory conditions.

In addition, with Oboe the control was tighter, as the pilot, who received track corrections continuously and directly in his headphones, could react instantly until the bomb-release signal was sent from the ground. In Gee-H it was the navigator who studied the display, advised the pilot and initiated bomb release when he judged the pulses to be aligned correctly. For these reasons, Gee-H was intrinsically less accurate than Oboe; yet it was adequate for many missions, and its use was refined with much success both by the RAF and the US 8th Air Force, who fitted the gear to large numbers of their aircraft.

Like Oboe, raids on specific targets called for careful pre-planning but, unlike Oboe, several aircraft could use the same pair of ground stations simultaneously. Saturation of the ground stations would result, theoretically, when the number of users reached 100. In practice, a somewhat lower number was preferable, but even so, the margin of availability was ample for most operations. For aircrew, it was convenient to navigate to the vicinity of the bombing area on the already-familiar Gee and then to switch over to H and align similar-looking pulses on the same indicator, with the aircraft's interrogating pulses replacing the Gee master pulses, and the two replies replacing those of the slave stations. Thus the display, though it now had a different meaning, was in the same form: alignment of pulses was the key to obtaining a fix or reaching a predetermined point.

H ground stations, essentially beacons responding to recognized interrogation pulses, embodied (like Gee slaves) means for maintaining a closely-controlled delay between reception and transmission to ensure overall system accuracy. Such ground equipment was designated Type 100 and came in three forms: static, heavy mobile and light mobile. The latter was exceptionally sophisticated in that any one set of mobile gear could be set up to work as master or slave in a Gee chain as well as an H beacon. In addition, pulse-width communication between ground stations permitted phasing (delay) corrections and interchange of messages by Morse Code.

Air Commodore E.B. Sismore, DSO, DFC, AFC, *Mosquito Pilot and Navigator*:

E.B. Sismore

In March 1943 we removed the W/T and fitted Gee to the Mark IV Mosquitoes. Operationally, it was very useful at high level, and much more value than expected at low level, since over the sea we could establish a firm track from the coast until the signal faded, and we got very skilled at reading an almost non-existent signal! Similarly, on our return, signals became useful fairly soon after leaving the Dutch or French coast, thus enabling a correct landfall in the UK.

I found myself being 'kidnapped' to teach Gee-H bombing after just one hour of ground discussion! After about eight weeks the task was done, and I flew from Swanton Morley to Gravesend to rejoin 140 Wing, to be met by a duty officer with a signal 'From AOC for Sismore: If you are not back at Swanton immediately I want to know why . . . '.

The target we used for training was the top of the tower of Ely Cathedral; this made it easy to measure errors on the photographs.

I was involved in only one Gee-H operation, on 23 May 1944, when a Mosquito formation bombed a gun battery on the Normandy coast from 16,000 ft, through cloud – alas, we had no information on the results. In the Ardennes offensive (December 1944) the UK weather was very bad and Thorney Island was about the only airfield base to operate (the nearest alternative was Prestwick). Three Mosquito squadrons bombed on Gee to delay the German advance and at least one village crossroads was left ablaze.

OTHER NAVIGATIONAL AND BOMBING AIDS

LORAN – LONG RANGE NAVIGATION (700)

This was an American system of master and slave stations radiating synchronized pulses. Its principle resembled Gee, and navigators were given similar charts overlaid with hyperbolic lines of constant time-difference. Whereas Gee, on wavelengths of 4–15 m, was virtually limited in range to line-of-sight from ground to air, Loran worked on wavelengths between 150 and 200 m and enjoyed the peculiar characteristics of radio propagation in that much longer waveband.

Radiation in that part of the radio spectrum naturally follows two paths: a 'ground wave' and a 'sky wave'. The ground wave (perhaps a slight misnomer, since it is receivable by aircraft flying at all normal altitudes) persists for some distance – typically hundreds of miles. The sky wave travels upwards at a steep angle, is reflected by the ionosphere, and so is detectable again, on or near the earth, at much greater ranges – a thousand miles and more.

The stations of a Loran chain, known as 'Type 700' when run by the RAF, were more widely spaced than those of a Gee chain; for example, some stations were located as far apart as the UK, Iceland and North Africa. Both ground wave and sky wave were used, and although considerable inaccuracies in sky wave could arise under certain ionospheric conditions, Loran provided a much-needed long-range navigation service to countless aircraft beyond the coverage of Gee. While at short ranges Loran's accuracy was lower than Gee's, its coverage was much greater. Among the many regions served by Loran were those target areas deep inside Germany where Gee was either not receivable or, if it was, the contours of its lattice lines did not permit good fixes. Aircraft could navigate on Loran in such conditions and, when fitted with dual installations, switch back to Gee for greater accuracy during the return flight to their UK bases.

At some ranges, both ground wave and sky wave could be received. Since the sky wave depended on the often unstable state of the ionosphere, the received signal could be far from steady. This effect was much noticed by those ground station operators who, trained on Gee, were transferred to Loran stations. For example, at the Port Errol Loran station (north of Aberdeen) it was often impossible to see clearly the pulses from the Loran station at Bizerte, some 1,500 miles away on the Mediterranean coast of Tunisia.

However, Loran continued into peacetime as methods were evolved to minimize these problems (e.g. 'sky-synchronized' Loran), and from the 1960s great improvements resulted from a change to the lower radio frequency of about 100 kHz – a wavelength of 3,000 m. At this frequency the ground wave is much more pronounced and long-distance communication more reliable, with the result that today, despite the advent of satellite navigational systems, Loran-C (as it is now called) is used worldwide and likely to continue into the twenty-first century.

DECCA NAVIGATOR

Another successful hyperbolic system was the Decca Navigator. This was conceived in America but developed in secret in Britain during the war under Admiralty auspices. CW (continuous wave) transmissions from ground stations replaced pulses, and the lattice lines did not indicate constant differences in pulse-arrival times, but constant phase-differences. The Decca system was successfully used by minesweepers needing to steer very accurate courses in the English Channel for the D-Day invasion fleets and, like Loran, use of the system still continues in peacetime for civil navigation.

H_2S

Although, in this book, we are concerned principally with ground-based radar and radar-like navaids, we must not forget airborne radar and the bombing aids that were entirely airborne, operating independently of ground stations. The first and best-known of these was H_2S, a British offspring of airborne radar, which presented in the bomber a map-like display of the terrain below and permitted operations analogous to visual bomb-aiming when targets were obscured by cloud or darkness. Since the equipment was entirely airborne, it was not limited by range from base stations. The basic H_2S worked at 10 cm wavelength, but 3 cm sets with finer resolution, both British and American, followed and were fitted extensively to Allied aircraft for use in Europe and the Far East.

OTHER AMERICAN SYSTEMS

Towards the end of the war the Americans developed several more blind-bombing aids of high precision, e.g., among others, Shoran (*SHO*rt *RA*nge *N*avigation), a kind of computer-assisted Gee-H. Electronic aids for accurate navigation and blind bombing had become established firmly and for all time. (For siting of RNA stations, see the map on p. 223.)

CHAPTER SEVEN

Radar and Navaids Abroad

PART ONE: THE ENEMY'S RADAR – MEASURES AND COUNTERMEASURES

Flight Sergeant C.W.H. Cox, MM, *Radar Mechanic, describes the part he played in the Bruneval raid in 1942*:

C.W.H. Cox

Bruneval started for me on Sunday 1 February 1942. I was a Sergeant Radar Mechanic at Hartland Point at the time, and I was sent posthaste to London on the noon train from Bideford, to report to the Air Ministry.

There I was joined by a Corporal Smith from Ventnor, and we were escorted to the office of Air Commodore Tate, Directorate of Radio. We stood at attention in front of his desk.

He looked at me. 'You are Sergeant Cox, Radar Mechanic?'

'Yes, sir.'

He looked at Smith. 'And you are Corporal Smith, Radar Mechanic?'

'Yes, sir.'

'You two NCOs have volunteered for a dangerous job.'

'Yes, sir,' said the Corporal.

'No, sir,' said I.

The Air Commodore looked at me in astonishment. 'You have not volunteered?' he asked.

'No, sir,' I replied.

'Well, there must be some mistake. I particularly asked for volunteers. Well now you're here, will you volunteer?'

'Well, sir,' I said, 'what's the job?'

'That I cannot tell you,' he replied. 'There's a war on, and people get hurt in wars, but I promise that you have a pretty fair chance of surviving.'

'Very well, sir,' I said. 'I volunteer.'

We were promoted to Flight Sergeant and Sergeant, and ordered to proceed to No. 4 PTS at Ringway Aerodrome, near Manchester. While we waited in the guardroom, we observed a number of aircraft in the sky, some towing gliders. I asked what PTS stood for and was told 'Parachute Training Squadron'.

Sgt. Smith and I looked at each other, both thinking the same thing. What on earth had we got ourselves into?

The following morning we reported to Group Captain Harvey. He looked us over.

'You don't know why you are here,' he said. We shook our heads.

'Well,' he said, 'in the first place, I must caution you that what I'm about to tell you is a number one military secret and you are not to whisper a word of it to anyone on this station. The staff know they have two men to train in a hurry, but what the reason is, only I know. You two men have been sent here to train as parachutists.'

I felt my heart stop, then start pounding like a trip hammer.

'You have to cram into a two-week course something that usually takes six months to learn. When you are trained, you will be dropped, with a few hundred other parachutists, near a German radiolocation station in German-occupied territory. Your job will be to dismantle this station and bring away anything new, or of interest to our scientists.' He paused for a moment.

'Now, we cannot force you to jump, and you did not know what you volunteered for, so if you refuse there is nothing we can do about it. Go out now and talk with the parachutists and their instructors. Take a ride to Tatton Park and watch the soldiers jumping, then come back and let me know if you're willing to go through with it.'

And so began our two weeks at Ringway. We talked to the instructors and parachutists. We went out to the park and saw two sticks of ten men jump from two Whitleys. We decided to go on with it.

Before I joined the RAF in 1940, I'd never been more than a hundred miles from my home at Wisbech; I'd never been to sea, nor in an aeroplane. All that was about to change abruptly.

First, I made two jumps from a captive balloon 500 ft up, and on the second jump, Sgt. Smith landed heavily and sprained his angle. From then on, I was on my own. It was impossible for him to finish his training in time.

I made two single jumps from an aircraft at 800 ft. Then I jumped with a stick of ten from 500 ft.

On 15 February I was informed that I must leave on the morrow for Tilshead, on Salisbury Plain, but that before I went, I must make a night jump, as the operation was to be at night.

A car took me to Tatton Park, where the balloon staff, the doctor and an ambulance were waiting. I donned a parachute and climbed into the basket of the balloon with an RAF instructor.

Up we went to 500 ft, then the winch motor stopped. It was strange in the balloon. In the bottom of the basket was a hole through which I was to jump. That hole looked like a bottomless pit.

The instructor said: 'Are you ready?'

'Yes,' I managed to say.

'Then let's have a good jump. Chin up, hands by your side, ready – GO!' and I went.

After the first 200 ft, I heard my parachute go 'plop', felt the tug on my harness and knew I was descending with my 'chute open. I kept my eyes on a row of trees silhouetted against the sky, to get an idea of my distance from the earth, then I saw it rushing towards me. I hit it! No bruises; no sprains; I had completed six practice jumps and my two weeks' training at Ringway was finished.

Next morning, after saying goodbye to Sgt. Smith, I left Manchester and headed for Tilshead. There I was introduced to the sergeants of C Company, 4th Parachute Battalion – a grand bunch of fellows, a lot of them Scots. I had a week of PT, route marching, unarmed combat, barbed-wire scaling, firearm practice and all the things that go to make a good fighter.

We were shown photographs of the station we were to raid – photographs that were used in pairs with a special optical device that gave details of the terrain in three dimensions. There were two models made of papier maché, one that showed the radiolocation station and the château behind it, and another made to a smaller scale but taking in the station, the château and the territory for approximately a quarter of a mile around them. We practised with the equipment we were to use, opening containers that were to be dropped full of arms, tools, explosives, cameras and ammunition. We also assembled a two-wheeled trolley that was to be dropped folded. The personnel I worked with were six Royal Engineers under a Lieutenant Vernon.

As I had previously been promised, I was allowed to go home to Wisbech, with instructions to report to the Air Ministry on the Saturday morning.

My family asked no questions, though they knew I was with the parachutists from the way my letters had been addressed. I took from all a fond farewell, as perhaps I would never see them again.

At the Air Ministry, I found Lt. Vernon there before me. We were introduced to a French officer and two English civilians who proceeded to give us all the information we would need if captured. We were warned that only rank, name and number were to be divulged to the enemy. We were also warned of their methods of dealing with prisoners from whom they needed information, such as putting an apparently British prisoner in a room with them who would get into conversation and skilfully extract the information they wanted; a concealed microphone would be relaying the conversation. We were also warned of the 'kindness' treatment. A nice room, good things to eat, with lots of wine. I told the intelligence men that I could stand a good deal of that sort of thing.

They were finally satisfied, and Lt. Vernon and I made our way to Tilshead.

The raid was set for Sunday 22 February, but due to the weather it was postponed five nights running. On Friday 27 February the weather was perfect. The buzz went round: 'Tonight's the night,' and we were glad. The waiting had been awful.

We left Tilshead at 8.30 p.m. on Friday and were driven to Thruxton Airfield, where two Nissen huts were assigned to us. We were given bully beef sandwiches and mugs of steaming cocoa. We picked our parachutes from a pile lying on the floor of the hut. They were a different colour from any we had seen – green and black camouflage instead of the normal yellow or white.

At 10 p.m. we received the order to don parachutes. We checked each other's straps and fittings, then walked around with the waddle that a parachute harness gives you. Then we formed up in tens (jumping sticks) and marched to our aircraft.

Somewhere ahead I could hear bagpipes playing. A lot of the paras were from famous Scottish regiments, and a piper, though not flying with us, was doing the honours.

We climbed aboard the Whitley. I was jumper No. 6 in Aircraft No. 6. With me was Major Frost, leader of the expedition, the Sergeant Major, and a sapper who was to jump No. 5 and release the containers in our aircraft when he jumped.

Somewhere ahead of us we could hear an aircraft's engines revving; then it took off and the others in front took off at one-minute intervals. I counted as five took off, then I knew we were next. Our plane moved forward slowly, gathered speed, and we were airborne.

We donned our silk gloves and crawled into sleeping bags, but it was too cold to sleep. Ten men in an enclosed space, dimly lit, going to they knew not what. But were we downhearted? I don't think so.

A group of three in the nose were playing cards. I tried out a song or two: 'The Rose of Tralee' and 'Because', but it was difficult to sing above the noise of the engines. Major Frost passed round a flask of Jamaica rum and we all had a sip.

I estimated we'd taken off at 2226 hours and until 2350 the journey was uneventful. Then we received word from the pilot that we were approaching our destination. Sleeping bags were discarded and the hole in the middle of the floor was uncovered. I could see through the hole at an angle. It was a bright, moonlit night. I could see the sea, then a line of surf and a short beach; then snow-covered ground. The aircraft swung in over the land, then turned towards the dropping zone. A little flak came, with tracer, under the aircraft, casting pretty reflections inside the hole. Suddenly the red light above us came on.

'Ready!' yelled the sergeant-major.

We all tensed; the aircraft slackened speed, then the light turned green.

'Number one – Go!' came the shout, then No. 2, No. 3, No. 4, 5, and then I was out in the slipstream. I could see a black shape with fiery exhausts above me. Then – bump – I was down.

I slipped quickly out of my harness, checked that my revolver and knife were still with me, then looked around and saw the lights of the container near me. I put them out hurriedly, then did the same to the folded trolley a few yards away.

The noise of the aircraft died away, and it was deathly quiet.

The first thing we needed, after two hours in the aircraft plus the hot cocoa, was to relieve ourselves. While we were doing this, another aircraft flew over, spilling its load of parachutists. With the help of the sapper who had jumped No. 5, I assembled the trolley and loaded it with all the gear intended for us. We left two Bren guns and ammunition for someone else to take away.

Thanks to the maps and models and the features of the terrain, I knew exactly where I was. I could see the château in the moonlight and followed a path with my eyes to a clump of trees which was where all the REs were to meet Lt. Vernon. The sapper and I made our way to the trees, dragging the trolley. Then machine-gun fire broke out at the radar station, followed by the dull crump of a hand grenade.

They also started fireworks in the village, and the rattle of machine-gun fire and shouts of the Germans and the British were almost continuous. Under Lt. Vernon, we made our way towards the station.

On the outskirts, Lt. Vernon told us to wait while he reconnoitred the station layout. We lay in the snow, listening to the sound of battle in the village. The cry of 'Caber Fee' – an old Scottish warcry – came clearly to us as we lay there in the snow.

After a couple of minutes, came a yell from the radar station: 'Come on, the RE!'

We rose to our feet and ran to the station, which was surrounded by a low but wide stretch of barbed wire. I reasoned afterwards that it was made that way to prevent interference to the transmission, but why it was there at all, I couldn't understand. There was a lot of shouting from the soldiers kneeling around to 'Keep down!'

The radar unit – called a Würzburg – was constructed as follows. Imagine a searchlight on a rotatable platform, mounted on a flat, four-wheeled truck. The four wheels had been removed and the unit was sandbagged to the flat platform level. Instead of a searchlight, the unit consisted of a paraboloid about 10 ft in diameter, and the whole thing could rotate through 360° and be moved with the touch of a finger.

The paraboloid could be raised or lowered, radiating the beam from sea level to several thousand feet. A small cabin on one side, 6 ft long, 5 ft high and 4 ft deep, contained the display and the operator. At the rear of the paraboloid was a container 3 ft wide, 2 ft deep and 5 ft high. This contained all the units with the exception of the display.

Tearing aside the rubber curtain that protected the units, we saw our prize, switched off but still warm. We learned later from the operator that he had plotted our incoming flight as we came in to land. He was about twenty years old, and terrified. He had been told that the English killed and ate their prisoners.

The top of the compartment at the rear of the paraboloid was taken up by the transmitter and, as we later learned, the first stage of the receiver. A large power pack with transformer and metal-finned rectifier occupied the bottom. In between the transmitter and the power pack was the pulse gear, on the face of which was a 3 in cathode ray tube – there, no doubt, to allow the crew to correct, if wrong, the pulse shape. The intermediate amplifier was positioned at the side of the pulse gear.

We were still under fire from the wood known as Presbytère (as we soon found out as zing! zing! went two bullets past my ear). One of the REs began to hacksaw the aerial from the centre of the paraboloid. Lt. Vernon had taken a photograph of this, which unfortunately later proved useless – someone had earlier taken a photo of the barracks and forgotten to wind the film on!

I was interested in the works, and decided to take all I could in the time allotted. We removed the pulse gear and the IF amplifier, ignoring the power unit. We then tried to remove the transmitter, but although we had a very long screwdriver, we couldn't reach the fixing screws. Lt. Vernon and I gripped the handles and the body of the transmitter, violently lifted it up and then pressed down, until with a rending sound it came away, bringing its holding frame with it. This was a stroke of luck, for when the equipment was examined in England, it was found that the frame contained the aerial switching unit that allowed both the transmitter and receiver to use the same aerial.

All this time, German bullets were zinging by, some striking the paraboloid. Each time we flashed a light to see what we were doing, there were howls of protest from our fellow parachutists, and I can understand how they felt – we were busy, but they were just standing or kneeling there, being shot at. We were just about to enter the cabin to remove the display when Major Frost gave the order to withdraw, so we did so, gratefully. We decided to abandon the trolley – the equipment was easier to carry without it.

We didn't move inland the way we had come, but followed the cliff edge where it went down in a steep slope to the village of Bruneval. As we began the descent, there was a huge explosion behind us. There was one less Würzburg. The REs had blown it up.

There was still a lot of noise coming from the village. We could hear the Bren guns echoing down the gully and the crash of hand grenades. Then, about a quarter of the way down to the beach, there came a terrific hail of machine-gun fire. The grass at our feet wavered and little spurts of snow showed how close they were getting. The aerial, which I was holding in one hand, was struck by a bullet, and one of the sappers had a groove carved in his boot. We did not learn until later that the Sergeant Major had been wounded in the stomach.

The firing stopped and a yell came from the village: 'Come on down – the village is taken!'

I was one of the first to reach the road where it merged with the beach. The first thing I saw, in the light of a flare, was a German against the wall of the blockhouse with his hands up, and one or two more still on the ground. One of the sappers was working over the beach with a mine detector, but he found none.

Corporal Jones and I took up our position under the cliff with the precious equipment we had snatched from Jerry. There we waited for the boats. It seemed an age, but we learned later that it was no more than ten or twenty minutes.

The original plan had been to radio the Navy that all had proceeded according to plan and we were ready to be picked up. But apparently, the stick consisting of half fighters and half radio crew had been dropped in the wrong place. The fighting men could hear the sound of battle and started to run towards it, while the radio crew, loaded with the radio and directing-beam equipment, could only walk. Major Frost fired two green Very lights, but there was a heavy mist. The Navy commander, however, when he received no radio signal, decided to come in and have a look-see, in the hope that we had made it. It was a great sight to see those troop landing craft coming in!

We waded out to meet them, and although the water was very cold, we didn't give it a thought. Corporal Jones and I, with two of the REs, climbed aboard one of the craft, still clinging to our precious loot.

Just as we were pulling off, a machine-gun opened up on us from the top of the cliff. About twenty-four Brens opened up on that one gun, and we had no more interruptions. The LCTs made their way out to sea, where we were picked up by a larger vessel, to which we transferred the booty and ourselves. Then we made full speed for Portsmouth.

Down in the captain's cabin, a member of the TRE, Dr D.H. Priest, was waiting to talk to me.

'Now, Flight Sergeant, I want a description of everything you saw before memory becomes clouded,' he said.

'Permission to be sick, sir,' I retorted, never having been to sea before.

'You can be sick later,' he replied. 'At the moment, greater issues than your physical comfort are at stake.'

I told him all I knew about the German radar, also the impressions I'd gathered of the construction. Then at last I was released and allowed to be sick, though I made a speedy recovery and drank a mug of strong, sweet tea. Then I fell asleep in the captain's bunk!

When I woke, the ship was silent and still. I climbed out of the bunk still dressed, and emerging into the daylight, I found the ship was in Portsmouth, tied up alongside HMS *Prince Albert*.

We had press interviews with photographers, and the crews of the Whitley bombers joined us all for a slap-up lunch. Then, after we arrived back at Tilshead to a right royal welcome, I was called away to the Air Ministry and the office of Air Commodore Tate. More interviews.

The radar equipment we'd taken from the Germans lay in the office. The consensus of opinion, at that time, was that technically it was crude and far behind us in development. For myself, I thought it was beautifully made, the way it all fitted together in units for easy servicing.

I was given two weeks' leave. My family had heard all about the raid on a German radiolocation station; they knew I was a radar mechanic, and they had learned from my letters that I was with the parachutists for some reason. They were not fools and could put two and two together.

From London I sent a telegram: 'All's well – arriving tonight.' When I got in around midnight, they were all sitting up waiting – my wife, my father and mother, and my baby daughter of six months.

'Hello, family!' I said, 'I'm a bloody hero!'

I never found out why they chose me and Smith, out of all the hundreds and hundreds of radar mechanics all over the British Isles! There must have been some reason, but I'm darned if I know what it was!

[*Note*: Bruneval was the first of two landings in German-occupied France in which radar mechanics took part. At Dieppe (August 1942) the radar mechanic was Jack Nissen, whose story is told in *Green Beach* by James Leasor. Jack's story would also have been included in this book had he not unfortunately been abroad when we tried to contact him.]

COUNTERMEASURES AGAINST RADAR

Throughout the history of defensive and military radar, thought has been given to ways of nullifying the other side's radar and of making one's own equipment less susceptible to the enemy's attempts to do so. (Such techniques are nowadays known as ECM and ECCM, for 'Electronic Counter-Measures' and 'Electronic Counter-Counter-Measures'.)

Deliberate interference can take different forms, the most basic being high-power radio transmissions on the radar's operating frequency. That is called 'active jamming' (as distinct from 'passive jamming' – dropping strips of metal foil, 'window', 'chaff' or '*düppel*', as known in the UK, US and Germany).

Active jamming transmissions may be continuous-wave or pulsed, or perhaps involve some especially violent modulation calculated to spoil the radar's display and prevent its operators from seeing targets in the normal manner. These possibilities were foreseen by Watson Watt and the early designers of the CH system, who wisely incorporated a number of palliatives against possible jamming (see p. 20) as well as the ability to change the operating frequency.

As the war progressed and many different types of radars and navaids came into use, the risks of enemy jamming increased; furthermore, the widespread German occupation of Continental shores allowed the enemy great flexibility in positioning jamming transmitters.

Accordingly, a special organization, known as J-Watch, was set up within the RAF to monitor all jamming transmissions. The aim was twofold: to assist the design of palliatives for our radars, and to determine the locations of jamming transmitters for possible air attack.

J-Watch teams were well-informed about the frequencies and characteristics of all known radars, and provided with comprehensive equipment including a range of different receivers and direction-finding aerials. They were often located at CH stations because of the advantages of a coastal site and the availability of high towers for mounting receiving aerials.

Roy Smith, *Radar Mechanic, describes his work on a J-Watch team*:

I was posted to Ringstead CH station for J-Watch training around November 1942. The J station comprised a hut close to one of the wooden receiver towers, with an assortment of aerials part-way up the tower.

There was no formal training programme; the four trainees were split between watches and expected to join in whatever was happening – although, with our aerials at only about 50 ft above sea level, I can't remember seeing very much! However, we did have access to a large number of secret documents, covering just about every kind of friendly pulse transmission, and we were encouraged to read them. Others were devoted to what was known about enemy equipment and emissions. (I still remember pondering over the one devoted to 'Bowlfire', later identified as Würzburg and Würzburg Reise.) There was also a display showing the name, location and frequency of every UK radar station.

There were only about twelve to fifteen permanent staff, made up of radar mechanics, radar operators and, to our surprise, wireless operators – on a radar site! I think the intention was to train one mechanic from each CH station to be able to identify, and report to J–Watch, any jamming they experienced, and to decide on the best way of overcoming it, with IFRUs, AJBOs, IJAJs and/or frequency changes, or some combination thereof (see p. 20).

At that time the J-Watch network consisted of units based in the CH stations at Stoke Holy Cross, Norfolk, Dunkirk in Kent, and Ringstead, Hants. They reported to 80 Wing at Radlett and also had access to TRE at Malvern, in each case by scrambler telephone. Each station was equipped with the same extraordinary set of gear – an R1155, a couple of Halicrafters, an S20 and an SX27 or 28. Except for the British R1155, these were American communication receivers, each of which covered a wide band of frequencies. Then some receivers made by TRE from modified Gee boxes, a wire recorder (this was before the days of tape recorders) – German-made – some Cossor 3339 double-beam scopes and a variable frequency phase-shift oscillator, built by TRE to be extremely stable and to produce pure sine waves. There was quite a bit more stuff, most of it purpose-built, but that gives the general picture. Basically, we were required to be able to monitor any frequency between 20 MHz and 3,000 MHz.

I eventually moved from Ringstead to Stoke Holy Cross, where again we never seemed to pick anything up. So we arranged to borrow a 240 ft tower and an adjoining hut at Great Bromley in Essex and see if we could do any better there. A group of us went down there with a few receivers and mounted our dipoles as far up the tower as the available coaxial cable would allow (not too high, unfortunately).

Before we had achieved any worthwhile results there, I was on the move again, to Dunkirk – the jewel in the J-Watch crown. There we had our own 240 ft tower, and a large hut which had housed the original CH, all surrounded by our own 7 ft railings, within the confines of A-site. Certainly, we had a lot more 'trade' there, and I well remember one occasion when we went down to Swingate near Dover in the radio van to investigate a problem they had. To our astonishment, we found ourselves between a very large gun (mounted on a railway truck, which from time to time emerged from a tunnel cut in the chalk cliff and fired a round across the Channel) and the German long-range guns on Cap Gris-Nez, which were firing much more frequently at Dover. The Swingate personnel seemed to regard this as quite normal, but we found it distracting, particularly when there was a loud explosion nearby and we were not sure whether it was our gun or an enemy shell landing.

Then we learned that we were to train Navy personnel in the secrets and mysteries of J-Watch. Our delight was unbounded when the first two arrived – two gorgeous Wrens! In our all-male preserve! Every week a new pair came, until all those required had been trained.

A few months later, all three stations were relocated. Dunkirk moved to Dover Hill (an ex-Coastal Artillery radar station on the cliffs behind Folkestone); Ringstead to Durlston Head (a similar site at Swanage), and Stoke Holy Cross to Bawdsey.

The new stations were a big improvement. We were much closer to the enemy, and at last we had gantries with turning gear which made d/f-ing much easier. We also got one or two new bits of equipment. We had often found it difficult, or even impossible, to synchronize our timebases so that we could examine and/or photograph jamming signals. The solution came in the form of a variable-speed camera, which we clamped to the front of our oscilloscope. It had no shutter, just a narrow, vertical slit. It held 25 ft of film and had to be loaded in darkness. (No problem for me; before joining the RAF I'd worked in a film-testing laboratory at Ilford Ltd.)

We would feed the scope with the IF signal from the appropriate receiver, switch off the timebase (so that there was just a vertical line), adjust the camera feed to what seemed to be the right speed, then switch on the camera and switch it straight off again; then take out the film, seal it in a can and arrange for it to go straight to 80 Wing; then clean the camera (because it was so fast that in that short time it had fed the 25 ft and whipped the last 6 in to pieces before we could stop it!). Since we were not using a timebase, there was no synch problem, and when developed, the film also showed the IF content, making it easier to calibrate the recorded signal. The whole thing was brilliant and worked like a charm.

In September 1943 I had my last J-Watch posting – to Durlston Head. There, my three major recollections are first, Fred Keys, our Corporal Radar Operator, who had served on the CHL in Malta while it was earning its George Cross. Also, he was on duty at the CHL at Swingate when the German battleships burst through the Channel and we got our first experience of jamming. Second, the night in May 1944, when I was in charge of the watch and we had our first (and, I think, only) enemy airborne jamming. From memory, there were three aircraft equipped with jammers swanning along the south coast while the rest of the wave bombed Plymouth or Portland. We were able to help in the destruction of one, which crashed on the Isle of Wight. A very hectic night indeed! Third, a call to an American 'Eagle' station on the night of 5/6 June 1944. We went up there in the radio van to investigate the problem and stayed on a while, mesmerized by the invasion unfolding on the PPI tube. Little did I realize that my two brothers were in two of those slow-moving dots.

By September, any enemy jamming sources were beyond our reach, so the station was decommissioned and we were all returned to the chain.

PART TWO: THE MIDDLE EAST AND FAR EAST

Dick Field, *GCI Radar Operator, 833 AMES, Middle East*:

In September 1941 I found myself on board the troopship *Strathaird* – formerly a P&O mailboat – bound for Egypt. For nine weeks we sailed, in convoy, first out into the North Atlantic almost to Greenland, then south-westward down mid-Atlantic to Freetown, thence to Capetown and round the tip of Africa into the

Dick Field

Indian Ocean. We called at Aden, sailed up the Red Sea, and disembarked at Port Said.

For three months or so, I and most other radar operators and mechanics waited in Egypt – in a variety of transit camps – until our new units were formed and sent out on duty. Thus I spent some time at Helwan, at Aboukir and at Tura, before joining 833 AMES and moving up into the Western Desert to camp at Gambut and become operational.

2 December 1941: FFI in the desert – trousers down, shirt up – come on, next man.' I draw the scene. We can see nine pyramids, some boats on the Nile, and sand.

4 December: We met a radar op. just back from Libya – he'd been up there for a year; half his party wiped out and he'd come down for a rest. It seems they send out a corporal and four or five men with a motor vehicle and a small instrument into the desert freelance to d/f tanks. Quite a game – you go in front of our tanks and when you pick up a Jerry, pass on the dope and cut and run. So, if we ever get out of this camp before the war is over, we may see some fun.

3 January 1942 – To Cairo: Transport met us in Cairo and brought us, by pleasant roads beside the river, on which the great curved booms of the Nile barges made a pattern against the red of the sunset, until we turned off uphill towards the bleak, limestone hills on the east bank. The foothills, of sand and slag and dust, undulated or broke into rugged crags; and scattered upon them were the tents of Tura.

We're told it is a bullshitting camp, and that we parade at 7.15 a.m.; so I get a

'FFI in the desert'; from an original watercolour by Dick Field.

shave in hot tea from the NAAFI. We turn in, wearing our clothes. My bed gives way under my weight. It is bitterly cold. Next day, we're told that we are to be policemen – radio and radar ops turned coppers. Somebody says there are six hundred unemployed radar ops doing general-duty work, sandbagging, guarding, fetching and carrying, clerking. Laurie gets very worked up: he swears and farts.

Friday 13 February – Posted: On 21 January 1942 Rommel advanced from El Agheila, whither he had withdrawn after the Crusader battle of 1941. His tanks overwhelmed First Armoured Division, and on 29 January, Benghazi fell. From February to March the British and German Armies rested at Gazala, and General Auchinleck considered – and rejected – the possibility of dismissing General Ritchie. Four of us are to go to 833 AMES. Leave tomorrow – my last guard 6–8.

21 February: Bypassed Mersa Matruh, stopped the night at Sidi Barrani. Only shells of buildings left – not much debris – an Eyetie lorry or two. I went down to the shore by the light of a thin moon: sand-covered sandbagged trenches, an overturned lorry, a little rocky bay, the sea breaking with white foam, no sound.

Next day – Halfaya (Hell Fire) Pass – CO warns us about mines – we are delayed an hour, and we bathe in the glorious refreshing sea. Oh the delight! I am second in, with a rush – wonderful!

28 February: We move up towards El Adem – they say this is permanent. A place called Buamud, approximately midway between Tobruk, El Adem and Gambut. We stick up aerials in a damn cold wind – bitter. We eat well – no outside supply, but still, grub is pretty good now – beef tonight. It seems we are to have some bullshit in the desert, would you believe it. Must be cleanshaven, no beards – and inspections to see that we've washed properly.

I am astonished, looking back, at how ignorant we were of the situation in the desert. We knew about the Gazala Line, and I suppose that we assumed – as did everyone from Ritchie down – that the next battle would be static: a tank-and-infantry battle like those in the closing stages of the First World War. I wrote in my diary of Buamud as a 'permanent' site; in fact, we were there – after lengthy preparations – for almost exactly three months. 833 AMES was a mobile radar station, organized to control fighters in a defensive situation. We were to work with fighters from Gambut to protect Tobruk, El Adem, and the immense dumps of material at Tobruk and Belhamed – though we knew nothing of the latter.

The core of our unit consisted of a transmitter, a receiving room, two aerials and two portable diesels to provide power. The transmitter and the receiver were housed in two great, high, old-fashioned Crossley lorries, each of which hauled an aerial and a diesel. Each aerial was built of an ingenious wooden frame, covered with chickenwire, in front of which were slung the dipoles; the whole frame was attached to a small cabin which was rotated by electricity. The diesels provided power for the whole affair.

The equipment was maintained by a group of radar mechanics headed by Sergeant Kistner, and operated by some twenty radar operators, of whom I was one, divided into three watches. There were supporting staff – drivers, cooks, GDs, and in charge of the whole unit, three officers: altogether there were between forty and fifty men, with sufficient vehicles to be fully mobile.

The unit existed to enable the controller to issue instructions to a fighter or fighters which would lead to a contact and a kill. The receiver van – usually known as the Ops Room – was set up with two cathode ray tubes mounted side by side. The right-hand tube was scanned by an electron beam from centre to edge, rotating in unison with the aerials. An echo picked up on the receiver strengthened the flow of electrons and made a blip on the screen, which was luminescent. Thus the echo of an aircraft appeared to move across the screen; friendly planes were equipped with IFF – a device which gave the blip a pulsating tail. The screen was divided into numbered squares corresponding to those on a map mounted nearby.

The left-hand tube was arranged differently. The trace moved from left to right across the screen, and the blips of aircraft were elongated downwards according to their height. But although it was easy to read the comparative heights of two or more aircraft, the system was by no means as accurate at recording absolute height.

The procedure was simple. The controller sat in front of the plan tube, with someone behind him and to his left who called out the plots of the aircraft with which we were concerned. A second man, sitting at the back, recorded the plots and all relevant information; and a third, at a map on the controller's right, charted the plots, and from them provided the controller with speeds (air and ground), direction (actual and steered), and relationships between aircraft. A fourth operator at the height tube gave the controller heights.

The controller spoke into a microphone directly to the fighter pilot. His instructions would normally sound rather like this: 'Red Two, vector two three zero, angels eleven; bandit dead ahead, distance two miles.'

4 May 1942: Our first stage here – the digging in and the settling down – is almost over. Nine ground gunners have arrived and are digging the canteen in. A few tents still have to be dug in; when that's done we're fixed, apart from small improvements in furniture, etc.

Jerry raids sporadically – one or two at a time. Last night we sent a hundred Wimpeys to Martuba. 833 hasn't done anything; they won't give us Beaufighters, and Hurricanes aren't fast enough. The railway is past us now; advancing 3–4 miles a day. Pretty smart work; saw what looked like an LMS engine on it, too.

26 May 1942: On evening parade, Adj. said: 'We must begin to rough it – be prepared to move – one kitbag on kit lorry permanently – four tents down and men sleeping in dining-tent – stores on lorries. We may not move, but let's be prepared.'

It was on 26 May at about half past three in the afternoon, that the forward movement of much German transport was reported. By 9.30 that evening the presence of Panzer divisions had been identified.

Plenty kites came over after dark – we stood outside and watched flares, bombs, ack-ack and onions over on the third escarpment. Suddenly from the north came a roar and the red arrows of kite machine-guns, and as we dived to the floor, a JU88 swept almost overhead at 150 ft, firing to the rear for dear life, the bullets spattering the ground across the camp. Some say it was a chase, others strafing; it was hot while it lasted.

27 May 1942: On watch 1–6 p.m. I was on the phone at 4 a.m., when AHQ rang for the CO and ordered readiness for evacuation. Jerry, they said, was menacing El Adem. CO came up, got the Crossleys started, ramps cleared, aerials partly dismantled. (We were still on the air.)

We were told: one kitbag, one bedroll. Everyone had to leave something precious. Only three weeks since we finished digging in! As we left our tents, gun flashes showed over the escarpment, and black specks appeared on the hillside. The CO said they were Jerries. (They might have been advanced units of Rommel's 90th Light Division. 27 May was the day when Rommel cut deep behind our defensive line, destroyed 7th Armoured Division and damaged 4th Armoured Brigade. On 28 May he was still advancing.)

About 9 p.m. we moved off. We didn't go in convoy. There was practically no traffic on the road. The moon came up; Tobruk barrage flared way back, and Campion got the Browning loaded up. The miles passed; bombs fell and flares lit up the road nearby. I heard later from the boys in the receiver truck (way in front) that a JU88 flew along the road machine-gunning and bombing a convoy just in front of them – they thought the transmitter truck had got it.

By late June, 833 AMES were back in Cairo. Dick Field summarizes the exploits of his radar unit as follows:

That was the end of our active part in the war. 833 AMES went to Palestine to guard Haifa and the oil installations; we stuck there for another two years. By the time I got home and was posted to Fairlight, the war was almost over; certainly, there was no more to do on the south coast of England than there had been in northern Palestine.

One might ask: what was our contribution to the war effort? After all, we were a special unit, designed to do a specific job. Our equipment was new and up to date. We were a self-contained and mobile unit; what did we actually do? Despite all the efforts that went into getting us to Buamud, we were only there a very short time. Moreover, even when we became operational, we needed the use of aircraft for calibration, at a time when there were other more pressing demands for them. We needed Beaufighters for their speed, but there were only Hurricanes, which were too slow to make use of the information we had to offer. To the best of my recollection, we had one contact: the fighter we were controlling found himself on the tail of an enemy aircraft, which escaped. Our controller claimed the contact – the fighter pilot replied that he'd seen Jerry anyway!

We were only available in the desert for so short a time because of Rommel's rapid advance. And because Ritchie's concept of the next battle was a static one, we wasted time digging in when we should have been calibrating and practising the drill without which we might as well have not been there.

Nevertheless, the memories I retain of that period of my life are not by any means all ones of disappointment and frustration. What stands out most clearly and indelibly in my memory is the inexhaustible ingenuity and creativity of man. Wherever we were, no matter under what conditions, this shone through. Put us somewhere for a day or two, and somebody was making a bed or a cupboard; a little longer, and we began to add refinements; before long, we were entertaining friends in our tents. I acquired a belief, which I have never lost, in the integrity of men, and in the force of their desire to be themselves.

[Dick Field, ARCA, ATD (London), died in 1986.]

Mick Miller *(died 5 December 1991) recalled*:

Mick Miller

After working on CHL and then GCI, I was posted at the end of 1942 to Renscombe Down, which of course meant that I was going overseas. I was at Easington at the time, and I'd had a date for the following day with a girl who was travelling from Thorne to meet me. When my train went screaming through that station, I chucked a note out of the window at the appropriate moment, and it was delivered to her house by a railway bloke!

At Renscombe we were put through a commando-style training with mobile CHL/GCI equipment. Eventually, our crew (8009 AMES) was posted to West Kirby, then on to Glasgow for the cruise to North Africa. I shall never, never forget that journey in convoy in midwinter, zig-zagging out into the Atlantic and then eventually through the Straits of Gibraltar in early January 1943 (with Spike Milligan on board) and at last landing at Algiers in blazing sun.

Then it was into battle in the forward areas of Tunisia supporting the 1st Army and American 5th Army. Very exciting and very scarey, especially when we had to push our equipment (in ten-ton lorries) over the cliffs (after taking secret bits out) and running for our lives for 7 miles along a beach to avoid capture by the Germans. By now I was a veteran, of course (though still an erk). The battle of North Africa was eventually won without us losing a single man.

So then we were off to Sicily and Italy, finishing up on Ischia in the Bay of Naples, from where we covered the Anzio landings. I finished my overseas travels in Malta and Gozo, eventually returning to the UK in June 1945.

[See following account of 8009 AMES's exploits.]

Robert Hyde and Arthur ('Tich') Childs, *describe their experiences of working on 8009 AMES (Mobile GCI/COL) in North Africa:*

(*Note*:) The following account is condensed from an original record compiled by R. Hyde and A. Childs, who have kindly given us permission to use their material. 8009 AMES moved into Italy after they left North Africa (see p. 181).

Arthur Childs

We boarded HMTS *Bergensfjord* at Gourock, in the Firth of Clyde, in early January 1943, in bitterly cold weather and with the troopship already well loaded, and were soon out into the North Atlantic. The ensuing days were made miserable by seasickness and overcrowding. For many, it was the first time away from home, and all we could see was the endless grey ocean and the other ships in the convoy, with no knowledge of our ultimate destination.

By 13 January the temperature had risen considerably, and the sea grew calmer. Two days later the convoy arrived at a point off the North African coast to the south-west of Tangier and turned north-east towards Gibraltar, which it passed under cover of darkness, with the Rock blacked out to port and the 'neutral' city of Tangier brightly lit to starboard.

Robert Hyde

We landed at Algiers on 17 January where, after a short break for a meal, we boarded a destroyer, HMS *Lammerton*, and left Algiers to dock at Bône, some 270 miles to the east along the Algerian coast, the following day. We were literally thrown off the ship, our kitbags tossed unceremoniously on to the quayside, and the ships were gone before darkness fell bringing the nightly visit of the Luftwaffe.

From the docks we were transported to a camp site outside the town, where we set up our tents to await the arrival of the radar equipment and to adjust to a climate where daytime temperatures were well into the nineties and dropped to freezing point at night.

When our equipment and vehicles arrived, all personnel were employed in removing them from the danger area as quickly as possible before the night raids started.

Radar Operator 'Tich' Childs was taken by the CO to RAF Headquarters, shown a large wall map and told to make a detailed freehand copy of the coast and road system between Bône and Bizerta and to observe strict secrecy about his activities. We were then instructed to remove all insignia, trade badges, etc. from our uniforms, so that dressed in Army khaki with 'Combined Ops' shoulder flashes, we were indistinguishable from the other Army forces in the area.

Then the CO held a briefing in his tent at which he disclosed to the senior NCO that 8009 AMES and 8010 AMES were to move to a forward position and, with great secrecy and under cover of darkness, to set up the equipment and become operational, at a site the exact location of which would not be disclosed until we reached the final leg of our journey.

We left the camp in convoy at 0045 hours on 28 January and travelled slowly, with no lights, eastwards towards Tunisia. We crossed the Tunisian frontier at La Calle and finally fetched up at Cap Serrat, where we were told that we were to operate from the French lighthouse at the top of the headland.

On arrival, we were rejoined by members of an advance party who had been brought in by landing craft from Tabarka by the Royal Navy to establish W/T communication with 894 AMES, a radar unit already operating at Morris near Bône,[1] and to set up a VHF R/T station for nightfighter control.

It was the intention that plots of aircraft and shipping movements observed on the PPI screens of 8009 and 8010 would be relayed to the Sector Operations Room at Bône from 894 AMES via an already installed landline, and that, conversely, 894 AMES would relay information and operating orders to the Cap.

On 3 February we dragged our radar units into a small courtyard within the lighthouse perimeter wall, removed their explosive devices, and their wheels, to lower them onto their axles.

Their tops were then whitewashed to match the general coloration of the lighthouse walls and outbuildings. All that then remained to do was to move the aerial trailer to the cliff edge, outside the perimeter wall of the lighthouse, connect up, and we were a fully operational radar station.

Strategically, we were in 'no-man's land' beyond the Allied forces' forward position at Sedjenane and Fort Monopole, and within range of German observation posts and patrols, therefore we were only able to move about freely and become operational at night. During daylight hours the aerial trailer was disconnected and manhandled back into the courtyard behind the walls, and all off-duty personnel moved down to a camp in the valley below the hilltop on which the lighthouse was situated.

To enhance the illusion that the lighthouse was deserted, a large herd of goats was kept there, which their Arab goatherds ostentatiously drove out on to the hillsides each morning and back within the walls each evening. This ploy was not solely for our benefit – it had been established some time before to cover the activities of a small detachment of French colonial soldiery who were also housed in the lighthouse, using it as a base for espionage and sabotage behind the enemy lines. We also found in residence two British Naval Intelligence Officers dressed as Arabs, and two French Naval/Coastguard personnel.

There was a strict rule to avoid making paths, so we all had to detour around bushes and under trees wherever we went. One day we were visited by a party of commandos who stayed at the lighthouse before a forthcoming raid. They were amazed to find the RAF in such a precarious forward position.

The first air attack we experienced was sudden and violent, with cannon shells and bullets pounding the tower, some to progress through the unguarded windows

[1] Bône is now shown on modern maps as Anaba.

and ricochet around the stairway. Then one morning we were jolted from sleep by the sound of diving aircraft and felt the tower shake and sway as bombs exploded around it. It seemed incredible afterwards that no one had suffered injury, and the spirit of everyone continued high with a great feeling of inter-dependency.

We lived on 'Compo' rations brought in by Arabs on the backs of mules. Each box contained a day's rations for fourteen men – hard tack biscuits, corned beef, soya links, a tin of combined soluble tea, sweetener and milk powder, tins of Maconnachie's beef stew, beans and fruit, plus a small quantity of toilet paper and 100 cigarettes. Just as essential as the food was the supply of diesel fuel oil for our generators. This was accomplished by naval troop-landing barges which came in at night on a nearby sandy beach with maximum speed and efficiency.

On the morning of 4 February we were attacked by three ME109s, but again suffered little damage except for a cut cable and a smashed switch where a bullet penetrated the aerial cabin. At 2000 hours on the same day, we pushed out the aerial trailer to its cliff-edge position and became operational.

On 5 February we were joined by 8010 AMES, who set up their station on the flat plain at the seaward end of the valley below the lighthouse, and camouflaged it with netting and foliage which had to be renewed daily.

On 21 February the receiver and its cabin suffered superficial damage from an air attack, and during that same evening the aircraft controller made our first successful interception with a Beaufighter.

During the following week the lighthouse was attacked twice, but again we were incredibly lucky and escaped serious damage and casualty. However, we were soon threatened by enemy troops moving from Tunis and Bizerta, and we then learned that both Sedjenane and Fort Monopole had been taken by German forces, despite strong resistance from the Durham Light Infantry, thus leaving no way that we could escape with our vehicles. By now we could hear the sound of continuous heavy gunfire from the south, and during the early hours of 1 March we received orders to evacuate the site.

We dismantled the equipment, removing the panels and electronic chassis assemblies from their racks, smashed them and obliterated all labels with hammers and cold chisels. Then we threw the remains over the cliff. All documents, maps, charts and circuit diagrams were soaked in petrol and burned in the lighthouse courtyard, during which operation we were again shot up by an ME109, attracted no doubt by the black smoke and flames from our bonfire.

We then removed the sump plugs and opened the radiator draining taps on both the diesel-electric generators and left them running to complete their own destruction.

After this we set out on foot, following the coastline track over the hills to Sidi Mechrig, approximately 12 miles westward as the crow flies. We had no Arab guides; there was no discernable track and the hills were separated by steep-sided valleys with streams and marshy areas. ME109s were much in evidence, at times passing not more than 150 ft above us as we lay face down in the sand or under trees and bushes. So the last arrival did not reach Sidi Mechrig until late afternoon, and in many cases the meal provided on our arrival was the first that day.

Shortly after dark, Flight-Lieutenant Herman arrived with a small convoy of lorries borrowed from 894 AMES, into which we were loaded. Without lights and as quietly as possible, we moved out along the dirt-track towards Tabarka – anxious to avoid the attentions of two German Tiger tanks which had been spotted on the open ground not more than a mile from our escape route.

We crawled slowly throughout that night, cold and uncomfortable in the heavily-overloaded lorries, and at last reached a sheltered location in the gutted buildings of an evacuated hospital at St Louis, near Tabarka.

We were, by this time, in a sorry state, with no personal kit or other equipment, five-week beards, and only the clothes we stood up in. We shared just twelve blankets between the entire complement of 8009 and 8010 AMES, and these were allocated to the sick. But on 3 March we were taken into Tabarka, where we received a hot shower, a medical check and a clean change of clothing. From here we were driven, via St Louis, to a campsite near Setif, where we were soon joined by the rear party from Tabarka, and thus we were all together as a unit for the first time since leaving Bône.

We stayed at Setif with 8010 AMES encamped nearby until 19 May, awaiting re-equipment and a new assignment.

[The background to the Cap Serrat operation was that the defeat of the German Army in North Africa was only a matter of time, with Montgomery's 8th Army pushing it back across the Libyan desert towards Tunisia, where it would be contained by the presence of the American 1st Army, with its only avenue of escape being from the tip of the Cap Bon Peninsula, from where it was believed they would be taken off by boats to Sicily less than 100 miles away.

Allied Command risked the lives of the crews and the capture by the enemy of what was at that time top secret equipment so that when the anticipated evacuation of the German Army began we would be in a position to control aircraft from the 8010 site and also Royal Navy surface vessels from the 8009 site.

Alas, this plan failed. The American forces allowed the Germans to break out of the cordon through a mountain pass at Kasserine and to start a pincer movement towards the northern coastal ports. At the same time, the German forces in the northern sector started a similar supporting offensive, cut off our access road and exposed us to the inevitability of a full-scale infantry attack.

This is why we received our orders to destroy all the equipment and documentation and make our way on foot to Sidi Mechrig.]

Shaw Taylor *(of* Police 5*), Early Light Warning Radar Operator, Far East*:

The man in the gold-braided white suit gazed at us solemnly. 'And that is why I have sent for you,' he said. Standing on the sun-baked airstrip, each of us to a man knew that victory in the Far East was down to us. There's no doubt that

Shaw Taylor

Lord Louis Mountbatten was the greatest PR man who ever lived.

The scene had been set earlier in the day. On the training camp in Central India, we radar operators had been given the useful task of whitewashing the row of stones that marked each side of the small airstrip. At 1500 hours, in best khaki, we were lined up at attention a yard behind the stones.

As the tiny Dove touched down and came to a halt, the Flight Sergeant ran his eye along the ranks for the fiftieth time, muttering a quiet imprecation at the jaunty angle of my bush hat.

The white figure, towering above his row of ribbons, gazed along our poker-backed ranks. In a quiet voice, just audible to everyone, he said: 'I can't talk to the chaps like this; can't you find me a box to stand on?'

A box instantly appeared from nowhere. Lord Louis mounted it and addressed us: 'Come on chaps, break ranks and gather round.' You couldn't help liking the man.

'Now,' he said, 'this is my problem. I wanted to take Burma from the sea but Winnie grabbed all the landing craft before I could stop him – for some little do they've got going on back there – so we'll have to do it the hard way; push down the road from Imphal.'

His voice dropped to a very confidential one-to-one tone.

'Now, I don't know what sort of air force the Japs have got tucked away there, which is why I sent for you. You . . .' he paused, 'are going to be our eyes. The Army chaps know you're coming, and they know we can't do it without you!'

I was still shaking with Errol Flynn fervour when I realized that he'd gone, and the Dove was a tiny dot in the sky.

In Imphal, Don Pannell, Pat Carey and I discussed what sort of unit we would like to join. In training, we'd been together on ELW and had a good time, but no one had ever told us what 'ELW' stood for.

'Right, my son,' said the P/O, 'let's see where we can send you. Any preferences?'

'I'd like to go on ELW sir,' I said.

The eyebrows shot up. 'Would you, now? Good on you – we need lads like you!'

He was just about to get two more. All three of us had noticed his increasing astonishment.

'You three!' said the sergeant, 'Down to 6101 AMES. We need a 15 cwt taking down. Which of you lot drives?' We exchanged glances.

'None of us, Sarge.'

'Well, learn tomorrow morning and be ready for off at 1500.'

'Where is 6101, Sarge?'

'Don't know. Haven't heard from 'em for a fortnight. It's all a bit 'ot down there.'

I nodded sagely. No doubt once we'd left the heights of Imphal we'd notice the rise in temperature.

'If you're lucky, Mandalay will've gawn by the time you get there – ask around.'

'What does ELW stand for, Sarge?'

He gazed at me pityingly. 'Early Light Warning, son. Early . . . Light . . . Warning!'

By dint of asking around (in one case, of a troop preparing to make a night crossing of the Irrawady who expressed the urgent request that we should not only dowse our headlights but place them for safety in a tender spot of our anatomy) we found 6101 at Monywa.

Mandalay had indeed fallen, and the big push down the road to Rangoon was about to start. We joined it, sometimes with it, sometimes ahead of it. After all, we were Early Light Warning, and you couldn't get earlier or lighter than 'Chiefie' Gale and his merry dozen.

The strategy seemed to be to push forward a few miles and then close for the night into a defensive 'box' – a square of slit trenches manned by a hotch-potch of troops.

It was not unknown for our radar truck to be parked outside the 'box'. In this case, a word with the troops in the nearest slit trenches was an imperative.

'Hey, Johnny – *do admi gharry – do admi* come back . . . OK? Nay bang bang!'

'*Tik hai, sahib* – nay bang bang, *sahib*.'

An early light warning Type 6.

You reckoned to make a good 15 yards before the first bullet whistled past your ear – a signal for the whole line of trenches to open up. Flat on your belly, you'd crawl back towards the trenches under a carpet of small arms fire.

'I said "nay bang bang", you foolish lad!' (a loose translation).

In the darkness, a row of bright eyes and gleaming white teeth would smile at you.

'Not this trench, *sahib* – that one down there!'

When people ask me if I came close to death in Burma, I have a simple answer: 'Yes.'

At Pegu, the final push to Rangoon was ready to start. The Japanese Army had been cut in half, as was pointed out to us by a portly major on the day we arrived (he was Captain Mainwaring of *Dad's Army* to a tee!).

'Situation this,' he said, pointing with his swagger stick. 'Reckon about fifty plus Japs over there . . . trying to get over there.' He swivelled, and I drew a mental line that went straight through my tent. Nothing happened. But there he was at breakfast the following morning.

'Reckon about hundred and fifty now . . . over there . . . .' our heads followed his cane '. . . trying to get over there!'

Tension grew each day. Then Pat Carey burst forth from the truck one day, waving a piece of paper:

'Chiefie, Chiefie, a signal, a signal! They don't need us any more. We've to move back to Maymyo!'

I doubt if any unit in the whole of the Second World War – possibly any war – struck camp as quickly as 6101 AMES. We were up and on the road within minutes, our three trucks kicking up the dust as we hit the rutted road north.

That night, the anticipated crossing took place. There was a massacre. I often wonder what happened to 'Captain Mainwaring'.

The hill town of Maymyo is a dream. We spent six glorious weeks there on battle fatigue leave before moving down the road again to Rangoon and the eventual Japanese surrender, taken by the man in the white suit.

On the day of our arrival in Maymyo we received an invitation from the Army to a dance that evening. The sight that greeted us is never to be forgotten. The Japanese had interned all the Anglo-Burmese families and quartered them in the town. The hall was filled with beautiful girls dressed in ball gowns which they had fashioned from parachute silk.

The band led into a slow foxtrot . . . I was a trained ballroom dancer. . . .

There will never be another evening like it. Nor another day like the one that followed. After breakfast, the lads of 6101 gathered round me.

'You seem to be quite nippy on your feet.'

'Well, I did go to a dancing school in Hackney. St Johns in the Narroway, under Johnson's the ironmongers. . . .' my voice trailed off.

Six hairy airmen grinned at me.

'Then you can teach us – can't you!'

I *was* wounded in Burma. Wounded by 'friendly fire', you might call it. Only it didn't feel too friendly at the time.

Alec Farmer, *(died 1993) ex-Radar Operator*:

Radar on the Cocos Islands (AMES 366)

Alec Farmer

[*Note*: It seems that the mobile CH sent to the Cocos Islands in 1945, to which Alec was attached, was not required for radar cover at that late stage in the war, since other radars had been set up for that area. However, there was a requirement for a navigational aid to assist incoming aircraft to find the tiny island base.

With RAF assistance, a small team of British scientists converted the radar into a one-off navaid. Although it worked on the well-established German Lorenz principle of overlapping beams, it was tuned to the Loran frequency in order that aircraft so fitted could use it with minimum modification. The name given – Loran-B – indicated the use of beams, as in the shorter range BABS (Blind Approach Beacon System), but this was not an official Loran designation.]

When I volunteered for the RAF in June 1941, I hied me to the recruiting office in Reading and asked what was on offer. The sergeant suggested Radio Operator. He said this was 'sort of to do with radio, but not Morse'. As an impressionable teenager, I was swayed by the recruiting blurb which went with it: 'Candidates must be above average intelligence and of undoubted integrity.' So I signed on at once, and it turned out to be radar!

At the end of April 1942 I got the call to be an instructor at Cranwell and spent a couple of happy years there. The senior NCO of the WAAF instructors was Flight Sergeant Avis Hearn – only a little mouse of a thing, but who had been awarded the MM for continuing to report from Poling during a blitz on that station (see p. 25).

Eventually, in 1944, came the call for overseas duty, and I went off to Stenigot, in Lincolnshire, where I became part of 366MU and we were all trained to drive. Later, 366MU were sent as a group to Chigwell and we breathed a sigh of relief as it was a pre-Western Europe supply station. We all preferred the idea of fighting the Germans to fighting the Japanese. We did the usual assault courses and also learned how to cook with a stove made out of a biscuit tin containing oil and water, which dripped down on to a hot plate where it sent the flame roaring along a trench, allowing us to cook for large numbers.

One weekend in December 1944, all passes were cancelled and we were ordered to report for kitting out. Surprise, surprise! We didn't get battledress blue, but KD (Khaki drill) for the Far East!

So the next thing we knew, we were on the high seas aboard the *Queen of*

Bermuda (known as the 'Queen of Blue Murder'). She was actually a very good troopship, and we had 500 WAAFs on board, although we didn't see them until we got through the Bay of Biscay, because things had been decidedly rough!

We finally arrived at RAF Worli (near Bombay) and some time later we were sailing from Colombo, where we'd been told we were to become part of 129 Staging Post. But what was that? we asked. The answer was that we were to form a brand-new air base on the Keeling Cocos Islands in the Indian Ocean (halfway between Ceylon and Australia). By then it was April 1945. We landed on the largest of the islands (7 miles long) and found it a virgin jungle of palm trees. We plodded from north to south to set up camp, only to be told that they wanted our CH station back up at the northern tip, so we plodded all the way back up again, to await the unloading of our lorries with their 105 ft aerials.

We set to work and got the aerials erected and connected up to the three-ton Crossleys that contained our gear. We knew that we had less than four weeks before the next 'regular' Jap recce plane was due over, and we were only protected by one Indian AA (anti-aircraft) battery which had no ammunition! Fortunately, the REs worked flat out and got an airstrip ready in three weeks, so that our Spitfires could be uncrated and operational.

Loran would have been the equipment of choice for the Cocos, with master and slave stations, but our group of islands were not spread out enough to enable any slaves to be far enough away from a master; so we suddenly found ourselves re-formed as AMES 366, and boffins like Freddie Lutkin (inventor of the Lutkin aerial array) came to join us and invent what was to become the very first Loran Babs beam. Loran-B was very successful, and one of the incoming navigators told us how he could put his feet up on either side of the tube while he was still on the deck in Colombo and literally 'left hand down a bit, right hand down a bit' guide his pilot to our tiny speck in the Indian Ocean.

The aerial towers were erected most precisely so that a double beam went north-west to Kankesanturai and south-east to northern Australia. The navigators in the aircraft had merely to line up their pulses to be of equal intensity and then they were homing in on our beam. We were such a tiny dot in the ocean that it was difficult for aircraft to fly to us, which they had to do as a staging post for their next step to Australia and on to Ceylon, or vice versa.

The islands were inhabited thus: Horsburgh was a naval base and also had a CHL; Direction Island had a Cable & Wireless station; Home Island was where the Clunies-Ross house was, and all the islanders (and eventually our Loran-B), and West Island had the airstrip and masses of Army and RAF.

The idea was that they were building up for the Zipper raid to free Singapore, and the West Island airstrip held two squadrons of Liberators and one of Spitfires, plus a flight of Mosquitoes. Fortunately, the Japs surrendered before the Zipper raid was needed.

I learned Malay and so became, on Home Island, the unofficial interpreter during a very happy eighteen months there. I got on well with the charming Cocos Islanders and went on their fishing trips and to their weddings and other celebrations.

We used to see films sent down from Welfare at an open-air cinema. Our CO let us have three of his sheets, which we sewed together and slung between two coconut trees as a screen. The projector was put in a tent, and we gave shows on successive nights, so that those on watches would see the film. The islanders had never seen this white man's magic before, and every last one of them turned up and insisted on sitting on the wrong side of the screen to watch it. They were so intrigued with it that they turned up on both nights. *Except* when the film was *Blithe Spirit* – all that stuff about spirits and things moving about in the air was too much for them, and not a soul turned up on the second night.

They were also very intrigued by the kisses. The islanders kissed by rubbing noses (which was called a *chium*, so they had to give a new name to the western-style kiss, which they called a *chium bunyi* (noisy kiss)!

I felt privileged to get to know these marvellous people and their magical islands.

Electric light being laid on the Cocos Islands.

A Cocos Island wedding, at which Alec Farmer was an honoured guest, perhaps because he took the trouble to learn their language.

PART THREE: INTO EUROPE

Ron Colledge, *Navigator of a Stirling bomber of 218 Squadron, who duped the Germans with their famed dummy 'invasion' in the Pas de Calais on 5 June 1944 with the aid of 'window'*:

Ron Colledge

Our preparation for the part we were to play in Operation Overlord began early in January 1944, although at that time we had no idea that there was any connection with the invasion nor of the role we would eventually play.

Along with other senior crews of 218 Squadron, we spent the rest of that month based at Newmarket learning the intricacies of a new navigational aid code named Gee-H – a more sophisticated version of our old friend the Gee box.

We found that Gee-H enabled us to obtain much more accurate fixes, and eventually, on our return to normal squadron duties, we were able to use it to good effect on bombing raids on railway marshalling yards and V1 (buzz-bomb) launching sites. On these raids we were able to release our bombs using the Gee-H equipment rather than the conventional bomb sight.

At the same time we were also carrying out short daylight flights over England, practising with our new toy, so that by the end of May we knew it really well and could use it confidently under most circumstances.

By then there was a widely-held hope and belief that the Allies would soon attempt a landing in Europe, and as we had been ordered not to discuss our current activities with anyone not directly involved, we naturally put two and two together and decided that when the invasion did come, we'd be a part of it. However, the exact nature of our role was still a well-kept secret, known only to the top brass and the boffins.

On 2 June and 3 June, we had two short dress rehearsals which involved setting lots of coordinates on the Gee-H set and thereby flying orbits, the accent being on quick and accurate setting of a long sequence of turning points.

We did nothing on 4 June, which was quite an anticlimax after the fairly intense activity thus far, but on 5 June we experienced the familiar butterflies when the news came through – 'ops tonight'!

On previous trips, the navigation leader had revealed targets in the Ruhr, Hanover, Berlin, etc., – when the bomb bays held our normal bomb load of high explosives and incendiaries – and areas like Kiel Bay, when we carried mines, and even French Resistance reception areas in the French Alps, when we dropped much-needed supplies.

But tonight our target was an area in the English Channel, and our bomb bays were empty. However, inside the fuselage was a huge quantity of 'window' – narrow strips of foil which had been used to confuse the enemy radar during our bombing raids from 1943 onwards.

On bombing raids, it was dropped by our aircraft in order to create a mass of echoes on the German radar screens, blotting out the vital single echo created by each bomber. Tonight we were hoping to fool the German radar operators in a different way.

Six of 218 Squadron's Stirlings took off from Woolfox Lodge, near Oakham in Rutland, some time before midnight. Each aircraft carried three navigators instead of the usual one. The first would carry out the normal dead reckoning navigation to get us to our operating area and, hopefully, back again. The second navigator would use the older Gee set to help the pilot maintain accurate tracks once the exercise had begun. My job, as the third navigator, was to use the Gee-H equipment to set all the turning point coordinates.

The plan was for the six aircraft to fly in two lines of three abreast with each aircraft about a mile apart, and the second line about four miles behind the first. Even on straight and level flight, these distances at night didn't leave much room for error, and as we would be flying a succession of orbits for approximately 3½ hours, positional accuracy and timing were crucial for the success of the mission – and for our own safety.

On reaching the operational area, I set up the first set of coordinates on the Gee-H set, and the skipper, aided by the Gee operator, brought the aircraft on to course for Cap Gris-Nez, near Calais. As soon as I had my pulses lined up, telling me we were over our starting point, I gave the order to start 'windowing'. That was the signal for several extra aircrew in the centre of the aircraft to offload bundles of window. Soon thousands of strips of silver foil were cascading to the water below.

As this continued, I had put a second set of coordinates on the Gee-H, and as soon as we reached this position, I gave the order to stop windowing. Simultaneously, the pilot brought the aircraft on to a reciprocal course with a 180° turn. As this was happening, I set a third set of coordinates, and as soon as the pulses lined up once more, with the aircraft now heading away from France, I gave the order to resume dropping window. We were now flying back towards our starting point, although on a track parallel to the outward one.

Then I set yet another turning point on the screen, but this one was fractionally nearer to Cap Gris-Nez than the first one. Once again: blips lined up; stop window; 180° turn; set new coordinates; on course; blips lined up; start windowing.

This sequence continued for the next three hours or so, with window being dropped on the parallel legs towards and away from France, but never on the turns. With the six aircraft in the formation, we were creating a huge rectangle of echoes, producing window the approximate size of an invasion fleet, hoping it would be picked up by the German radar operators and interpreted as such.

Even though the aircraft were flying at some 200 m.p.h., the accuracy of the Gee-H set enabled us to cause the window to creep across the Channel at 5 knots, the approximate speed of a large fleet of ships. This was achieved by each successive pair of turning points being set fractionally closer to the French coast (see diagram, p. 140). It was in this way that we created our phantom fleet.

At the same time as this was happening, Lancasters of 617 ('Dambusters') Squadron were carrying out a similar spoof towards Le Havre, giving the Germans yet another headache.

Eventually, the last order to 'stop window' was given, and we set course for Woolfox. Fortunately, all six aircraft returned safely and, after debriefing, we went to the mess for the usual post-op. breakfast.

After a normal night op., we would then have snatched a few hours' sleep. But sleep was farthest from our minds that morning, and we stayed in the mess listening to the radio. And presently we heard the BBC announcer tell us, and the rest of Britain, that what we strongly suspected had really happened – the invasion of Europe – nearly 400 miles west of our little decoy operation!

I think we then went to bed!

[History has recorded that this ruse proved highly successful.]

Ron Colledge (second from right) with a crew from 90 Squadron on the morning of their first operation.

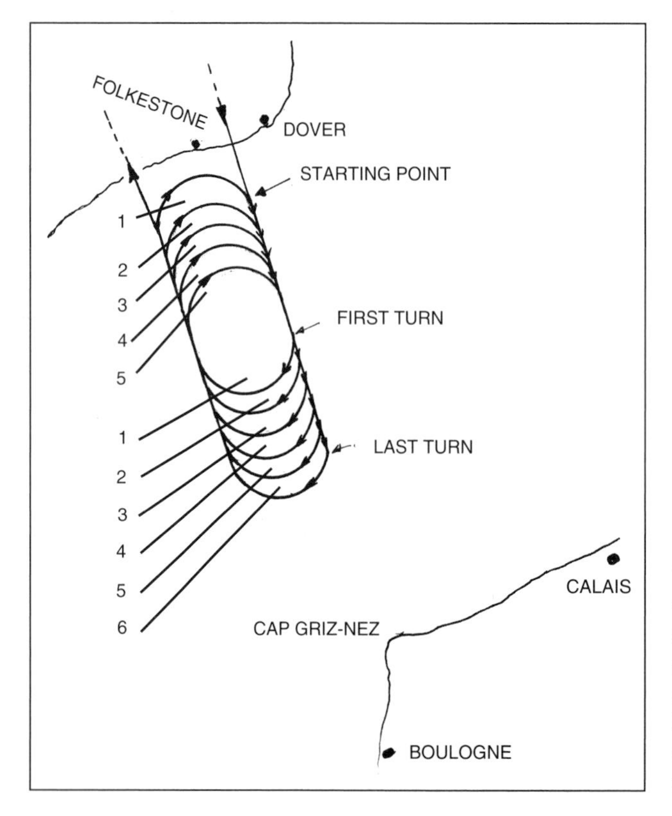

The phantom invasion fleet was created by aircraft dropping window in a series of turns, gradually advancing towards the French coast. (For simplicity, only a few turns are shown.)

Flight-Lieutenant E.H. ('Ned') Hitchcock, *Electrical Engineer Officer, Royal New Zealand Air Force*:

E.H. Hitchcock

RAF Radar on Omaha Beach

Not many people know that an RAF radar unit landed on D-Day, in the midst of bloody Omaha Beach! This US Navy photograph with the caption 'Underwater Obstacles on Omaha Beach' shows a beach studded with heavy timber tri-poles. On the horizon there is a dense mass of shipping. The sea between is empty. To the left appears a grounded LST, to the right a tank deep in the sand. In the foreground is the heavy barbed-wire defence.

A military historian studying this photograph might be puzzled by the presence, centre stage, of British vehicles. Two burnt-out wrecks are Thorneycroft three-tonners, and immediately behind is the shape, so familiar to radar staff, of an Austin three-tonner housing a 20 kVA diesel generator. Why should such vehicles be in the midst of 'Bloody Omaha' on D-Day itself – the beach where so many American soldiers gave their lives storming Fortress Europe?

About five o'clock on the afternoon of that day I had rather similar thoughts.

The underwater obstacles on Omaha beach, revealed as the tide receded.

The beginning of the wet landing had been easy. Truck after truck of our radar convoy had plunged down the ramp from our LST and roared shoreward. But alas, the water, instead of shallowing, steadily grew deeper. About the time it reached our waists, the truck in front stalled. Ours immediately followed suit, engine noise ceased, and all around pounded the relentless sea, already tearing at the canvas sides that protected the diesel generator.

Far in the grey distance lay the beach. We could see the occasional shellburst. There seemed to be very little American activity; it all seemed to be suspended – and little promise of welcome. We could see no other vehicles rushing ashore. It was all rather isolated and lonely.

Four years earlier, I had arrived in Liverpool from New Zealand on board the *Empress of Asia* in 1940, having just completed my degree course in engineering, and having already been accepted for training in radiolocation, as it was then called. I soon found my way to Yatesbury in Wiltshire, to the RDF Training School, where even our notebooks were classified 'secret'. We had been honoured with the rank of leading aircraftman before we even left home, and in due course I was promoted to corporal, along with another chap whose name might be familiar – Arthur C. Clarke.

Feeling it was time to apply for a commission, I found that I must become an electrical engineer in order to do so. With dizzying speed I went through an officer cadet course at Cosford, and then on to Henlow for the electrical course, which was intense.

After this, I shot off to Swanton Morley, in Norfolk, to be in charge of electrical and instrument sections of three squadrons of 2 Group's medium bombers. But not for long! Somebody suggested that my place should be in the newly-established electrical-mechanical engineering section at 60 Group, 60 Group being responsible for ground radar in Britain. About the time I arrived, 10 cm radar had come, adding paraboloids, turning gear high on the towers and transmission through waveguides – more like plumbing than electronics.

To cope with all these developments, the new Section TM4 had been established, headed by a livewire Aussie. There we had a mix of design and development work, particularly for the new centimetre wavelengths; of coping with emergencies in old, overworked gear, and of acceptance inspections.

We Join the Offensive

Late in May 1944, I was working at Group one morning when a colleague put his head round the door.

'Want to go in with the invasion, Hitch?'

'Sure,' said I.

Next day: 'Get your kit – we're going!'

We learned that two mobile radar units had been assigned to go in with the invasion, and that a number of specialists in various aspects were to be attached, for the initial period, to assist with setting up complex technical equipment in battle conditions. Norman Best was to be GCI specialist, and I was to be electrical engineering specialist. And fate decreed that we were to join the unit allotted to the Americans and scheduled to land on what was to be known as the infamous Omaha Beach.

GCI – The Invasion Role

We gathered that in a seaborne invasion of a hostile shore, the best time for counter-attack is on the first night, or in the early stages of build-up. Air activity at night could be difficult to counter, so a necessary defence for the invaders would be effective nightfighter protection. Mobile GCI units were to be landed close behind the initial waves of the attack, and to be operational in support of the beachhead on D-Night. Because the Americans had no available fully-operational system, one unit had been assigned from the RAF to the American Sector. And in mid-channel there would be shipborne units (Fighter Direction Tenders) to provide cover over the invasion routes, and link with the beachhead units (see p. 68).

The Assignment

Our first move was to collect gear from 85 Group at Uxbridge. In addition to the usual field service items were some that underlined aspects of the way ahead – anti-gas impregnated battledress, an escape map and a service revolver meant business. There was at the same time desperate activity – all the ground RAF units which operated in Army territory were having their khaki clothing recalled and being reissued with RAF blue. It was said that the RAF went into battle in blue – more of this later.

Back to 60 Group that night, and amid the farewell party, another grim note: WAAF friends putting rank badges on loops that could be slid off – snipers were said to be selective! The next day we drove down into the sealed area of the south coast, where no civilian movements were permitted in or out, and no communication was allowed between civilian and military. The Second Front, so long awaited, was under way.

Camp D2

We joined Radar Unit 15082 – already ensconced among some thousands of American troops. Strict discipline – no short cuts across open grass, everything camouflaged. The Americans were friendly, helpful and efficient. More deadly serious equipment was issued – an American assault respirator, worn on the chest in a waterproof bag (destined to be a lifesaver!); supplies to make us completely independent for forty-eight hours (including three condoms!), and maps of the landing area showing fortifications and machine-gun sites. Our briefing explained that we were to land at H-Hour plus five (about full tide) on Sector Dog-Red, entering by a cleared lane, and that a beachmaster would direct us to our exit.

We Set Sail – Twice

In the late afternoon of 4 June we set sail for France from Portland. Our slow fleet would take all night to cross the Channel and arrive at dawn on 5 June. But next morning I awoke to find land close on our right – we must have turned back! What could have happened? Was it all off?

We spent the day pottering about in a borrowed dinghy, rowing around among the ships. Later, of course, we learned of the critical decision to postpone the landings for a day to minimize the effect of expected bad weather. That afternoon, we set off again, and woke to grey skies and a barely visible French coast.

We Go in to Land

At about 0900 hours our LST suddenly set off from the middle of the invasion fleet – straight in – ours leading, the other four following. The recce party was third. A patrol craft tossing about in the rough seas came close: 'What wave are you?' I didn't hear the reply, but the patrol seemed satisfied: 'In you go!'

As we neared the beach we could see clearly that it was not yet captured. The men ashore were taking cover from enemy fire; there was a vehicle burning; as we watched, an explosion blew a figure high in the air.

Aboard our vessel was a US observer, who had experience at Pantellaria. He, we heard, had assessed the situation and concluded that the last thing needed ashore at this stage was a collection of technicians armed with radar aerials. Rather relieved, we turned seaward, presuming we could land next day.

We stood off while naval guns pounded the shore. We saw the Vierville clock tower destroyed (we later learned it was suspected of housing German artillery observers). Mercifully, we knew nothing of the desperate battle by the American infantry to gain a foothold (this was the sector eastward of us, where the Americans had been carried by strong tidal currents). Nor did we know of General Bradley's debating whether the Omaha landing should be abandoned.

About four o'clock in the afternoon we were concluding that it would be useless to land now – no chance of working that night. Then, suddenly, *in we went*! It was now low tide, so we could be landed below the beach obstacles which the Army engineers had not yet been able to clear, because of enemy fire. Then followed the debâcle.

The Debâcle

The unplanned landing at low tide instead of high had disastrous results. Some vehicles were landed on sandbars and stalled as they drove into deeper water. Others sank in patches of soft sand on the long run up the beach and were immersed as the tide rose. Those reaching the shoreline found that the wire and earth barriers had not yet been breached and there was no way off the exposed beach. They became sitting targets for enemy shellfire, and shrapnel-punctured diesel oil drums fed the flames.

On our LCT, the ramp splashed down as the vessel grounded; the vehicles roared down the ramp; the water rose steadily around our waists; the engine gave up, and we sat – thinking the thoughts with which I began this tale.

Suddenly, past us there surged a Thorneycroft – great bow wave, cab high above water – and leaning out, a grinning face under a tin hat, hand-signalling to us what might have been charitably interpreted as a V-sign. Just the irrepressible humour needed to jerk us back to practicality!

I waded ashore to where our rescue Diamond-T crane waited, and managed to drag a cable back and grope under water to hook up. By the time it became clear that the surging sea had embedded the wheels too deep for retrieval to be possible, the water had risen to cab-top level. There was no way ashore except a swim in full kit, made possible by two factors – nightly keep-fit runs back at 60 Group, and that assault respirator, giving buoyancy!

The crane crew had already one man wounded, and after I staggered exhausted up the beach between the obstacles, I could see nothing and no one – no beachmaster, no medics – just dead and wounded, and abandoned vehicles.

After a brief rest, leaning against one of the vehicles, it seemed to me best to get busy; the urgent task being to save what equipment we could. Flames threatened an undamaged truck. I managed to pull out a wounded GI from his doubtful shelter underneath it, and drove my first ever heavy transport clear of the flames.

Then a bulldozer suddenly appeared and cleared away the barriers, and there was a way off the beach, and our group seemed to come together again, rescuing what vehicles could be driven up to a field in the narrow valley and collecting wounded for evacuation. We had suffered heavy casualties – ten dead and forty wounded. The Americans had suffered horrific casualties, and the beaches were strewn with their dead.

In the midst of all this, some of us found a place to sleep, under a hedge in the grounds of a seaside villa. I managed to borrow a blanket, and I don't recall discomfort from wet clothes. There was wry compensation in that the only air attack on our location came from a lone Ju88 flying very low to avoid the hail of fire from the assembled shipping. (This uncontrolled ack-ack fire was to make the nightfighter task more difficult.)

D-Day Plus One

Up at dawn, some sodden biscuits, and off to rescue our Type 14 transmitter, caught in soft sand and then by the tide. A dead American leaned against the wheel, seaweed draped over all. We requested help from a bulldozer which was busy rescuing other bulldozers. Shelling started, and the engineers removing beach obstacles took cover. The LST was shelled. The bulldozer arrived, extracted the Type 14 like a cork from a bottle, and towed it, still sinking into sand, past the LST wreck. Then came sniper fire from the bluffs, and the driver prudently abandoned the tow: he was too good a target. (We soon learned that walking briskly from cover to cover baffled the snipers – don't stand still!)

It appeared that further landings had been abandoned. Had it all been a failure? Were we just a few stranded on an enemy shore? Then came relief – American tanks advancing from the next sector (misnamed 'Easy Beach'). Then a little later came one of those indelible moments in the memory – a group of men crowded round a radio vehicle listening to the BBC news – to be told that the invasion had been successful and that men and materials were pouring ashore on the other beaches.

We carried on collecting our battered remnants and started the task of putting together what we could to become operational. Later, we moved to a camp site nearby.

D-Day Plus Two and Later

The American commander said that we'd better get out of that RAF blue – it was too much like German field grey, and he couldn't guarantee that his men might not mistake us for the enemy! And miraculously – in the middle of an invasion – our American allies produced from nowhere a miscellany of assorted khaki and we were instantly transformed into Americans – gum-chewing and all!

A suitable operational site having been selected and tested for mines by careful backing of the Crossleys, some replacement gear arrived and we were on the air! On the night of D-Day plus one, 1½ enemy aircraft were shot down[1] – the first GCI-controlled interception from the American beachhead.

Within a week, we were hitching a return lift on an American LST from Utah Beach back to Portland.

Back at 60 Group, we were set to work on countering the buzz-bombs. These were programmed to change course after launching, to prevent tracking back to the site. Attacks on those sites would be helped if radar range could be extended. Transmitter h.t. had been increased, and an extended aerial array might help. First, I located some GCI aerial mesh frames at the maintenance unit in Carlisle. Then a few days on the drawing board designing a frame extension which was made up at the Kidbrooke Depot. Next, with a Kidbrooke party down to Wartling, and the extension frame was mounted. (I gather the Germans soon introduced mobile launching gear: the inevitable move and counter-move!)

As the Liberation Army advanced, plans were made for the ground stations of

[1] It sometimes happened that two aircraft or ground-based units attacked and brought down the same enemy aircraft, each claiming a kill. Because it was impossible to decide whose fire had been the more successful, the credit was divided between them. Hence a score of half an aircraft.

the radar navigational aids (Gee and Oboe) to follow up. A new wing organization was set up and given the name of 72 Wing. I was put in charge of the Electrical-Mechanical section, whose main task was to service the very large number of generating sets, from Lister diesels down to light-weight petrol sets suitable for airborne transport.

No turning gear to plague us, but a whole new set of problems – those 110 ft timber towers! They were beautifully designed, lightweight and transportable, but had an infinity of small pieces to maintain. There was a desperate rush to work out what equipment was needed; mobile workshops and the provision of spares.

Our convoy landed on Sword Beach on 5 September 1944. All very civilized this time – even a bulldozer to pile sand at the ramp for easy exit. We learnt that we could take over buildings previously occupied by Germans, and their taste was good!

But the speed of the Allied advance across France meant it was soon time to move forward, and Mons was chosen for the next HQ site. It took two days for the convoy to reach Belgium – driving past slag heaps in the mining areas – dreary surroundings after our outdoor life in Normandy, but all compensated for by the warmth and friendliness of the city – with the added link of New Zealanders having been there in 1914–18.

Radar was back in the firing line during the German Ardennes offensive. An Oboe unit had no warning: the story goes that a crew member looking at a footbridge down in the valley suddenly realized there were German soldiers crossing. The unit made a hasty exit, struggling with winter mud and the need for help to extract highly-secret equipment from very preoccupied Americans. (Von Rundstedt later disclosed that he had detailed an armoured unit for the specific purpose of capturing intact all the 72 Wing units.)

Not long before VE Day, we delivered a new power unit to a station in what was to become the Russian Zone. We were told that civil affairs officers had displayed photographs from Belsen, not too far distant. These had been dismissed by the locals as typical Allied propaganda. Yet, in that village, we saw a factory with the workers – mostly Russian girls – camped in it. The villagers must have known that this was forced labour; the girls were virtually slaves and could now easily run riot.

We had wondered why those villagers were so terrified of the rumour that they were to be in the proposed Russian Zone. Now we understood.

Gerald N.S. Taylor, *Radar Mechanic*:

The Story of 15121 BDS – A Mobile GCI Radar Unit, July 1944 to May 1945:

15121BDS (Base Defence Sector) was one of five mobile GCI units which went to France in 1944 as part of the RAF's 2nd Tactical Air Force – part of the

Gerald N.S. Taylor

Allied Expeditionary Air Force. Its function was to provide air cover over the battlefield and tactical air support for the armies fighting on the ground, as well as airlift facilities for airborne forces and photographic reconnaissance. It was intended that these GCIs, which were part of 85 Group, would provide defence of the base areas against air attack at night.

This particular unit comprised four primary radars, one IFF ground interrogator system and both ground-to-air and ground-to-ground communications systems. The main convoy consisted of about twenty-eight vehicles, augmented in March 1945 to a total of 105.

The first site on which the convoy operated was on the east side of the beachhead, near Coursells. It took some forty-eight hours of sweat and toil to get everything erected and working, much to the wrath of Wing HQ, but with a lot of new equipment and several non-existent handbooks, this was hardly surprising. No sooner was most of the equipment on the air than instructions came to dismantle and move back about 4 miles to Hermanville, as Monty wanted our field to put a large number of his guns in for one of his famous barrages.

At dusk that evening, Bomber Command made a raid on Caen with nearly 500 Lancasters and Halifaxes: an awesome and unforgettable sight from 5 miles away. The Monty barrage followed at dawn, so there was not much sleep that night. It was not just the noise – part of the German trench we were sleeping in collapsed with the vibration.

It took another three days to get the station working again, and it was about 9 July before operations started in earnest against German aircraft which were intruding over the beachhead at night. Nightfighter Mosquitoes, usually fitted with MkVIII AI, flew out from the UK in pairs and patrolled the beach-head for about two hours, being relieved by another pair at the end of the patrol. As can be seen from the photograph of the scoreboard, our first partial success was a damaged Me210 on 11 July, with the first kill a Ju88 one week later, on 20 July.

The main German targets seemed to be the ships anchored offshore and the Mulberry harbours, rather than military targets inland – perhaps because the latter were heavily defended by AA batteries, most of which seemed to be completely trigger-happy. It only needed a dog to bark, a truck to backfire or someone to loose off a rifle round for the whole sky to be one mass of tracer, fired off in apparently random directions. It took several minutes to quieten down before someone coughed and the whole cycle was repeated.

The July figure of five kills and one damaged in the three weeks was bettered in August with ten kills and one probable. There was then a single FW190 shot down on 1 September, after which orders were received from Wing to pack up and get on the road eastwards. Paris had fallen on 25 August, Rouen on the 29th, and what was left of the Wehrmacht was rapidly getting out of France.

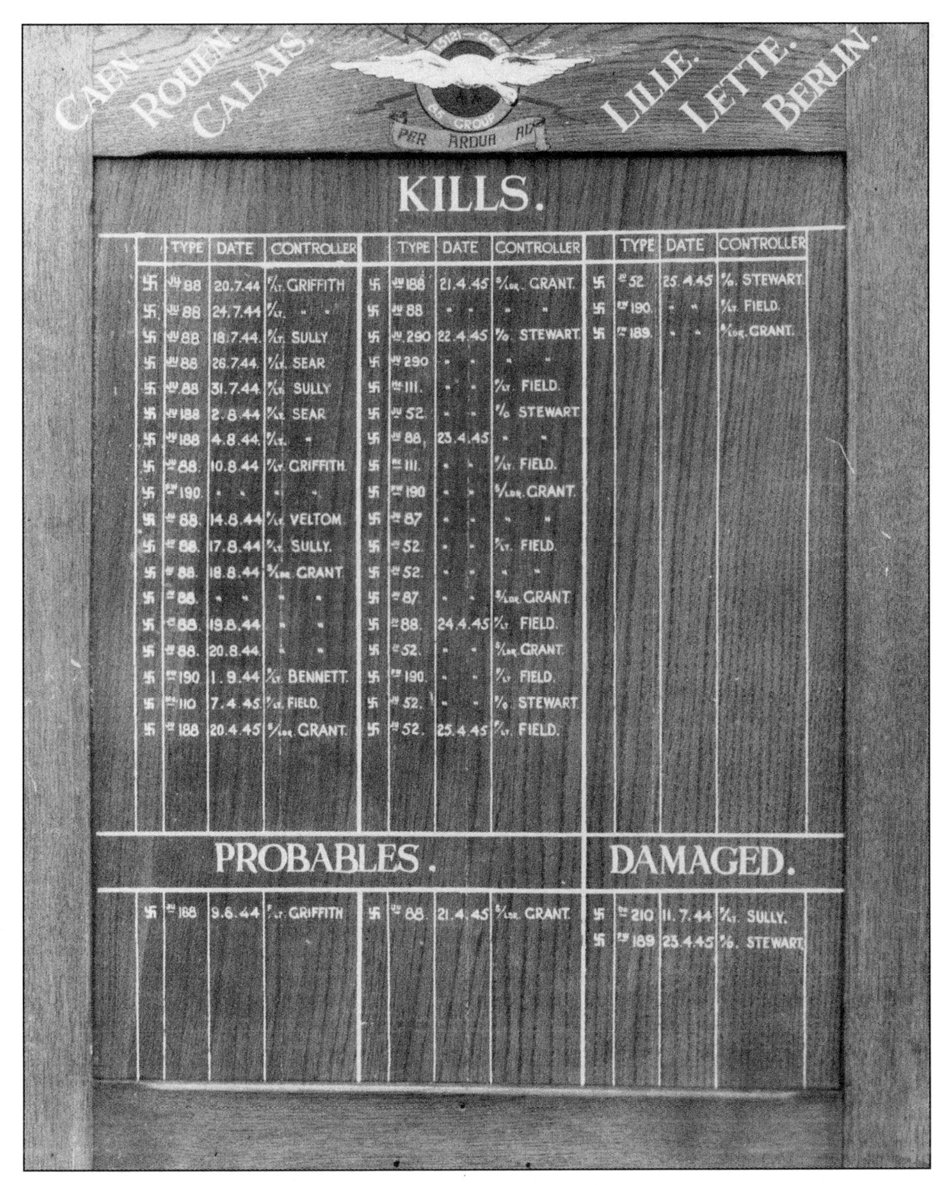

15121 Unit's scoreboard.

Rouen

The road to Rouen was packed with military traffic, all travelling eastward. Fortunately, our route was not on the direct road to Paris, which was heavily congested. The convoy spent the night parked on the verge of the road on the outskirts of Rouen, where it was an object of much curiosity to the local population.

All bridges over the Seine had been destroyed, either by bombing or by explosives. However, one had been repaired enough to allow one-way traffic with care. After a delay, the convoy got across the river next morning, but became split up in the process. What happened next was to affect the fortunes of 15121 Unit for the next four months!

Unlike some cities, Rouen had not been extensively damaged. Allied bombing had been confined to the bridges, and relatively little fighting had taken place there. Nevertheless, there was some damage. Our Type 15 Aerial Vehicle had become separated from the rest of the convoy and was travelling down a wide street littered with blocks of masonry which had fallen from the buildings lining the road. There were telephone wires, electricity cables and overhead tram cables hanging in great loops down the middle of the road. While the driver was trying to avoid some lumps of masonry lying in the road, the top of the aerial framework, which was bolted to the side of the aerial cabin, hit a heavy tram cable. The driver immediately stopped the truck, and the passenger climbed up to look at the damage. It was difficult to assess how bad this was, as the IFF aerial and several other pieces of equipment were also stowed on the cabin roof. Certainly, one of the wooden aerial support frameworks was broken, but nothing looked beyond repair.

At this point, one of the despatch riders appeared and led the vehicle to where the rest of the convoy was forming up. The CO was told of the accident and said that a proper inspection could be made at the temporary Wing HQ set up to the east of Rouen. This was duly done, and a very pessimistic report was produced: a lot of repair work would be needed, and the parts would have to come from the UK. It might take several weeks before the Type 15 was serviceable again. The CO was then dressed down by the Group Captain and told that the unit was in disgrace and would have to stay in the Rouen area until further notice. This turned out to be four months!

We were quartered in a large château on the escarpment to the east of Rouen, and the radars were deployed on flat farmland a few miles away. After a few days there was virtually no enemy activity in the area, and the war receded eastwards. In fact, apart from continual maintenance of our equipment, there was nothing to break the monotony of watchkeeping during the whole period from early September until Christmas.

Calais

To everyone's delight, orders came immediately after Christmas to pack up the convoy and move to Calais. At last someone had remembered our existence! Morale rose – but not for long. It soon became clear that getting on the road again would be easier said than done. The radar vehicles had suffered severely by being out in the open air for four months. In addition, the weather was exceptionally cold, with a severe frost night and day. It was so cold, in fact, that the electrolyte had frozen in the batteries, and radiators had burst in spite of antifreeze. Tyres had deteriorated; there was water in the fuel tanks – springs, brakes and suspensions had rusted up. In those vehicles where the cab and steering wheel had to be removed before the radar aerial could be turned, the seat upholstery had rotted. It required a major effort to get all the engines running again and the vehicles roadworthy.

The convoy eventually set off for Calais in the first week of 1945. The new site at Calais was up on the cliffs among the heavy guns and massive concrete defences which the Germans had left behind. There was not enough room to deploy the four radar aerial vehicles in the normal arrangement, with each one 100 yards from the ops cabin complex. With the cabins closer together, more blind arcs had to be accepted. In addition, the ground around the Type 15 aerial was far from flat, and heightfinding was therefore very unreliable. Heights derived from the Type 13 were not affected by uneven ground and were used instead of those obtained by the Type 15.

The operational reason for placing the convoy on this site was that German troops were holding out in an area near Dunkirk and were being supplied by air-drops at night. It was hoped that nightfighters could deal with this situation. For some reason, the operation failed to work and was abandoned after a few weeks.

Lille

After some six weeks at Calais, the station was packed up and moved the comparatively short distance to Lille. Here, it was parked on an airfield, which at least was flat. Everyone went home on ten days' leave while the gear was given a thorough overhaul, ready for an active role in Germany.

Lette

Some time towards the end of March, we received orders to move eastwards into Germany. Following the Ardennes counter-attack by the Germans, just after Christmas, the Allies had regrouped and stockpiled a mass of equipment just to the west of a line from Arnhem in the north to Saarbrucken in the south. A general advance started on 8 February, and by 20 March this had reached the Rhine, which was crossed in several places during the next four days. By 26 March the Allies were pouring across in a number of places on a wide front.

Around this time, 15121 Unit got on the road, crossed the border into Belgium and continued on into Holland, finally entering Germany near Venlo. Our briefing was that we would be attached to the US 9th Army under General Simpson and would get fuel and rations from the Americans. The 9th Army was operating under Monty, so technically the unit was still under British control. We were to keep as close to Simpson's front line as possible, consistent with the safety of the men and equipment. We were to operate offensively, with the object of destroying as many enemy aircraft as possible and disrupting the Luftwaffe's operations. We would be free to decide when and where to operate the equipment to achieve these objectives.

By the time we crossed the Dutch border into Germany, our convoy had grown to 105 vehicles, needing a fleet of despatch riders to marshal everyone along the correct route. The roads were full of American trucks, all moving east as fast as possible. Petrol was a problem: each vehicle had to carry two days' supply, and the route had to be planned to ensure that fuel dumps were available. We reached the Rhine at Wesel on 31 March and had to wait until the next day to cross on one of the two pontoon bridges put up by the Americans.

It was a frightening experience. The river was in full flood after the spring thaw and was at least 500 yards wide. The roadway was supported by inflated rubber boats; steel hawsers connected to the river bank prevented it from being washed downstream. On driving on to the roadway, it dropped about a foot and rose again behind the vehicle. We were stuck in a traffic jam for forty-five minutes in the middle of the river, and as we sat and watched those hawsers, I remember thinking: what a way to spend Easter Sunday!

The cause of the traffic jam was obvious as soon as we got off the bridge – the whole town of Wesel had been bombed flat – not a building higher than the ground floor left standing. Bulldozers were trying to clear the road, but there was only a single track through the rubble, which was often 30 feet high on both sides. (A classic case, this, of 'overbombing' by the RAF in spite of being asked by the Army to go easy on high-explosive bombs.) A particularly bizarre sight was a large tree on the outskirts of the town standing next to a bicycle shop which had been hit by a bomb. The tree had lost all its leaves, which had been replaced by hundreds of bicycle tyres!

Just north-east of the Ruhr, 15121 Unit stopped for about a week or so and went operational. The scoreboard records the name of the place as Lette, which cannot be located on a map. It may have been near Koesfeld, about halfway between Wesel and Munster. One ME110 shot down on 7 April appears on our scoreboard.

Berlin

A bit of an exaggeration, perhaps – maybe it would be more accurate to call our next stopping point 'Elbe'. The rate of our advance depended on the Americans: sometimes we had to wait a day or two, sometimes it was very rapid. The route to the Elbe was by an autobahn, which meant that the speed of the convoy could be increased from the normal 30 m.p.h. to nearer 40 m.p.h. The bridges had a clearance of only 4 m (13 ft 1½ in), and as the Type 15 aerial vehicle had a height of 12 ft 9 in, it was a case of shut your eyes and hope!

While travelling across France and Belgium, we had tended to park the convoy along the roadside each night and sleep in the vehicles, but once we were in Germany we had no compunction about commandeering accommodation as and when it was required. The route lay from Münster to Osnabrück, Minden and Hanover. At Hanover we parked on a large airfield which was full of German aircraft, including a large number of JU88 nightfighters with Lichtenstein (50 cm) radar. This equipment was a good example of the German tendency to overdesign their hardware. For example, while the quality of their components was far better than ours, it was sheer lack of imagination to use castings for frameworks instead of simpler and much cheaper pressings. Castings make modifications very difficult – often impossible. With new equipments having a service life of six months or less before they were jammed out of existence, the ability to quickly modify or radically change the design was essential. Several bits and pieces from a Lichtenstein and other equipment were brought back to the UK to illustrate the matter.

Although the 9th Army had now reached the Elbe, it had not fully cleared the land on either side of the road, so we had our retreat cut off at one stage. These pockets of resistance became more numerous as we approached the Elbe. An advance party had picked a site for us on the outskirts of the village of Keine Schwechten, in the Stendal district, about 5 miles west of the river. The site was a potato field in which the crop was being rapidly devoured by a plague of Colorado beetles! We pressed on regardless, and the equipment was erected and working in the record time of 4½ hours. We then had our first look at the airspace over Berlin, right at the edge of the PPI.

At night there was quite a lot of activity, with many aircraft climbing out and heading south in the direction of Dresden and the Czech frontier. The Allies were on the west bank of the Elbe, about 60 miles from Berlin, the Russians at about the same distance from Berlin, but on the east banks of the Oder and Neisser rivers. The RAF had bombed Berlin on the night of 12/13 April, and the Russians began their final advance on the city on 16 April, which was about the time that 15121 Unit arrived at Schwechten.

On the night of 20 April, one of our Mosquitoes shot down a Ju188, and from then on the success rate rose rapidly, to a maximum of seven aircraft on the night of the 23rd. An increasing number of these aircraft were Ju52 transports, as people tried to escape from the doomed city.

Four Mosquitoes were controlled at a time: two were on patrol over the city, while another pair were in reserve, orbiting around our AI beacon. At the end of an hour, the first pair would return to the UK while the second pair became operational. As can be seen from the scoreboard (see p. 149), there were at least two controllers on duty at a time, the first using the Type 15 ops cabin, with the second either in the Type 13/14 ops cabin or on standby and waiting to relieve the first.

There was absolutely no opposition from German aircraft, and it seemed that the Luftwaffe were quite unaware that there were British aircraft just waiting for them to clamber up to a reasonable height before shooting them down. The GCI experienced no jamming on any of the radars, and no Würzbergs (German 50 cm radar used for AA gun control and for GCI) were picked up on the receiver of the Type 11.

There was a danger of our aircraft being shot down in error by Russian AA fire. Two precautions were taken against this. First, there was a code, changed nightly, for flashing the aircraft's navigation lights if AA fire was around. This was considered a pretty hopeless solution, as the navigation lights were unlikely to be seen at any reasonable height, particularly if searchlights and exploding AA shells were around. Most AA gunners were trigger-happy, and the Russians were reckoned to be as bad as the rest in this respect.

The second precaution was more drastic: every night, before ops started, we would receive the coordinates of a line, running north–south, which had to be drawn on the PPI display. Our aircraft were not allowed to cross to the east of this line unless an interception was in progress. At first, the line was not even on the display, but it soon appeared, and each night it moved steadily westward and reduced the area in which the Mosquitoes could patrol. It was made plain that if one of our aircraft did cross this line, even under control, the Russians would not consider themselves responsible for the consequences: a case of 'shoot first and argue later'.

It was the presence of this line which finally put an end to our operations. By 26 April the line had reached the Elbe, and there was little point in risking the loss of an aircraft by flying it out from the UK and back on the odd chance that a few German aircraft might fly westwards over our front line.

Our instructions regarding the navigation lights code and the position of the north-south line reached us via the Special Liaison Unit (SLU), which, we understood, had direct contact with the Air Ministry. One evening, shortly after our arrival at Schwechten, a message was delivered to the CO by the SLU, saying that a German Panzer unit with a lot of tanks was occupying a wood about 8 miles to the west of our site. The map reference was given, and we were warned the wood would be attacked from the air with bombs and rockets at dawn. And so it was. The incident caused some speculation as to how the Air Ministry knew about a posse of armour in an obscure wood near Berlin. (The mystery was not solved until 1976, when the secret of Ultra was revealed and it became clear that German Enigma-encrypted messages had given the game away.)

Our CO was determined to get to Berlin and, if possible, to be the first Brit. to get there. He had a Bren gun mounted on his staff car, and with two motorcycle despatch riders to provide communications, he set off for the Elbe. Here he met some American guards who warned him that the Russians were on the other side of the river and that they would let no one move eastwards.

He promptly crossed the river on a small ferry, and was immediately met by a Russian guard who would not let him proceed. An officer appeared; there was a lot of mutual backslapping, and the CO was taken to meet the local commander. After a few vodkas, it was explained that, much as he admired the desire to reach Berlin, his orders were to allow no Allied troops to enter Russian-held territory. And – except for a lot more vodka – that was that.

At Schwechten village, we had commandeered the Gasthof zur Erholung – the only hotel – and enjoyed unprecedented comfort, including fresh meat, eggs and vegetables. This hotel became our HQ, from which orders were issued to the local population via the major. These orders were necessary because at least half the local population were displaced persons, which was simply a euphemism for slave labour. Most of these wretched people were Russians and Poles, with a few Dutch and Belgians. The Germans had rounded them up in their own countries and shipped them in cattle-trucks to replace German farmworkers, who in turn were called up into the Wehrmacht.

As soon as the Americans had occupied the area, the guilt-ridden German farmers threw the displaced persons out, and as a result there were large numbers of starving men roaming the streets dressed in nondescript clothing and with their feet bound up in rags for lack of shoes.

The Russians, who had been the worst treated, didn't seem to understand what had happened. The Poles were properly organized and gave the CO a list of houses in the village where SS troops in civilian clothes were hiding. We passed this list on to the American commandos, and they were promptly dealt with. Meanwhile, the major was ordered to feed the displaced persons and house them temporarily in barns until the arrival of Russian troops, which was expected shortly after we left on 6 May.

A nation at the moment of its defeat is not a pretty sight. It was made a lot worse by the presence of the displaced persons and by the awful horror perpetrated by the SS just before our arrival. They had herded hundreds of them into a church and machine-gunned the lot. The local commander of the American troops ordered his men to visit the church and take cameras with them, so that they could show 'the folks back home' that this sort of outrage was not mere propaganda. For the RAF, the visit was voluntary.

Perhaps worst of all, because it was so universal, was the attitude of the German people. Not only did they reject any responsibility for the war, but they referred to the displaced persons as 'animals' and could not understand why we treated them as equals. We had found this lack of remorse, the perpetuation of the 'Master Race' myth, and the transference of all blame to Hitler, not just in East Germany but pretty well everywhere along the route from the west.

Early in May, orders came from Wing HQ for us to pack up and return to Brussels. We set off on the road back on 6 May with a strong feeling of anticlimax. Our expectation had been to reach Berlin, with the added thought that we might be the first British unit to get there. We had achieved our primary objective of harrying the Luftwaffe almost, though not quite, to the very end, only to find ourselves prevented from finishing the job and forbidden to cross the Elbe.

On the evening of 8 May we stopped in a field near the autobahn to spend the night. While we waited for the cooks to produce a meal, the small generator was cranked up so that we could get the news on the radio. What we heard were the celebrations going on in London, the crowds around Buckingham Palace, Churchill making his speech, and interviews with the crowds thronging the streets.

We didn't even have a bottle of beer between us! It was all too much!

Peter Harrild, *Technical Officer, 1942–5, Mobile Gee-H*:

Mobile Gee, Oboe and Gee-H stations, together with a Wing HQ (72 Wing) were being formed before D-Day, in preparation for them to be transferred to the Continent as soon as possible. These were destined to follow the retreating

Peter Harrild

Germans across France and Germany, and thus extend their cover and provide navigational and blind-bombing aids for targets deep into Germany. They were also used for the tactical bombing of oil refineries and troop concentrations and the disruption of troop movements, particularly during the Ardennes offensive.

The first two mobile Gee-H stations (114 and 116) were formed in May 1944, using equipment similar to that used at the fixed ground stations. Such mobiles were called 'Heavy' Type 100s (as opposed to 'Light' 100s, which used equipment that was much smaller and lighter and which could be used as backup for either Gee-H or Gee).

In about September 1944, when most of France was in Allied hands, they moved over to France and were soon on sites at La Roches (in the Ardennes) and at Commercy (in Hautes de Meuse). Two further Heavy 100 mobiles were formed and went over to France at the end of 1944 (these were 115 and 117), and early in 1945 a third pair (118 and 119) went over. Equipment from Grangewood and High Street had been used for the last pair, and these stations therefore closed in December, with most of their mechanics being posted to the four new mobiles.

By the end of the war there were six Heavy 100 mobiles in Germany. There were also six or eight Type 9000 (Oboe) mobiles, seven or eight Gee mobiles and a large number of Light 100s acting as Gee stations.

This is an abridged account of the wanderings of one of those six heavy 100s (AMES 117) and is formed from extracts from the Commanding Officer Peter Harrild's diary for 1945 and from letters to his wife, Joy.

Friday 8 December 1944: AMES 117 spent the night at Dover Castle.

Sunday 10 December: 5.30 a.m. – Brought the convoy down from the castle to embark on the two tank landing craft. Channel too rough to cross. Embarkation Officer in Dover emphasized that once we were on board we were not to go ashore again. So we spent Saturday night, all day Sunday and Sunday night aboard the TLCs, and during the stormy night of Saturday the two metal TLCs, moored together in Dover harbour, heaved up and down and banged against each other all through the night. The only time I've ever been seasick!

Monday 11 December: Landed in France. Spent first night on French soil in a large château standing in its own grounds, with a marvellous view and in lovely country.

Saturday 16 December: Convoy set off for Mutzig in very bad weather – snow, ice and cold. This was the day that the Germans started the Ardennes offensive, though we didn't know it at the time. It took us three days to reach our destination (350 miles), having had much trouble in getting the heavy technical vehicles up steep, snow-covered hills. We eventually arrived on 18

December, dead beat, with the prospect of starting to put up the tower the next day.

Included in our convoy was a water bowser, which we had filled with 300 gallons of good English water before we left. On investigation at Mutzig, we found we had got 300 gallons of good English ice (and a leaking water bowser when it thawed!).

Operational on Our First Site Near Mutzig

18 December 1944–4 January 1945: Three days' hard labour, 19–21 December, were spent on the technical site (a few miles from the village of Gresswiller, where we were billeted) erecting one of our two towers in icy cold weather. We shared the site with a Type 9000 unit, whose CO was also in charge of the whole site and who liaised with the nearest American HQ. (Alsace was in an American Zone, and this meant, among other things, that we drew American rations).

From Operational Log: '22/12 1800 hrs. Station Operational on Mutzig site. Phasing 1130.'

On Christmas Eve we had a test operation for 117, with 114 and 115, during which fifteen aircraft were seen at 1415 hours. It was later reported that eleven American aircraft had used us successfully.

New Year's Eve: Very little to spend money on, except our whisky and gin ration, which is two bottles per man per month and costs about 80 francs. New Year dance and general party in the local café with most of the locals there, finishing up with everyone kissing everyone else.

1 January 1945: Flap about evacuation overnight. Only a rumour.

2 January: More flap. Ordered to stand by. Packed everything in the tech. vehicles.

3 January: Still standing by. Unpacked vehicles. Only one Chevrolet serviceable.

5–27 January 1945: Retreat to Commercy and Mons. Our route to Commercy lay over the Vosges mountains, and in heavy snow we made very slow progress up the icy, snow-covered roads. We had many stops, and after one of them we realized that the next vehicle in the convoy (one of the tech. three-tonners) was no longer following us. We turned round and went back and found it, with the rest of the convoy, still stationary at the place where we had last stopped. I went to expostulate with the driver, opened his door and he fell out – fast asleep! We eventually reached Commercy dead beat at 7 a.m., having been driving for sixteen hours.

We were billeted in a school at first, but later moved to a small house which was much warmer and more comfortable.

But in no time at all, AMES 117 were on the move again!

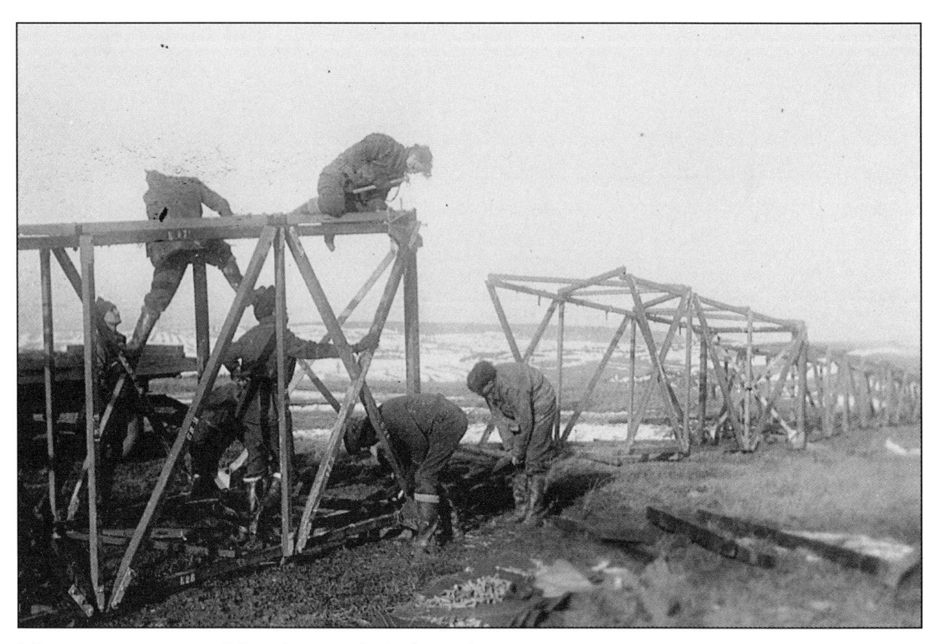

The tower party assembling the mast in bad weather.

The mast erected. The wooden 105 ft transportable mast was used for several mobile equipments including CH (AMES Type 9) and Gee-H. Its square cross-section and tapered construction enabled the several sections to fit within each other for transit. For deployment each unit had to be manhandled off the transport trailer and laid out on the ground. A metal baseplate, to which the mast was hinged, was staked to the ground and the sections bolted together. A giant Meccano job indeed; heavy-going in mild weather – a nightmare in bad. When all was firmly bolted together on the ground the fun began! With the aid of a jury pole and winch (often lorry-mounted) the mast was hauled by rope from the horizontal to the vertical. The tension on the rope was enormous and often the winch had to be restrained from slipping. Everyone was relieved when the mast became upright, the guy ropes were attached and it was safe. Not a job to relish under poor conditions!

1 February–3 April 1945: St Avold.

2 February: Bolting mast together. Difficulty with last two sections.

5 February: Mast and arrays finished. Started to hoist after lunch. Mast twisted when initial weight taken. Bottom two sections and derrick damaged. Started repairs.

7 February: Finished guys. Cast off tackle. Ready at last at 1200. On test 1900. All equipment very damp.

We are now at our final destination (I hope!) and are billeted in a decent-sized house in which we all fit quite comfortably. Central heating throughout and bags of hot water, and – luxury of luxuries – a real proper WC (two, in fact)!

10 February: The Yanks in Luxembourg entertained us to lunch in a large hotel which they had taken over as a mess, complete with waiters, etc. – just like dining in London! It seemed completely unreal, but the lunch was excellent and far from unreal! The French people told us all about the Gestapo during the occupation, and how Hitler, Rundstedt and Von Papen had once stayed here; how they hid escaped prisoners in their cellars, and how the Gestapo chief, who lived next door, came and removed their wireless just before the Americans arrived.

13 February: I heard the first lark this morning. (I'm getting into awful habits out here of just *taking things* such as houses, furniture, etc.)

I'm beginning to think that the Far East is a real probability – my release group must be way up in the forties.

21 March: Baseplate in position. Tower arrived 2 p.m. Laid out and first three sections on. (We had been asked to put up another tower on the same site for a mobile Gee unit – AMES 7912.)

22 March: Tower finished. Arrays on. Sandbags filled. Almost ready for hoisting. Operation with 115.

23 March: Raised tower at 11 a.m. without a hitch except for top guys taking no weight. Feeders finished.

During February, 117 was used for ops by 3 Group, 2 Group and the US Air Force, mostly on targets 100–175 miles to the north of us.

By 9 March, the Allies were up to the west bank of the Rhine in the north, but there remained one large pocket of Germans in the salient formed by the Moselle from Koblenz to Trier and along the Siegfried Line through Saarbrucken and back to the Rhine beyond Wissemburg.

The Allies attacked on 15 March; good progress was made west of

Zweibrucken, but east of there the Germans held firm. However, the salient was cut off by General Patton reaching the Rhine north of Koblenz and then turning south and reaching Worms on 21 March, where he joined the XXth Corps, which had burst through the bulge south of Trier, In a few more days all organized resistance in the salient behind Saarbrucken came to an end.

3–24 April: Our third site at Edenkoben. Arrived on site at Edenkoben, 20 miles south-west of the Rhine. Mannheim had been occupied by the 7th US Army on 29 March. Site too small for tower. Found new one on football pitch. Easy site, lovely weather, good crew, work on tower progressed apace.

5 April: Diesels up; tower up 4 p.m. Operational for test 7 p.m.

16 April: The Adj. and I took the afternoon off and drove through the country in search of champagne. It is the most lovely country. All the fruit trees in full bloom; all the little villages so neat and tidy and charming, linked by miles and miles of vineyards.

The unit is split into frat. or non-frat., and we're having a debate next Sunday on the subject. Personally, I'm all for non-frat. after some of the stories we've heard since we've been out here, and remembering what happened and what might have happened in England. But part of the trouble is that the villages round here have hardly been touched by the war, and the country is so beautiful that it's hard to imagine that anybody living among such beauty could think of making a brutal war and doing the foul things that we know the Germans have done.

The French, of course, are far better at it than we are and have got the right idea, having had firsthand experience of German brutality. I think that we and the Americans still don't really believe the stories we've heard.

24 April: We're to leave here tomorrow.

28 April–6 August: Our last site at Wildenreuth, near the Czech border.

29 April: Arrived at our last operational site at Wildenreuth after four-day journey of 400 miles. Had a good trip, though more than our fair share of transport trouble. Saw a lot of utter devastation in some of the large towns and cities.

30 April: Tower erected; operational for test at 1600.

The appalling stories that are now being unearthed are unbelievable. We've had quite a few ex-prisoners of war who have been released by the advance, including five staying with us who've been prisoners for five or six years. The stories they have to tell are terribly gruesome and absolutely barbaric in their cruelty, especially the treatment of the Russian prisoners.

My language is becoming awful, and also my morals as far as acquiring things are concerned. Goodness knows what I shall be saying and doing by the time I get back to England!

[*Note*: Peter Harrild did get back to England in August 1945, and was reunited with his wife, to whom he had been married for only one week before AMES 117 was assembled, trained and sailed for France.]

Keith Benson, *Gee-H Radar Mechanic, AMES 116, Europe*:

Keith Benson

On 22 January 1944 I was at Grangewood on a Gee-H Type 100 course. The training took three months, and with Hastings so near by, we had plenty to do with our off-duty time.

By May I had become a member of AMES 116. We left Grangewood for RAF Trelanvean, in Cornwall, where we were to crew the first of the Heavy Type 100 mobile units, which was sited at Kilter Farm. A new mast, with aerials attached, had been erected by No. 2 IU from Kidbrooke, but we had brought with us both the Tx and Rx, which had belonged to AMES 113 at Grangewood.

Our crew consisted of two officers (one technical, the other administrative) and thirty-six men, of which about fifteen were radar mechanics and operators. AMES 116 was completely self-contained and was technically under the control of 83 (Signals) Wing.

The convoy consisted of five prime movers – Austin vans, of which one contained the Rx Type 1441 and another the Tx Type 1448; yet another held the amplifier, and a further two housed a Mark II, 20–kVA Lister diesel generator with an emergency supply of diesel oil in forty-gallon drums.

In addition, there was the 105 ft wooden mast in six sections – carrying the aerials, which had to be dismantled when we moved and transported on a trailer towed by a three-ton Crossley. In the Crossley was a hand-operated winch to help us erect the aerial tower once it was assembled.

The unit also had two general-purpose trucks and a water bowser and the CO's jeep. Our CO in charge of the whole convoy was F/O Frank Garlick and the Admin. Officer was F/O Bacon.

Our technical site at Kilter Farm occupied a field overlooking Falmouth Bay. The 105 ft mast was made up by joining together six sections horizontally on the ground and then, using a jury pole, two men had to operate a small hand-winch, pulling the whole assembly vertical and guiding it into position by the wires attached to each corner. The tower itself stood on a 4 ft square steel plate staked into the ground, and the mast was supported by four steel guy-wires attached to four similar steel plates, similarly anchored by stakes and sandbags. The winch had been temporarily mounted in the Crossley, which was also suitably staked to the ground and weighted with sandbags, to prevent the whole lot tipping over when it took the strain of the tower as it was winched upright. And all this construction work, and its demolition, was to be our job in future whenever and wherever we moved.

The mobile station became fully operational on 24 May, although the full crew were not yet gathered at Kilter. Once up to strength, we'd be a full heavy Type 100 mobile unit, ready and raring to go!

One day I walked, with a WAAF operator friend, to Helford Water, where we had a cream tea. And when we returned to camp we heard the news: the date was 6 June!

Within twenty-four hours we were off to Renscombe Down for training in aerial construction and erecting, and by July we were at Hursley, near Southampton, ready for embarkation. We were to be attached to the 8th US Army Air Force, as the Cherbourg Peninsula was in their sector. The difference between their treatment and ours was amazing!

Since we were going abroad, the NAAFI had allowed us to *buy* twenty Players, forty Woodbines and three 2 oz bars of chocolate. At Hursley, the Yanks *gave* us each six packets of 200 Lucky Strikes, Chesterfields and Camels, some tobacco, one or two pounds of chocolate, sweets, toothbrushes and paste, shaving kit, and – to raffle off round the unit – pocket wallets and watches! We also 'acquired' a folding camp-bed each. The Yanks really did know how to treat their boys when they were going overseas. Later, a picket boat came round the harbour delivering K-rations for us all.

On 29 July we landed on Utah Beach and waited for low tide. All was quiet, with little air activity, and we watched the beachmasters shepherding their flocks of disembarked vehicles, with bulldozers ever ready to push to the edge of the minefields any lorry foolish enough to break down.

In glorious sunshine we watched all this, until at about 1500 hours it was our turn to disembark and make our way to an orchard, where we made ourselves as comfortable as possible, ate some bread with hot soup from self-heating cans, then settled down for the night.

Our first operational site was at Anseville-en-Saire, quite a few miles inland from where we'd landed. We erected our tents (complete with our recently-acquired camp-beds), set up a marquee as a mess hall, built earth-and-oil-drum cookers, and lastly, toilets. As we were still in the American section, we drew their rations – peanut butter and white bread – and with the beautiful weather, it all seemed like a delightful camping holiday, with the added spice that most of us had never been abroad before.

We got out and about, sampling the local Calvados (reputed to be made from anti-freeze) and the rough cider, which was very rough indeed. To crown it all, Hitler's so-called impregnable Atlantic Wall, which he'd been so proud of, had been breached, and we spent some of our spare time investigating the tunnels and the big gun emplacements, and the German living quarters.

On the Tech. site, Stan Bratt and I formed ourselves into the 'Shithousehausan Construction Co.', priding ourselves on our master craftsmanship (as we continued to do later, on all our sites).

So there we were – nicely settled at Anseville – when on 30 August we received orders to up sticks and move on. We struck camp, and with everything loaded, set off eastwards through La Pernelle and on (through what would later be known as the 'Falaise Gap') to what should have been an overnight stop near Caen. We saw plenty of evidence of the recent fierce fighting; only bodies had been cleared away, but dead horses, which had been used in the Germans' flight, were everywhere.

We camped at a château which Rommel had been using for his HQ, drew English rations, and settled down to wait for the front line to advance.

When our convoy was given the OK, we rolled onwards, passing through Paris, which had just been liberated, and where the people seemed glad to see us, though I suspect chiefly because of our (and the Americans') free-spending attitude.

On we journeyed, through the recently-freed towns and cities of Meaux, Montmirail, St Challon-sur-Marne and Bar-le-Duc. Finally, we reached Commercy, a small town not far from Nancy. It had taken three days of hard travelling, and we had moved some 400 miles. I had been sitting all that time in the back of one of the diesels, and the whole unit had lived off K-rations and tea. But it seemed such an adventure!

We were directed to our billets at Commercy, and I was told that ours had been a brothel during its German occupation. Being in the American sector again, we still qualified for their excellent rations, though we had to wait a while for the ration lorries to catch up with us, since they (quite rightly) had to give priority to the ammunition units. But the American practice was that if you were within 50 miles of the front line, you could draw your PX rations – free. We took full advantage of this and lived like kings.

Commercy itself showed little sign of war. While we were there I saw General Patton – resplendent with six-shooters – who came by with his staff in his jeep to give us all the once-over. I also saw – live – Bing Crosby, Bob Hope and Dorothy Lamour, who visited the small local cinema while one of their 'Road' films was showing.

Our technical site was in an old Napoleonic fort a few miles east of Commercy, which had been enlarged for the Franco-Prussian War. There was plenty of room for us to erect our tower, set up the equipment and, after being calibrated, become operational. At the time I didn't know very much about the operations we were performing, but I hope we were of use to the war effort. I do remember standing on top of a pillbox and watching several Lancasters in the region of Metz, bombing a target on which we had directed the markers.

Then we had a tragedy. Going up to the site one day, our CO, Frank Garlick, and Bill Dawkins were crossing the canal over a bridge which the Americans had re-built, constructed mainly of wood. Its surface was covered in black ice; Frank Garlick was driving, and I suppose he must have just touched the brakes, for without warning the jeep turned at right angles and went straight through the bridge's flimsy parapet. He and Bill were both flung into the ice-encrusted canal. Only Bill managed to get to the bank and pull himself out. He raised the alarm, but alas, to no avail, and it was Stan Bratt and I who grappled our CO's body from the canal.

A full military funeral was held for him under American auspices at the cemetery in Commercy. His death brought a sadness to the unit, for he had been well thought of and was sadly missed.

The funeral of 116 AMES's CO Frank Garlick in Commercy.

Soon the front line advanced, and the Yanks moved forward. We spent Christmas at Commercy, and our cooks did us proud. Then, in January, the Ardennes breakthrough came and we had a visit from AMES 117, who had had to leave their forward site. While they were with us, our transmitter broke down and they very kindly lent us theirs for a day or two, to tide us over. They left us after about a fortnight, and life carried on much the same, with the war on course again after that costly hiccup.

I had home leave in March 1945, and on my return to Wing HQ in Mons, found that AMES 116 had moved to Langenfeld, in Germany. While there, I sat a trade test and got my LAC (effective from 1 April).

On 22 April we moved on to Neubronn, a small village some 10 miles from Bad Mergentheim.

Then on August 5 we were called back, via Frankfurt, Bonn, Maastricht and Brussels, to Wing HQ at Mons. And here AMES 116 was disbanded and the unit personnel were split up.

Alf Cassidy, *RCAF Radar Mechanic on Oboe* (9432 AMES):

[*Note*: Oboe was the codename for the secret blind-bombing radar system. The official name for a fixed or mobile Oboe ground station was AMES Type 9000, or 9K.]

Alf Cassidy

In January 1941 the Canadian government undertook a commitment to the British government to recruit and train 5,000 radar technicians and officers to serve in the RAF and the Allied air forces under its command. Upon completion of my training under this plan at the University of Saskatchewan and then at the Radar School, Clinton, Ontario, I arrived in England in October 1942.

I was first posted to a CHL station at Great Ormes Head, in North Wales, and later to another CHL station at Strumble Head, in South Wales. During this time I was cycled through the RAF radar school at Yatesbury to learn about new developments in centimetric radar with all its mysteries of magnetrons, klystrons, E waves, M waves, circular waveguides, rotating joints, parabolas, phantastrons, echo boxes, etc.

Shortly after D-Day, I reported once again to Yatesbury for the Type 9000 Mk II course. The high level of secrecy relating to 9K was immediately evident when we went to classes in a compound within another classified and restricted compound, from which we were never allowed to take out our notes or notebooks.

At the end of the course I was posted, along with most of my classmates, to RAF Renscombe Down, near Swanage, to join other RAF and Royal Canadian Air Force personnel to form a new mobile Oboe unit. Here we learned to drive trucks, to use small arms and other skills in order to move and operate as a mobile unit. When we had mastered these new skills, we travelled to Cardington to pick up our radar vans, trucks, diesel generators, tents, workshops and all the other bits and pieces that made up a mobile unit.

At last, with all the necessary forms signed, we were on our way to Salisbury Plain, driving in convoy all the way. Somehow we novice drivers managed to navigate the narrow roads and innumerable intersections and arrived at Old Sarum without mishap. The assembly area was a memorable sight – rows and rows of RAF and Army trucks and equipment waiting their turn to be moved across the Channel. But we didn't have long to wait before we were on our way to Dover. This time it was late at night – our first experience of driving in the blackout! But we had only to follow the small tail light on the vehicle in front. Our headlights, like all the others, were just little slits in the blackout covers – not much help.

We arrived at Dover the following day and loaded our assigned landing craft. These craft did not have sleeping accommodation, so we slept wherever we could find a spot to stretch out or curl up. Fortunately, the Channel was calm and the crossing very smooth.

Laroche

We awoke at daylight the next morning to find ourselves on the beach at Boulogne. From there we headed off for Mons, Belgium, our Wing HQ; then, after a few days, we were on our way to our first operational site – Laroche in the Ardennes, not far from a little place called Bastogne. Little did any of us know at the time how pivotal that area would become in just a few weeks.

It didn't take long to set up the radar vans, diesel generators, workshops and operations office on one of the highest points in the Ardennes and very close to the German border. The equipment was very soon tuned up, tested and operational.

During testing and non-operational times, the dual parabola antennas (4 ft diameter versions of the modern TV satellite dishes), mounted on the roofs of the operational trailers, were always turned away from Germany to avoid detection of any of our test signals. Then, shortly before 'zero hour' (the time when control of the first Pathfinder aircraft would start), these dishes would be slowly rotated and tilted up to the bearing of the rendezvous point of the first aircraft. From outside the trailer, this action always reminded me of the rotation and elevation of the big guns on a battleship – ominous, powerful and deadly. And although our salvos were totally silent, they were nevertheless effective up to 300 miles distant.

Inside the crowded trailer, tension and anticipation mounted as the controllers, radar operators and mechanics waited as the countdown continued to zero and the transmitter was switched on.

The attack would have commenced some 200–300 miles away, deep in the heartland of Germany. An operator would slowly move the antenna back and forth, and then, all of a sudden, a blip from the transponder transmitter in the aircraft would appear on the large CRT. The operator would continue to make fine adjustments of the antenna to keep the signal tuned in. An electronic marker would be moved over the blip, and 'lock-on' would be achieved.

The tension gave way then to the routine of controlling the aircraft down the 'beam' towards the target. This routine would depend upon the role of that transmitter for that particular raid. If that role was the 'Cat' (or tracking station), the signal sent back to the pilot would be determined by the distance from the 'Target Marker', which was a very accurate preset radar range from the Tx to the target.

Morse 'dits' would be sent if the distance was too short, and 'dahs' if it was too far. These would merge to a steady note right at the target range. The pilot would adjust the heading of the aircraft accordingly until he was flying an imaginary 'beam' which would take him right over the target.

At the same time, another Oboe ground station – probably a similar mobile unit in Holland – would be operating as the 'Mouse' (release station). As the aircraft moved along the tracking beam from the Cat towards the target, the Mouse Tx would send signals to the navigator indicating the distance to its Target Marker (which was also a very accurate preset range to the target).

When the aircraft was over the Target Marker, a signal would then be sent to the navigator to 'release'. When the release signal was given, the aircraft transponder/transmitter would be switched off and the blip would disappear from both the Cat and the Mouse scopes. The antennas of both units would then be turned back to the original bearings, and the 'routine' would continue for the next aircraft scheduled to fly down the beam.

This routine would be repeated in the other four trailers on the site, with each controlling a separate aircraft with different designated times. This entire coordinated operation would continue till the end of the bombing raid.

Operations

The Oboe scope, used in both Cat and Mouse modes, had four range scales: 300 mile range with 25-mile marker pips; 25 mile range with 5-mile pips; 5 mile range with 1-mile pips and 1 mile range scaled to 10 in (i.e. 1 in = $^1/_{10}$ mile and $^1/_{10}$ in = $^1/_{100}$ mile. This made it easy to read and set to a range of 0.01 mile, or 52 ft.

The 1-mile pips, generated by a stable oscillator, were divided in frequency by 5 to produce 5-mile pips, and again by 5 to produce 25-mile pips. (The same principle is used in modern quartz-controlled digital clocks and watches.)

To set a range of, for example, 264.23 miles, the 300 scale would first be selected and the Target Marker set on the tenth 25-mile pip = 250 miles. Then on the second 5-mile pip to give 260 miles. Next, on the fourth pip of the mile range to give 264 miles and finally to 2.3 in on the mile range.

Mutzig, France

In the first week of December, orders came through that a new mobile unit was to be formed, and our trailer and crew were selected with more from three different sites.

We met up with the others at Mons and deployed to a new site in the Vosges Mountains near the town of Mutzig, about 30 km from Strasbourg.

The site overlooked the Rhine Valley, and the Rhine itself could just be seen in the far distance. We had hardly become operational again at this new site when the Battle of the Bulge began, and our friends who we'd left at Laroche barely had time to move out with their radar trailers before the site was overrun by the Germans. Most of the other vehicles, such as workshops and diesels, had to be burned when they became stuck in the mud and snow.

When the American Army in our area moved out to support the forces in the north, our CO considered it prudent for us also to make a withdrawal. We deployed to Bacarrat until the military situation stabilized. It wasn't long before we were back at our site in Mutzig and operational again.

After many operations in February, March and April, it was all over at last in Europe – VE Day, 8 May 1945. There was no further need of Oboe in this theatre of operations.

Back to Canada

Although the war in Europe was over, the war in the Far East was not. Some personnel from our unit were posted to mobile Loran units for the purpose of pushing the range of this important navigational aid further in that direction.

Oboe mobile trailer at Mutzig in 1945. This unit had previously been based at Tilly Whim, near Swanage in Dorset.

Those of us who remained waited patiently for our next orders, wondering if we, too, would be needed in the air offensive against Japan. However, we were soon advised that we had all been assigned a repatriation number, based upon our date of enlistment and upon how long we had been overseas. (This number would determine the order in which we would go home.)

My turn came in August, and it was with great sadness that I said farewell to all my friends with whom I had shared many experiences in the past year. It would be many years before I had the pleasure of meeting some of them again.

Reflections

When I look back on my radar days, I am always amazed at how much was accomplished in such a short time. The few early radar stations on the south and east coasts of England, which were instrumental in the summer of 1940 in changing the course of history, were soon an extensive defence system all round England, Scotland, Wales and Northern Ireland; then in North Africa, the Middle East, India, Ceylon, New Zealand and Australia.

It also amazes me how quickly Oboe was 'invented' to meet the needs of Bomber Command and then tested and operationally deployed. Oboe was truly the beginning of pushbutton warfare – for better or for worse?

Tom Hatcher, *Oboe Radar Operator (9442 AMES)*:

Tom Hatcher

In August 1944, at Durnford near Swanage, our crew was formed into a unit, complete with its complement of controllers (experienced ex-aircrew), technical staff, and auxiliary trades such as drivers and mechanics, a medical orderly, cooks and admin. staff.

It was 20 September before we embarked for France, and after a smooth crossing, we had a nice, dry landing on Mulberry Harbour at Arromanches. From there we made our way to a château near Caen, where we were issued with khaki, lest our Air Force blue be mistaken for German field grey.

The convoy set off on 24 September on a two-day journey to Wing HQ in Mons. After a few days there, we moved on again, travelling through Dinant, Marche and La Roche to our first operational site, at Barraque Fraiture, in the Belgian Ardennes.

We quickly established our technical and domestic sites – the former consisting of two Oboe trailers, each with its own transmitter, receiver and other technical equipment, with workshop trailers to provide the necessary backup. Power came from diesel-electric generators and alternators – self-propelled on Austin flat-bed lorries.

We quickly settled into a well-ordered and effective routine, and soon moved out from under canvas to take up residence in the Château Ste Marie at Salm Château, where we were dry and comfortable. A vast improvement!

The Oboe operator's work differed from a radar op's in that with Oboe we knew the timing of the operations in which we were to be involved. There were the pre-operation duties of setting up and testing the equipment – all to be done with meticulous care. Then came the anxious minutes of the operation itself.

In any one operation, contact with our single aircraft was but a short-lived affair, his Oboe equipment being switched on and responding to our signals for only a short time during approach to the target – something of the order of 10–15 minutes.

Our initial concern was that he should respond to our signal, 'come up' and lock on in place and on time. We would silently *will* him to remain steadily on course throughout the operation, and then – safely switched off – to be on his way without mishap. The worst experience was to see a signal disappear abruptly with its run incomplete.

At Salm Château we could not get out much at night. There were tales of Germans still remaining in the surrounding hills and woods, and we all – tech. and non-tech. – took turns at guard duty. But we valued our daytime off-duty hours all the more, and we saw as much as we could of the neighbourhood. The nearest town, Vielsalm, was within walking distance, and a special perk was to go on the ration run to Mons – an interesting place to explore, after a pleasant run through the countryside.

However, in December Hitler embarked on his Ardennes Offensive, and so began the Battle of the Bulge. We had no real knowledge of what was happening, but clearly something untoward had occurred and it was vital that our equipment should not fall into enemy hands.

So we were ordered out, with a hasty dismantling of both sites. The tech. site was a sea of mud; lorries and trailers with their onboard technical equipment had to be extricated by the Matador towing trucks, which were invaluable with their powerful winches. But notwithstanding the hard work and united effort of men and machines, it proved impossible to extricate one of the workshop trailers, which had to be destroyed.

Once off the site, we joined a seemingly endless stream of American Army vehicles returning from what had been the front line. It was a most astonishing sight. The overriding impression was of mist, snow and mud – a sort of cold, moist, grey cocoon which enveloped everyone and everything and added a curious sense of unreality to what was actually a very serious business indeed.

The convoy made its way, via La Roche, Marche and Dinant, to Rosée, where it remained until 20 December before moving on to Wing HQ in Mons. We spent Christmas Day 1944 in Mons. It was not a very memorable Christmas, and it most certainly was not a merry one.

On Boxing Day we departed Mons and journeyed via Valenciennes, Cambrai and Walincourt to set up a technical site at Selvigny. Here we were billeted in a large, well-appointed château which had previously been commandeered from its owners by the Germans. There was an enormous cellar – plenty of bottles, but no wine!

In our leisure time we visited Cambrai, and sometimes got even as far as Rheims, and – on one memorable occasion – Paris! The Folies Bergères! Les Showgirls – Les Danseuses!

But, in due course, the German Army was driven back, and we were ordered to return to Barraque Fraiture. We left on 29 January 1945, and took the convoy via Rosée to the old Belgian town of Durbuy, where we established our domestic quarters in another château and in the Hotel Albert.

Signs of recent battles were all around us. There was extensive damage and destruction of property; destroyed and abandoned tanks littered the countryside. The dead lay where they had fallen in the snow by the roadside. Minefields and suspected booby-trap areas were marked in many places, and no one took any unnecessary risks. With the snow melting, there was mud and water everywhere, making any movement off the road very difficult.

The unit quickly re-established itself in well-ordered routines for both the technical and domestic sites. Off duty, we visited surrounding places such as Liège and Spa, and with the coming of milder weather, we were able to appreciate more of the surrounding countryside.

But the war had moved on into Germany and the time came for us to leave Belgium. Dismantling began again; transports were loaded, and on 18 April the

In the mud of the Ardennes, Belgium.

convoy crossed into Germany over a temporary pontoon bridge across the Rhine at Remagen.

After several days' driving, we settled in under canvas at a place called Quechbron on 21 April. The technical site was established on nearby higher ground. By 23 April we were able to move into billets in Weikersheim – my billet had been the old gendarmerie.

We enjoyed our life at this site, with plenty of interesting visits to places such as Heidelberg, Rothenburg and Nuremburg. The countryside was beautiful and we got plenty of swimming and cricket, not to mention some of the lavish entertainment we shared with the Americans. On 28 July there was a show in a large, open-air natural amphitheatre with Jack Benny, Ingrid Bergman, Martha Tilton, Larry Adler and Dave Le Winter.

But there were other, more sombre occasions, such as the time I was at Wing HQ in Mons, when I was asked to be one of the RAF party to attend the funeral of a local Resistance hero. He had been killed by the Germans and was now to be reburied with full honours at Jemappes, near Mons.

On 8 May came VE Day, but we stayed in position for the time being, until 11 August, when we journeyed north to Fort Schaar, near Wilhelmshaven, where a technical site was set up and a regular watch system established.

The war in Europe was over. AMES 9442 had carried out its duties, and it could only be a matter of time before disbandment came.

Bill Evans, *Radar Mechanic on Gee-H*:

AMES 117 Goes to France

[*Note*: This account can be read in conjunction with Peter Harrild's, on p. 155).]

Bill Evans

At Renscombe we practised building and erecting a 105 ft wooden tower on a football pitch. One day, I was on the winch inside the Crossley with a Scottish sergeant operator. Something went wrong and the tower started falling towards the Crossley. I learnt very quickly: (a) some remarkable Scottish swearwords, and (b) that you can move extremely fast when your life is in danger.

The next move was to Cardington, where the old airship hangar was being used as a mustering point for AMESs. We met the rest of 117 and received a bowser, three Canadian Chevrolet trucks, a W/T van and a mountain of stores – all of which had to be stowed.

Thence to Dover for embarkation and straight onto a tank-landing craft. The Channel was so rough that we were being pitched about inside the harbour. After two days' waiting on the wallowing craft, with nowhere to sleep, we finally set sail for the beach near Boulogne on a gorgeous day. The Navy had their washing drying on a line stretched above our vehicles.

By this time we were in khaki, as RAF blue was too close to German field grey for comfort. Because the RAF had bombed Boulogne to rubble and we had RAF roundels on our vehicles, the locals spat on us as we drove through the town.

Our projected site was near the German border, away in Alsace, near Mosheim. We arrived in our civvy billets at 50 rue des Moulins, Gressweiler, where we found a German greatcoat hanging behind our door. It was so cold that there was an eighth of an inch of hoar frost on the bedroom walls!

During our second night there, at 2.30 a.m. we heard a great commotion downstairs. It turned out that the farmer's son had deserted from the German Army and had arrived home. We rose and joined the party. The unaccustomed Schnapps brought back my fifth-form French, and I gave a rendering of 'There's a Tavern in the Town' (freely translated).

We built and erected our tower in freezing conditions. It was so cold that after the mid-morning cocoa no one would go back out to the nuts and bolts until the sergeant mech. appeared at the door and, in the accent of Violet Elizabeth in the 'Just William' stories, said: 'If you don't come out this very minute I'll thqueam and thqueam until I'm thick!' We trooped back outside.

It's difficult now to imagine the tensions that build up when working at minus temperatures in snow – diesels proving difficult and even the smallest task an uphill struggle. But Christmas night 1944 was a highly emotional occasion. We were using a local restaurant as our dining hall, with the locals coming in as well.

They decked a big Christmas tree; the drink flowed; they had only just been freed after four years of subjection. Much singing and jollification went on, and then – at midnight – a hush fell while the local people sang 'Silent Night'. The emotion was palpable, and I, for one, found myself crying.

The Battle of the Bulge was raging north of us, with the Americans getting mauled for a time. We were in a US 'rest' area and made friends with some of the GIs. Many had done twelve weeks' training in the Mid-West, crossed the Atlantic in one of the 'Queens' (15,000 of them to a ship), docked at Cherbourg and trucked to the front. They didn't know which way was up. We swapped some of our good cold-weather clothing for swish-looking but not warm US windcheaters, boots and the like. The CO allowed us to look like Fred Karno's Army as long as the work got done.

US rations were superb. At American railheads, used to giving out daily rations for a whole division, the chaps couldn't be bothered breaking up boxes for a unit of forty men, so if eggs were on the menu, it was a crate of eggs; if chicken, a box of chicken! I recollect going on watch where, for our dessert, we *each* had a 12 lb tin of large pineapple rings.

With a temporary German advance, we had a crisis instruction to leave the tower and take our secret equipment right back over the Vosges to Commercy. In snowy and icy conditions, with at least eight different kinds of vehicle, that journey was an experience. The bowser was solid ice. We kept going through the night and stopped next morning. After an hour's rest, the CO led off in the jeep, but the driver of the second vehicle had gone to sleep, so the rest of the convoy couldn't move. An irate CO returned, wrenched the driver's door open, and the sleeping man fell straight out on top of him, with both of them ending up in a snowy ditch.

Another memory of that fearsome journey over the Vosges is of when the Crossley, which was towing a trailer, had to add the 15 cwt wagon and the bowser (both of which had broken down), and tow them as well, like a train. Doing 4 m.p.h. up the hills, a chap with a watering can stood on the bumper and topped up the boiling radiator, then leapt down and ran forward a hundred yards or so and filled the can from the stream beside the road, then waited for the caravanserai to catch him up again.

Our next site was at St Avold in Lorraine, near the German frontier. We got into a large, comfortable house there, but the site itself was on sloping ground, which made erecting the tower a problem. We drove a truck under the top end of the tower and stood on that to finish it and mount the aerials. After erection, the dipole was seen not to be vertical, so I went up with a shifting spanner to fix it. While I was up there, a driver – positioning a box-back Rx vehicle – managed to snag one of the guy-ropes. The tower oscillated wildly, and I shouted dreadful things to the people on the ground. I dropped the spanner, so they shouted dreadful things back up to me.

As the Allies pushed on, we were resited to Edenkoben, in the Pfalz. We were on a large playing-field on top of a hill, in good weather at last, with a huge equestrian statue of Kaiser Wilhelm looking down upon us. I remember when the stores corporal broke his ankle playing football against the Free French, and as he lay in the US Military Hospital, a visiting general came round the ward giving out Purple Heart medals to all the inmates. He rather reluctantly had to decline his.

Our final move was to Wildenreuth, just short of the Sudetenland, in Bavaria. We settled in a country hamlet, Gossenreuth, the Gasthof being our HQ, with animals housed under the same roof with us. The SS had declared that they would fight to the last man in the mountains of Bohemia. The RAF suggested that they wouldn't if Mosquitoes and Gee-H could do anything about it, so that was the reason we were so far east.

Being in a US sector, we always had the Union Flag flying, and this attracted British and Dominion ex-prisoners of war newly freed by the German guards. We would talk far into the night with them, and they shared our beds, using the ones belonging to the men on watch.

For off-watch entertainment, we formed a glee club; we played cricket, shot deer and went to the Beyreuth Festspielhaus – not to hear Wagner but to a USO show.

Just before VE Day, we had a long weekend in Brussels. The round trip is enormous, but we thought little of it at the time. In fact, the distances we travelled across Europe, with half the road bridges blown up, now seem remarkable.

So, after an easy time at Gossenreuth, we upped sticks at last and returned to Mons, a place thick with rumours of what was going to happen to everyone. We youngsters had high demob numbers; the CO feared he was destined for the Far East. But I was sent to the new Rhône Gee chain in the South of France, and later, after qualifying, I was one of the perhaps few radar bods who went into radar development, spending six years from 1949 on H2S Mk 9, destined for the V Bombers.

Ray Barker, *Radar Mechanic*:

The Continent, January 1945, AMES 7932 (7K)

We embarked at Tilbury in rough weather, and it took us three very seasick days to cross the Channel to Ostend. We reported to Wing HQ at Mons, and from there I was posted to a station near Louvain, in Belgium, where we were billeted in a château on the estate of a sugar baron; another château there had been used as Rommel's HQ. Our A-site was a short distance away in open country. Attempts were made to get the local Maquis to guard the place at night, but this was not successful, as they would disappear with the tents and heating stoves with which we had provided them.

The Maquis were collecting all the local girls accused of collaborating with German troops, shaving off their hair and subjecting them to indescribable indignities. They could never understand why we disagreed with this treatment and refused to join in their 'fun'.

I hadn't been there long before I was posted to form a new unit, AMES 7932 – a combined Gee master/monitor station which was to be deployed at Roermond, in Holland, on the German border, to prepare for the crossing of the Rhine. We found AMES 103 already sited there, living in tents.

We were unable to settle on our site as it was in the middle of a German minefield. This was cleared by the Americans, whereupon our CO insisted on being the first person to test its safey, and he drove a wagon over the whole site before he would let us bring the rest of the convoy onto it. Then we got busy and were operational within three days.

But within a couple of months another unit arrived to take over from us; we did this the quickest way by leaving our equipment *in situ* and taking over their convoy. We then set out on what was to be our convoy's last journey. Crossing into Germany itself, we passed signs which said 'YOU ARE NOW IN ENEMY TERRITORY – WEAR YOUR TIN HAT!' Then, in front of a whole row of dragons' teeth: 'THIS IS THE SIEGFRIED LINE', followed by a washing-line full of issue underwear, with another sign: 'AND THIS IS THE BLOODY WASHING!'

We travelled down the west bank of the Rhine (where hardly anything was left standing, other than chimney stacks) to Bonn, where we were accommodated in a bombed-out hospital. Here we waited for the pincer movement of our troops to capture our next location – Winterberg. I visited Beethoven's birthplace (and had to pay an entrance fee), and we played about with some of the abandoned small craft on the river.

After crossing the Rhine via a pontoon bridge (quite an experience), we eventually arrived at our destination, which was on the summit of Kahler Asten – a mountain in the Hochsaurland. Once again we found AMES 103 – 'Birnbaum's Original Circus' already ensconced there.

There was a large, round tower on the summit which had housed a German met. station and a high-frequency transmitter, so we decided not to assemble a full tower, but to take advantage of the existing one. We hoisted only the top section of our tower and fastened it to a convenient concrete block on the roof of the tower which had previously housed some of the enemy's met. equipment. The feeders were run down the outside of the tower and into the Tx vans. We were operational very quickly and giving extended coverage to the aircraft bombing deep into Germany.

The Americans had brought a high-powered signals unit on to the site, and the master sergeant in charge told us that it would blast us off the face of the earth. When we became operational, he came up to us and said: 'Jeez! what have you got there? You win!', and promptly packed up his equipment and departed!

We began to experience infiltration by small numbers of German troops who assumed we were still a German Army station. On one occasion, the cookhouse staff went into the marquee to prepare breakfast and found a few German troops waiting to be served! Fortunately, none of the escaping Germans caused us any problem – we fed them and transported them to the nearest prisoner-of-war camp. There was just one exception, though, on the day that a fanatical German officer and a few of his men decided to shoot his way out, and bullets were flying about the camp. It so happened that on that particular day a posse of high-ranking RAF officers and their minions were visiting the site. No one had ever seen a group of people turn tail and disappear back to Wing as fast!

In due course it was decided that a further Gee chain was required which would give full coverage over Berlin, and we had to organize a crew to erect the towers for this. About ten of us, under the command of our CO, Flt.-Lt. Steel, were sent off, together with an MT driver, an MT mechanic and one GD. We were away from our unit for about ten days, and we had just completed the last tower in the region of Hamburg when VE Day was declared and we were ordered to dismantle them all!

The first tower collapsed like a pack of cards and became what was probably the first victory bonfire, much to the disgust of a visiting officer who had joined us for instruction in tower-erecting. He actually wanted us to go into the woods, cut down trees and manufacture a new one!

I stayed at the Winterberg station for almost a whole year, being demobbed at last in June 1946, at Olympia. I returned to my home in a South Yorkshire mining village, only to discover – after almost six years of involvement with high-level electronics – that we still did not have a supply of electricity in the house!

Note: The above story, and the one on p. 37, are taken from Ray Barker's Book, *Reflexions on a Chain of Events*, and is published by kind permission of the author.

Denys Clutterbuck, *Radar Operator on LWS (Light Warning Set) 6081*:

Denys Clutterbuck

We arrived at Renscombe Down in February 1943 and learned what a LWS was (see photo on p. 132). The idea was for the L-crews to operate as near the enemy lines as was feasible, passing information back to the larger FDPs (Forward Defence Posts), who in turn passed it back, plus their own, to GCC (Group Control Centre).

L-crews were operating in Africa, and that was where we thought we were going. Instead, they gave us vehicles and sent us to Scotland, where, in a desolate spot near Galston, we erected our steel-framed operational tent, designed for desert warfare.

Thereafter, we moved around the country, living in tents. Then they gave us new radar equipment mounted in a van, which was a big help.

Then they told us we were henceforth on Combined Operations, and sent us to HMS *Dundonald*, the Navy shore station at Troon, in Ayrshire. There we paraded and marched to a band every morning with men from all three services. Training consisted mostly of assault courses and 'wet landings' from landing craft along the coast. We came away from Troon wearing bright new Combined Ops badges, and somewhere along the line we had collected rifles and Sten guns. It dawned upon us that we were destined for the Second Front.

But we missed D-Day, and many D-plus days. We were part of 84 Group, 2nd Tactical Air Force, and for weeks there was no room on the beachhead for 84 Group. Some Allied commanders had hoped to take Caen by the end of D-Day, but the Germans were still holding it six weeks later.

When we did set foot in Normandy, we found the French had had time to assess the generosity of their liberators; there were notices up in the bars: 'IN FRANCE IT IS CUSTOMARY TO TIP THE BARMAID.'

We soon made up for lost time, and we were close enough behind the tanks and infantry to catch some reflected glory, graciously waving back to the cheering crowds lining the streets of liberated towns.

At Hoogerheide, about 12 miles north of Antwerp, the radar van was on a hill as usual. I was in it one day, yawning in front of an empty tube. My companion was behind me at the plotting table, writing a letter. There may have been nothing on the tube, but there was something in the sky, and it was heading straight towards us. Suddenly, there came an explosion, as of a bomb uncomfortably close, and the van rocked violently. We scrambled out and saw, down the hill, 50 yards beyond our line of tents, a crater. Gazing at it were our shaken crewmates.

We heard later that down there a scene had been enacted that would not have disgraced a Hal Roach comedy. Syd, a radar op., had come out of his tent for a breath of fresh air and seen a V1 coming straight towards him, its engine cut off, its wings rocking. He put his head back inside the tent, pointed frantically, his mouth working soundlessly, then threw himself flat on the ground.

The tents escaped with a few loosened guy-ropes.

Then the Germans started to launch V1s from bombers. It was at Hoogerheide that I first saw this on the PPI – two aircraft on converging paths, each launching a V1, the target being the Scheldt estuary. It was interesting to see the two echoes each divide into two, the fainter echoes of the V1s following the original path, the stronger ones of the aircraft – their job done – receding.

The Rhine

We were perched on the Calcar Heights. Ahead and below was the Rhine. Just across the way was Calcar, flattened and deserted. The only intact objects around were newly-erected noticeboards with posters reading: 'YOU ARE WITHIN SIGHT OF THE ENEMY' and 'THE PENALTY FOR LOOTING IS DEATH.'

It was 23 March 1945. The biggest artillery bombardment the world had known started at 2200 hours. It was the beginning of Montgomery's 'Operation Plunder', to breach the Rhine. Two nights before – had we known it – 5,500 guns, British and American, had moved up behind us. When the barrage ended next morning, the Germans had been at the receiving end of approaching ten million shells.

When the guns stopped, there came the distant, thin whistle of a single, defiant German shell.

Below us, assault craft crossed the sluggish river. We followed more sedately later, over one of the Bailey bridges thrown across by the sappers.

Across the Rhine, we lived sometimes in tents, sometimes in improvised billets. There was a half-gutted barracks in Oldenburg where we slept on the floor and rats ran over us. I cannot recall that we ever put up our Yagi aerials again. If we did, the watches were uneventful: the Luftwaffe had ceased troubling us.

The Allies had instituted a route system on the Continent. The route symbols, together with regimental insignia, were displayed at road junctions. Main junctions were a riot of regimental colours.

Our route was the Blue Diamond route. It ended at a sort of country hotel – modern for the time – which was soon christened 'The Blue Diamond Cafe'. There, we finished up in comfort. It was the end of the line. And the beginning of the end of LWS 6081. After VE Day, my crewmates disappeared one by one, posted to other units, either in England or Germany, and I eventually found myself at Burtonwood, an ex-Yank camp in Lancashire.

And there I met Audrey, the WAAF I was to marry.

Roy Smith, *Radar Mechanic*:

[*Note*: With experience of the Chain and of J-Watch (see pp. 35 and 119), Roy volunteered for overseas service. After taking the Yatesbury centimetre course, he was posted to Germany, as he explains below.]

Four of us were sent to 2003 AD Wing in Amsterdam. We examined and dismantled the entire German chain from Zandvoort to Den Helder and the Dutch Freisian Islands. It was all carefully labelled and shipped back to the LMCD (Luftwaffe Material Concentration Depot) in Amsterdam. This was particularly interesting for me, since I was able to think back to the descriptions in the signal detectors at J-Watch.

The majority of sites consisted of a mixture of Pole Freyas (long-range warning, no heightfinding) and Würtzburg Reise (Giant Würtzburgs), although on one island there was also a Wassermann, with a 100 ft-plus, very slowly-rotating array, driven by an enormous motor. There were quite a lot of centimetre horns which were used to D/F on H_2S emissions.

My own impression of the German set-up was that although the sets were well constructed, the whole thing, thankfully, compared very unfavourably with our own.

Specifically, I never saw a single PPI display. The normal grouping was a Pole Freya, to give long-range warning and to alert *two* Giant Wurtzburgs – one to plot the nightfighter, the other to plot the selected hostile bomber. These projected green and red spots of light respectively on to a vertical form of the Seeburg Table – a glass wall bearing a map of the area (coastline, etc.). Only when the Würtzburg had locked on to a target did any heightfinding data become available, and only one interception at a time from three radars was possible. Compare this with the capability of one GCI 'Happidrome'.

When we had completed the last island and the last of the radar was safely housed in the LMCD, we returned to our own units for the gradual run-down to demob – most of it dreadfully boring.

But one last recollection: for some months I was in charge of a radio factory in a small town called Wulfrath, where our squadron was then based. The factory was used to store anything which might have any connection with radio or radar, and we finished up with thousands of resistors, capacitors, inductors and transformers, together with sundry other odd bits and pieces, but no radar!

When the day came to shrink the unit back into Wing HQ at Krefeld, I was instructed to pass on our stocks to any British unit which would accept them. The majority were happily accepted by a nearby REME (Royal Electrical and Mechanical Engineers) unit who, however, rejected out of hand our 'odds and ends'.

My instruction then was that they must be destroyed before we moved. Chief among them were about a dozen large, well-made wooden crates, about 2 by 1 m by 1 m, each containing two sprung cradles, with each cradle holding one V2 gyro. Beautiful pieces of precision machinery. Regretfully, we put them to the hammer.

From subsequent reading, I learned that at that very time there were teams of American technicians scouring Germany searching for V2 gyros!

Olive Carlisle (*née Marshall), WAAF Signals/Radar Officer*:

Olive Carlisle

Like so many girls, I joined the WAAF to be a heroine – driving our brave pilots to their fighter planes. I was summarily side-tracked.

After radar training at Yatesbury, it was off to Canewdon, and soon afterwards to Worth Matravers, a marvellous station which we left in precipitous haste, having come off nightwatch and been told to pack our kit and board a train for Wylfa, in Anglesey, to a cold, bare house.

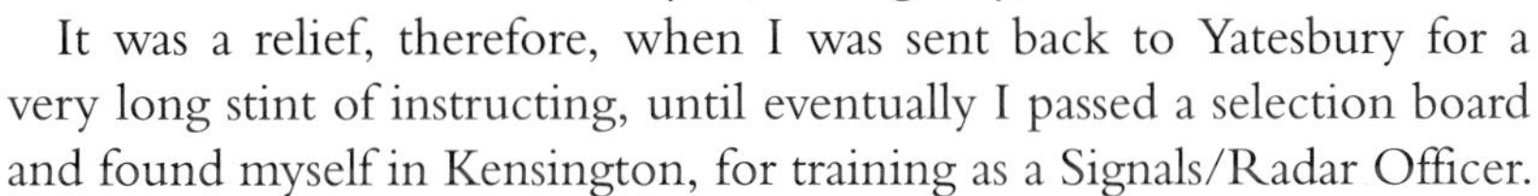

It was a relief, therefore, when I was sent back to Yatesbury for a very long stint of instructing, until eventually I passed a selection board and found myself in Kensington, for training as a Signals/Radar Officer.

There we were given a crammed mechanics' course and had to pass tests on the Morse Code. We also did tough square-bashing round the Albert Hall! Then to Bowness on Windermere for the 'finesse' bit.

With 75 Wing, my main field of work was inspecting, helping in the calibration, and even wiring, of electrical calculators – always under the suspicious eye of a CME (what a competent and special breed these men were!), usually ex-Dollis Hill. Many an exhilarating mile I've travelled in the sidecar of a CME's motorbike!

I covered all CH stations from Great Bromley to Ventnor, and for the latter I was issued with a special pass to cross to the Isle of Wight, unaware at the time that D-Day was only a week away.

I remember marvelling at the thousands of trucks, etc. lining the roadside and sheltering under every leafy tree, with the Solent seething with every kind of camouflaged craft.

Postings, postings! My next was to Dunkirk, near Canterbury, where the section consisted of wireless operators, mechanics and, later, teleprinter operators, who were housed underground. We seemed to be the testing ground for many types of aerial arrays.

The marvellous cameraderie at the station was threatened only temporarily once, when a 'regular' Flight Sergeant, at least ten years my senior, arrived and almost immediately requested a transfer – 'I've never had to work under a woman before and I don't want to start now!'

Fate stepped in. Freezing fog and sub-zero temperatures had rendered the equipment at the top of the transmitter tower unserviceable. In murky twilight and a howling wind, the Flight Sergeant and I climbed the ice-covered rungs of the steps to the very top, and having completed our task, descended even more perilously. Shortly afterwards, he asked for his request for a transfer to be scrapped, and he happily lost the last trace of misogyny by eventually marrying a delightful WAAF from the section.

72 Wing, Mons

The advent of VE Day seemed to me to wipe out the reasons given for turning down my frequent requests for a transfer to 72 Wing at Mons. The Powers That Be

Some of the headquarters staff of 72 Wing at Bonn on VJ-Day. Olive Carlisle is the female in the centre.

seemed to agree, because I found myself one day at Croydon, boarding a bucket-seated Dakota, bound for Brussels. From there by truck to Mons, where I was billeted with a Belgian couple not far from the mess in Boulevard Albert-Elisabeth.

Apart from two code and cypher 'Queens' at Mons, it was a completely male society. One learned to leave the mess tactfully when a pianist played 'Goodnight Ladies'. Travelling around France, I'm quite sure the locals considered me to be a 'Forces' Comfort' and I remember a friend being told by one of them that he thought I'd make an excellent farmer's wife (if I were available).

But my life there was easy compared with that of the men subjected to the adverse and most inhospitable conditions of some of the outstations. I have in mind especially Mount Ventoux, where crews were marooned in deep snow (sometimes for weeks) far from the base camp, when even caterpillar-tracked trucks were 'grounded', and often skis had to be used. These men really were the unsung heroes of the less glamorous but all-important links of the Gee chains. I was privileged to cover most of the Gee chain stations from the north – Aarhus, in Denmark – to the south – Carcassone, in France.

So the war got me well and truly bitten by the travel bug, and after it was over, I explored most of the rest of the world as a pioneering stewardess with BOAC.

Robert Hyde and Arthur ('Tich') Childs, *8009 AMES in Italy*:

Note: This account takes up their story after they left North Africa (see p. 127).
We left Bizerte harbour on 29 September 1943. After an uneventful crossing, the two LSTs carrying our personnel, vehicles and equipment anchored off the Salerno beachhead. After some delay, we landed and then moved south along the coastal road. The journey was slow, on roads not built for heavy traffic and with all bridges down, which meant that rivers and streams had to be forded – hard work with our heavy and cumbersome radar vehicles.

We finally found our site from the given map reference, halfway up the side of a steep gradient to a small peak, some 400 ft above the seashore, near the small town of Pisciotta.

We set up a tented camp in an olive grove, on the same level and adjacent to the technical site. The radar vehicles were stationed along the verge of the road, close to the rock face to reduce obstruction, with the exception of the aerial cabin, which was positioned on a level plateau where the road doubled back upon itself.

Both the domestic site and the radar vehicles were well screened and camouflaged from observation by sea and air, with the exception of the aerial, which had a clear, unobstructed sweep of the approaches to Salerno and Naples. This was the role assigned to us – the protection of Allied shipping convoys approaching the west coast of Italy.

Within two days of arrival we were ready for operations, but then we found that the 323 Wing Filter Room was not yet ready to receive our plots. No landlines had been laid either, so all plots would have to be transmitted by wireless telegraphy, a most unreliable medium, especially in our case, with a range of hills peaking to 3,000 ft between us and the receiving station.

By mid-November, however, landlines had been laid by the Army Signals Corps, and we began plotting Allied shipping movements along some 120 miles of sea lane, to maximum ranges of over 60 miles, and even further under conditions of 'abnormal propagation'. Aircraft we could plot to the extreme range of nearly 200 miles.

The volcanic island of Stromboli, at a range of 92 miles to the south, gave a very clear permanent echo which we used as a reference against which to check our range and azimuth calibrations and operational signal strength.

The landlines gave trouble, partly because they were indirect (i.e. they were routed via Army telephone exchanges), and partly because they were repeatedly cut by saboteurs. To mitigate the problems, the W/T link was improved by obtaining better equipment and moving the W/T station to a new site higher up the hillside. VHF R/T equipment was also obtained and brought into operation, with the attachment of F/O Annand and P/O Hughes as Controllers (GCI).

For security reasons, the road through the site was closed to civilian traffic by a boom with a guard post permanently manned by the RAF Regiment.

That Christmas of 1943 we performed our own concert party in a marquee, which was converted into a dining-hall at one end and a bar at the other. We ate fresh meat for the first time since leaving England – pork and wild boar (shot by the CO) – and the local vino flowed and our spirits were good.

Meanwhile, the Allied 5th Army had moved up from Salerno, entering Naples on 1 October. Then on to the Volturno river, which they crossed in mid-October, until eventually they came up to the Gustav Line – the fortified German defence position along the Rivers Liri, Garigliano, Sangro and Rapido; and here they were, still stuck at the end of the year.

On 12 January the battle for Northern Italy commenced with attacks all along the Gustav Line, partially as a diversion for the seaborne attack at Anzio, which was launched on 22 January. The key position in the German defence line was, of course, the town of Cassino and the mined and heavily-fortified defensive positions in the hills surrounding it. And here the Americans, Free French and New Zealand troops were repulsed with heavy casualties.

In February our old and somewhat inefficient R/T equipment was taken out of service and we became hosts to an American mobile VHF R/T unit. The marquee dining room was replaced with a large, wooden building, complete with elegant and artistic murals by the twin brothers Humphries.

The weather was dreary with heavy rain and gales, and early in March a landslide demolished part of the road between our camp site and the marina where our MT section was located. But presently the weather improved, and we started swimming and sunbathing at a rocky beach at the base of the cliff. Our ablution facilities were greatly enhanced by an excellent outdoor shower, contrived by diverting a small natural spring. We acquired a little farmyard of laying hens and a fattening pig, and in addition we managed to obtain several defective radio sets which, when repaired and adapted to our 240 V AC supply, allowed us for the first time to receive BBC news direct and keep ourselves up to date with the progress of the war. Life was improving for 8009 AMES!

Early in May, considerable aircraft activity was observed on our screens, and on 11 May the Allies launched a full-scale attack at Cassino, spearheaded by Free French and Polish units plus 8th Army troops diverted from the Adriatic front. These succeeded in breaking through the defences, and on 23 May the German forces withdrew to Rome, thus releasing the Allied forces pinned down on the Anzio beachhead.

With this dramatic collapse of enemy resistance, it was apparent that our stay at Pisciotta would soon end, so we began preparations for movement, including killing and eating our little collection of livestock.

As expected, on 4 June we received instructions to move to a site 6 miles to the south-east of Cassino, and on the morning of 6 June – D-Day – we departed with mixed feelings – glad to be moving forward again, but with regret at the loss of the amenities we had enjoyed during our time at Pisciotta.

Pisciotta to Tarquinia

Our journey took us back along the familiar route to Salerno and then around the lower slopes of Vesuvius, smoking heavily and blackened by the ash fall and larva flows from the recent major eruption.

Our new operational site was on the vast, open plain confronting the mountains and the town and monastery of Cassino to the north. We had difficulty in finding both the map-referenced site and a safe route to get to it, due to uncleared minefields and, up in the foothills, where the final assault had been made, the bodies of Polish soldiers still lying where they had fallen – awaiting the clearance of mines before they could be recovered for burial.

The original intention was that we should become a central control station and filter room, with four early-warning radar units plotting into us, to give cover for the battle line to the immediate north of Cassino. But events on the European war map were now moving too quickly.

We had moved out of Pisciotta on D-Day, and even as we were setting up our equipment at the new site and becoming operational, the Allied forces' beachheads were being consolidated in Normandy, while on the Italian front the prospect of a protracted battle to liberate Rome had disappeared when Von Rundstedt had declared it an open city and removed all his forces to the north. And so, after being operational for only two days, we were ordered to move on to Rome.

We reached Rome in the middle of a very hot day, passing the Coliseum and the other historic buildings, but with no time for sightseeing, as we still had some distance to go.

Our new operational site was on the large coastal plain to the north of the port of Cevitavecchia and roughly south-east of Tarquinia. We were operational

8009 AMES on the way to Rome in June 1944.

Rome, 1944.

within twenty-four hours, and a mobile filter room was erected nearby to receive our plots and those of the four early-warning radar stations.

But the German retreat continued, and soon the mobile filter room was dismantled and removed and we were left standing by, pending further orders. In due course these arrived, and we were on the air to detect and plot aircraft moving in the coastal approaches to north-east Italy.

Early in July we received our new mobile, twin-channel, VHF R/T equipment to replace the single-channel, transportable equipment that we'd had to make do with since arriving in Italy. Thus we were once more fully mobile in every respect.

On 6 August we plotted over a thousand Allied aircraft, bombers and fighters, moving in large formations from our local airfields into the south of France. Further intense activity was observed and plotted on the 13th, and on 15 August we were woken in the early hours by large formations of troop-carrying aircraft towing gliders, flying low, their engines at full throttle. We plotted them over the south coast of France and back again later in the day, and as they passed low overhead we could see that their exit doors were wide open. An invasion force, codenamed 'Anvil', had landed in the south of France to join up with the forces liberating the north.

On 9 September we received orders to cease operations and dismantle the equipment. At midnight that day, Cevitavecchia was declared a non-military port. Two weeks later we were on the move again, heading for a new location some 6 miles north of Leghorn, near the small village of Guasticce.

Guasticce – The Final Chapter

Here, our CO managed to commandeer a large, rather dilapidated farmhouse, which provided more than adequate living and messing space for both officers and men, and still left room on the top floor for indoor recreational use, including a photographic dark-room.

In the large general messroom on the ground floor, we built a stage and installed our carefully-transported piano, and the concert party immediately began rehearsing for the Christmas concert. This room also doubled as a cinema for the weekly visit of the RAF mobile cinema unit.

Winter set in, with heavy rain throughout October which threatened to flood our technical site, so we had to move it to higher ground. We again had a magnificent Christmas dinner that year, with our own concert party's variety show, which would not have disgraced the Palladium.

Into 1945, with the weather still cold and wet, we were kept busy with formations of Allied bombers moving up over France and back again, plus the occasional detection of hostile interceptors.

But early in March, Allied forces crossed the Rhine in strength at Remagen, and it came as no surprise to us when, on 29 April, the German forces surrendered in Italy, followed on 7 May by their total surrender in Europe. On the same day we received orders to cease operations and withdraw all technical vehicles into the MT vehicle park on the domestic site. (We had only just carried out this order when we received its countermand, and once again we set up our station and resumed operations, to provide a 'practice' facility for a locally-based fighter squadron.)

But on 20 August we were ordered to close down and pack up equipment in readiness for a move to Capua, about 20 miles north of Naples. Here all our vehicles and trailers were checked for completeness of content, sealed and taken into storage, and by 16 September we were reduced to a 'personnel only' basis and finally disbanded to await individual postings to other units in the Mediterranean, pending return to the United Kingdom and final demobilization.

CHAPTER EIGHT

Recruitment and Training

In the decades before the war, several major British companies of the radio and electrical industry had built up prestigious research departments, matching in their levels of professional expertise the government-funded scientific organizations such as the Royal Aircraft Establishment, Farnborough. These great private companies, in common with the scientific Civil Service, provided career opportunities for fully-trained degree-standard professional engineers, some of whom were to become involved in the pioneering work on radar.

Many remained in their companies' laboratories on secret radar development work for the government, while a few transferred to the growing team of scientists at the Bawdsey research station under Watson Watt, and thence to its offspring TRE (Telecommunications Research Establishment) under A.P. Rowe. By this means a collection of some of the best and most innovative brains in the country was focused on the development of radar. But the need for another kind of expertise was soon to arise.

Once war started, the rapid installation of new radar stations and the need for uninterrupted early-warning around the clock demanded large numbers of operators, mechanics and technical supervisors. On-the-job training on radar stations was limited by the availability of suitable trainees and the extent to which operational equipment could be spared, so special schools were quickly set up at Yatesbury, Cranwell and Clinton, Ontario, and a vigorous national recruiting campaign was initiated for those with suitable experience and background. To preserve secrecy, all radar activities were classified as 'radio' while 'wireless' was used for communications – a distinction unexplained and the cause of some puzzlement to the uninitiated.

Advertisements included:

> Serve in the WAAF as a Radio Operator. You need good eyesight, a 'quiet tongue' and should be quick to learn. Essential qualifications are an alert mind and the ability to keep cool and self-possessed. Enrolment subject to passing a selection board.

Many young women satisfied these requirements, as did men lacking technical knowledge of radio but displaying 'above average intelligence and undoubted integrity'. And for radio mechanics:

> Only highly skilled radio men may be accepted. Should be radio engineers capable of servicing modern superhet sets. Men who have held an amateur transmitting licence may be accepted. . . .

Prewar radio was so popular that wireless shops with competent repairmen were widespread: they, and knowledgeable 'hams', were candidates for training as 'radio' mechanics, and the RAF was quick to absorb them.

When established, the 'radio' schools provided a wide range of radar courses for operators (usually six weeks), mechanics (eight to ten weeks, later more), technical officers (varying lengths) and special subjects, including navaids and centimetre-wavelength techniques.

Trainees were given more technical detail than was needed in the normal course of their work. Operators, who might have been trained merely by rote, were taught about the behaviour of radio waves and how the cathode ray tube worked. Again, mechanics were instructed meticulously in aerial theory, and while they themselves could do nothing to affect the radiation patterns, this enabled them to appreciate fully the design features of equipments they would service.

For most trainees this 'overtraining' imparted confidence and enthusiasm. It has been remarked elsewhere that German policy was different; while their equipment was well-designed and solidly made, the technical standard of their servicemen is said to have been comparatively weak.

SECURITY

Such tight security measures were enforced throughout radar courses that this policy of overtraining did not compromise security. Personnel not directly involved in radar – especially those who risked becoming the enemy's prisoners – were denied knowledge of it; yet this could lead to problems, as David Speake recalled:

> I went with a party from Ringstead (CH) to a dance at a nearby American base. In the course of the evening I was in conversation with a member of an aircrew, and hearing that I came from Ringstead, he asked if I knew anything about 'chaff' (window). Being security-conscious I pleaded ignorance, whereupon he told me he didn't know how it worked but that it was his job to dispense it from the aircraft and, since he usually forgot while over the Continent, he got rid of it over the Thames Estuary on the way back!

Nancy Paterson *(née Hunter), Radar Operator, Instructor, ROM and later Mechanic, recalls her part in training*:

Nancy Paterson

In 1943 the call-up ages of men rose to include mature men who had given up good and settled jobs. Training schools were busy, and these men were sent directly from square-bashing to active stations. I was an i/c watch (aged 19) at CHL Cocklaw, west of Peterhead, and I can remember at least four such men posted to us. I had two on my watch plus two fully-trained, and as we were an acting GCI, this put quite a strain on the rest of the watch. I think the older men found it hard to be bossed by a girl half their age. We had them plotting and recording, but strobing and PPI reading took longer to explain.

Two months later, at CH Netherbutton, Orkney, we received 18-year-old mechanics who had been partly trained and sent out to finish off at stations.

I was posted soon after to Cranwell, where I did my ROMS course, and thence to the maintenance squad. This was my first chance to use my training; I had done the odd shift in transmitter blocks and had been allowed to help boffins from Malvern, but at Cranwell I worked with the mechanics. I think our small hands were much appreciated and were used to find and pick up dropped items in inaccessible places. My first job was to grease the nipples on CHL aerial-turning gear. I wasn't sure if this was a real task or a tease, but I donned my overalls and climbed on to the roof.

Eric Hendy, *a wartime member of No. 8 Radio School at Cranwell instructional staff, remembers*:

Eric Hendy

From September 1943 the growing demand for airborne radar resulted in a changeover of instruction from ground to airborne equipment. This included IFF, Gee, Air Interception Mks 8 and 10, H_2S, Monica, Fishpond, Village Inn, Blind Approach Beacon Systems, Radio Altimeter and Rebecca/Eureka. This change resulted in all operator training ending; only radar mechanics were trained thereafter. In the early stages of airborne radar, training was limited to that needed for particular squadrons – Fighter, Bomber and Coastal. (This resulted in the suffixes 'F', 'B' or 'R', where the 'R' stood for Reconnaissance – mainly done by Coastal Command.) Later, when personnel could be trained in other airborne equipment, the basic category Radar Mechanic (A) would cause fewer problems of cross-posting within squadrons.

H.C. ('Tony') Horwood, *Radar Mechanic Instructor (died September 1995)*:

AB Initio

H.C. Horwood

At the outbreak of war, the RAF was faced with an enormous training problem to provide sufficient personnel to maintain the developing wireless equipment together with the newly-born RDF equipment.

The ingenious solution was to use the existing knowhow of the lecturers in civilian technical colleges throughout the land. After intelligence and aptitude tests at induction centres, suitable recruits were sent to a technical college for an *ab initio* course in radio. The course lasted about six months and was extremely comprehensive – from Ohm's Law to superhet. via AC and DC theory, valve types, characteristics and uses, tuned radio-frequency receivers together with Hartley, Colpitts and tuned-plate-tuned-grid oscillators, to mention but a few of the topics.

The theory was taught by a member of the technical college staff, as was the more practical aspect – namely, using hand tools and, in particular, soldering and building circuits.

Each course consisted of about twenty recruits. The RAF presence was usually in the form of a pilot officer or flying officer together with a senior NCO. They were responsible for liaison with a local RAF station and arranging civvy billets for the trainees. On one morning each week, the senior NCO would march the recruits, equipped with soap, flannel and towel, to the local public baths, where 'five inches' of tepid water was drawn off for each recruit in succession.

At the end of the course, those who had passed went on to training in service equipment. In the case of radar, the bulk of the training was done at No. 8 Radio School, Cranwell, and No. 9 Radio School, Yatesbury. Some trainees were given further training, and some were remustered to another trade. Others were sent on loan to the Army to maintain searchlight radar.

The *ab initio* course was not a male preserve. An example of WAAF participation was given to me by the then ACWs Jo Abley and Jean Carpenter who did their *ab initio* at Hull starting in May 1944. They arrived at Yatesbury just before Christmas 1944, and after a sixteen-week course, passed out as Radar Mechanics (Ground). Their course was made up of ten WAAFs from Hull Technical College and eleven from Leicester Technical College.

The *ab initio* courses without doubt provided a thorough background in radio engineering – a view supported by those who underwent the rigours of radar training.

Squadron Leader George Danielson, *Chief Instructor at No. 9 Radio School, Yatesbury, for most of the war*:

George Danielson

I came on to the RDF scene in 1938 at Bawdsey Manor, by which time Watson Watt had departed. I well remember the great thrill and excitement of the tests being carried out between Bawdsey (in the dark room with just the flickering green trace on the CRT), and the Blenheim aircraft, piloted by Flight Lieutenant 'Blood-orange' Smith. It was the job of us first half-dozen to acquire all the knowledge then existing and then pass it on to a select band of others, including Marcus Scroggie and Orr-Ewing.

I always had an affection for those 360 ft towers, and it was once my ambition to climb at least one at each CH station, starting off with Bawdsey, Stoke Holy Cross, Great Bromley and Canewdon, but in the end I hadn't enough petrol to go careering about all over the place, though I picked up two or three more along the south coast later – one at Pevensey.

The training moved from Bawdsey to Yatesbury in the cold winter of 1940. We had six-week courses which included detachment to ops stations, and the mechanics' courses were six to eight weeks. The airborne equipment training went to South Kensington (a most unlikely spot). At Yatesbury we had the WAAF training under Flying Officer K. Lethbridge and the RAF under Flt. Lt. Gardner. Squadron Leader Tippet was in charge, but before long he moved to Cranwell and I replaced him. There was a special short course for senior officers who just needed to know what radar was about without many technical details – for COs mostly. This was run by the excellent Flt. Lt. John Ree: 'You ask, Sir, what is that pair of wires sticking out there: that, Sir, is a stub; it stops energy going that way. It's as if you wanted to build a wall here but couldn't for some reason, so instead you dig a trench a quarter wavelength away to serve the same purpose.'

We had an American Officers' course too, which ran for a long time, and also for Canadians. Then there was the Radar Operator Mechanics' Course – the trouble we had with Ohm's Law, reactance, resonance!

We were required to run all kinds of courses by all kinds of people, not only 60 Group, and I would always say yes, whatever the request – I reckoned No. 9 Radio School could tackle anything!

I can't quite recall when the 'immediate LAC' rank came to an end, but I remember Bob Flook making scathing remarks about newcomers who didn't know a parade ground from a fire bucket who came in and did a 'pansy' little course and then blossomed as an LAC!

But I shall never forget those early days at Bawdsey. The atmosphere! Seeing this thing that so very, very few people knew about – the green glow in the darkened room, the wiggle of the trace and the knowledge that the elusive deflection represented an aircraft, that his range was there on the scale, and that with a bit of calculation and line-drawing, we could get a good idea of the height. So we could place this fellow in space, and neither he nor anybody else in the outside world knew that we knew. Quite something. Even the later Oboe, and the knowledge that we could place our aircraft to an accuracy of the width of his wings, didn't quite equal those first months.

David McClelland, *Flight Sergeant, RDF Mechanic (later Flying Officer Pilot)*:

At the outbreak of war I was a constable in the Birkenhead Police Force, where, as well as normal duties, I did some part-time work on radio communications equipment. By the middle of 1940, when the war hotted up and invasion appeared imminent, the government was appealing for experienced radio engineers or technicians to volunteer for the RAF, so I put in an application to the Chief Constable to leave the force, but he sent for me and told me I was wasting my time (and his), as the police was a reserved occupation and there was no chance of my leaving.

David McClelland

After a few weeks, however, I tried again. This was in early September, and the Merseyside blitzes had just begun. On this occasion the Chief Constable sent the application to the Home Office, and in a few days a letter arrived, signed *personally* by the Home Secretary, Sir John Anderson. It read tersely: 'Release this man immediately.' By 11 September I was in the RAF!

At Padgate I was given a trade test and graded as an AC/1 Radio Mechanic. After square-bashing at West Kirby, I arrived at Yatesbury late one evening. I had expected to be involved in ground or aircraft R/T equipment, but I was in for a big surprise! Next morning, I and a lot of other sprogs were marched down to the gates of No. 9 Radio School. When I saw the various antenna systems, particularly the rotating CHL arrays, I began to suspect that I was into something special.

The new intake (about 350 of us) was assembled in the NAAFI and addressed by the CO, Wing Commander Kidd, who warned us of the dire consequences that would result if we ever spoke of what we did at No. 9 Radio School.

Back in 1937 I had obtained an amateur Radio Transmitting Licence. I was surprised and pleased to find that many others on the course were also radio hams, even Squadron Leader Danielson, our Chief Instructor (see p. 190). Pre-war British radio hams were all technically experienced, as they had, perforce, to construct and often design their own transmitting equipment. Commercial communications receivers were readily available 'off the shelf' if one had the money, but most of us built our own. (I have read somewhere that before the war, Hermann Goering suppressed the German amateur radio movement, considering it potentially subversive. When interviewed in captivity after the war, General Martini, Head of Luftwaffe Signals, bemoaned the fact that his radio technicians had been mostly of poor quality.)

My course companions and I were completely amazed by the revelation of an up-and-running UK defence radar system. At the end of the course I and several others were selected as mechanic instructors. After attending a short instructors' course, I was then attached to Flt. Lt. Radcliffe, a theory instructor on MB2, RF6 and CHL. After a week he left, and I took over.

There were names to conjure with. Arthur C. Clarke, who amazed us all with his plans for moonflights and other space enterprises, which earned him the nickname of 'Spaceship Clarke',[1] and M.G. Scroggie, a prominent writer in the pre-war and postwar radio technical press. There were many other technical wizards. I was flattered when Scroggie asked me to read and comment on the proofs of the first edition of his book, *The Foundations of Wireless*. This must have been the most successful radio textbook ever – I think it sold over a million copies.

I remember a CHL installation with separate Rx and Tx antennas (before automatic T/R switching). Synchronism between Rx and Tx antennas was achieved by a Wheatstone bridge arrangement. This consisted of two rotary wire-wound potentiometers (one in the Tx hut, the other in the Rx hut). Their sliders rotated in angular synchronism with the line of shoot of each antenna. The Rx antenna was synchronized with the Tx antenna by the operator observing a centre-zero voltmeter, which indicated the balance, or lack of it, of the bridge.

The fun bit was that both operators turned their respective antennae by means of pedals attached to a crank, chainwheel and chain system taken from a pushbike! Was such a Heath Robinson set-up ever used operationally, I wonder, or was it just a Yatesbury mock-up? (It was – see p. 71. – Pat Sparks)

At night in 1940 and 1941, German bombers overflew Yatesbury, making their unhindered way to blitz the Midlands, Merseyside and Manchester. We could hear the 'woo-woo-woo' of their unsynchronized engines and, looking

1 Subsequently, Arthur C. Clarke became world famous as a science fiction writer and accurately prophesied satellite television.

up, see their long-drawn-out condensation trails. However, later on, with the arrival of GCI and the Beaufighter, the odds changed in our favour. I remember how thrilled we were by the arrival of our first GCI.

I remember, too, the visits we had from royal personages, including King George VI, Queen Mary and the Duke of Kent. When Queen Mary came, I happened to be walking along the narrow path leading to one of the huts when the royal party came out through the door. I stepped into the mud, stood smartly to attention, and remained at the salute until the party had gone by. Queen Mary inclined her head as she passed by and rewarded me with a gracious smile.

I left Yatesbury in June 1943 to remuster to aircrew, and was commissioned as a pilot in August 1944. I was a bit miffed when I had to hand in all my notebooks, which were then incinerated, particularly as they contained a lot of non-secret, general material which could have been of use to me afterwards.

Arthur Rous *(died 1994), pre-war RAF 'regular' Wireless Operator, later Warrant Officer Radar Mechanic*:

Arthur Rous

I was at Yatesbury when the wireless operator school moved there from Cranwell in the winter of 1938–9, and again in 39–40 when the radar school moved from Bawdsey. A few of us went from Bawdsey with the road convoy – quite a journey. It took three days at the great speed of 12 m.p.h., complete with an AA route!

The convoy got stuck in Long Melford – a mast on a Queen Mary low-loader jammed under a railway arch. Part of it had to be dismantled. It wasn't long before locals were coming out of their houses with mugs of tea and buns to sustain the brave boys in their plight. Then on to Duxford and Abingdon, reaching Yatesbury on the third day.

Incidentally, I was at Bawdsey at the time of the Zeppelin spying flight. I wasn't on watch but I heard that the echo was the biggest ever seen at Bawdsey. (See p. 1.)

Dr John H. Bryant, *of the Department of Electrical Engineering and Computer Science, University of Michigan, tells the unusual story of how an American came to be commanding a British radar station in 1942*:

In the spring of 1940, scientists and engineers in the United States were focusing their attention increasingly on the reality that scientific and technical manpower and industrial facilities had to be mobilized for the impending war. The National Defense Research Committee (NDRC), formed in June 1940, was a civilian organization with a budget and authority to organize and support new programmes and establish new facilities when required.

A step-function advance in preparedness for the US, the NDRC was equipped to host the British Technical Mission to the United States and Canada,

Dr John H. Bryant

better known as the 'Tizard Mission' (August–October 1940). The purpose of this mission was to enlist the effort of the American and Canadian engineering and scientific communities for development and applications work, and to get the large productive capacity of electronics and other industries in these two countries devoted to wartime product development and production. This was to include radar, fire control, underwater detection, communications, turrets, superchargers, chemical warfare, rockets and explosives.

Sending this mission in late August 1940 with the most valuable fruits of British defence research – samples, detailed drawings, construction details, applications and tactical information – was a bold, high-risk venture. There were misgivings, to be sure, and hesitancy about giving such vital details to the United States, a neutral power. There was also concern about whether any reaction would be prompt enough to make a difference. Reaction was, in fact, prompt and responsive, and led to a remarkably successful programme of cooperation between the three nations.

The axiom 'to transfer information, send people' is amply illustrated by members of the Tizard Mission. For radar and navigation there was Edward G. Bowen, a charter member in 1935 of the radar development team under Watson Watt, and the distinguished scientist John D. Cockcroft, who had played a key role in mobilization of British scientists for radar and related work. Cockcroft had completed his direct involvement in siting and installing the first dozen or so CHL radar stations, and on his return was due to be appointed head of ADRDE, the Army radar research and development establishment at Christchurch.

Cockcroft and Bowen travelled extensively, presenting and explaining what they brought, including the cavity magnetron, which was copied at the Bell Telephone Laboratories in a matter of weeks and was in production at Western Electric before 1940 was out. These and airborne radars built to early British design were soon being shipped from US and Canadian production to the UK.

Cockcroft and Bowen recommended that civilian laboratories be established for design, development and application of new radars and related systems and equipment. The Radiation Laboratory at the Massachusetts Institute of Technology (microwave radar and long-range navigation), the Radio Research Laboratory at Harvard (radar countermeasures) and the Applied Physics Laboratory at Johns Hopkins University (the proximity fuse) were established.

NDRC contracts also supported the work of individuals and groups of investigators at various academic locations. Contracts, negotiated with thousands of industrial firms, ranged from establishing new facilities for the manufacture of coaxial cable or furnishing supplies and equipment, to the production of radars, proximity fuses, countermeasures and navigation equipment. All of this was intended to ensure the supply of a wide variety of radar and associated equipment for a large number of different applications from American and Canadian production for Allied use.

The Need for Radar Officers

There was an urgent need for trained staff including radar officers, but in the US there were no established radar schools. In early 1941 James B. Conant, President of Harvard and Vice-Chairman of NDRC, started discussion about sending Signal Corps officers to Great Britain for radar school and operational training in radar.

Action was prompt, with the British agreeing to give up space in their schools, but in turn hoping to get useful work from the Signal Corps officers. The Electronics Training Group (ETG) was established in the Signal School at Fort Monmouth to recruit and train new officers for radar. These men were sent in groups of approximately fifty, and Group 1 departed for the UK in August 1941.

I was in Group 12, a year later. By the time the training programme was terminated in November 1943, 907 Signal Corps officers had completed their training in England – 547 in British Army radar and 450 in the RAF.

Arriving in August 1942, my group was sent to Bournemouth for a few days, and then in small groups we went to operational radar stations: in my case to RAF Rhuddlan, Flintshire, Wales, on a CH radar. By 9 September about 40 per cent of our group was at Cranwell radar school.

Here we had a fourteen-week course on ground-reporting radar – a stimulating experience. The instructors were university faculty members in uniform for the duration, all excellent teachers who enjoyed intellectual discussion on their subject.

My interest in graduate school was stirred by this. They also conveyed the reality of (1) the urgency of making full use of equipment and facilities through good maintenance and ongoing training of personnel, and (2) expecting upgraded and new equipment from advancing technology.

Commanding a British Radar Station

On graduating on 19 December 1942, two of us in the class were posted as commanding officers of radar stations. For me it was RAF Skendleby, near Alford, Lincolnshire, under 73 Wing with headquarters at Malton, Yorkshire. The main radar of the station was a CHL, reporting to Filter Room via RAF Stenigot, a CH station about 15 miles to the north-west.

We two were not the only ones to hold British commands. On various occasions thousands of British troops served under the command of these US officers at a time when combined military operations under Supreme Allied Headquarters were still in the future.

Working in the RAF organization was an interesting experience. Our site of perhaps an acre was enclosed by barbed-wire with a small guardhouse at the gate. One morning the guard called to tell me a gentleman was there to see me and asked if he should send him in. I said no and walked to the gate. I was greeted by a friendly and distinguished-looking man who mentioned names and an event which showed familiarity with 73 Wing organization. He casually showed his identification and explained that he was from the Air Ministry on a regular visit to inspect government property.

I told the guard to take good care of our visitor and went to my office and called Wing HQ. When told that no inspection had been set up I knew I was being tested, so I went back and showed our visitor on his way.

In due course I was relieved of this command and sent to join the technical staff at Wing HQ. Welcomed into this group of three very capable radar officers, I was made a participant in the lively activity. Calls from the stations for information and assistance ranged from routine to emergency need for a part for a set out of operation. I marvelled at how well they could deduce the source of a problem merely through a phone conversation with a radar mechanic. Accompanying them on visits to stations, I was impressed at how much they remembered about particular installations.

I also travelled on my own, visiting CHL stations in Yorkshire and Lincolnshire, and participated in the installation of a GCI. I got back to Skendleby once to install a Mk III IFF unit of US manufacture on the CHL set. By that time the station also had WAAF personnel.

I visited TRE at Malvern for several days once and got an impression of how a wide range of equipment had been developed and constantly updated. I saw some items that were new to me, including what I later learned was a cavity magnetron in operation on a bench.

My tour of duty in Britain ended in mid-1943. After my experience with British operations, my sense of urgency often did not fit well with the more laid-back approach of the USA.

I went overseas again, to Italy and southern France, where I had responsibility for an SCR–527, 200 MHz, search and GCI radar. In France and Germany, our unit had an MEW (Microwave Early Warning) radar. This long-range 10 cm transportable radar incorporated filter room functions and had multiple controller positions for GCI intercept and air traffic control. The MEW sets had no heightfinding, the British Type 13 radar often filling that requirement well.

In civilian life it has been my privilege to visit Great Britain regularly on business, technical and holiday visits. My interest in the country and feeling at home there undoubtedly stems from my year with the RAF in 1942–43. Since turning historian ten years ago, I have spent a good deal of time at the Public Record Office, at TRE and the Science Museum. On 21 February 1990 it was also my privilege to participate at Birmingham University in the 50th anniversary commemoration of the first operation of the cavity magnetron.

Retrospective

The question naturally arises whether the Electronics Training Group was a success. From the individual participant's point of view, I believe that for most it was, and for me it certainly was. From the US Army Signal Corps' point of view it must have been a success. I assume that the ETG programme was a success from the British point of view, but not as much as hoped because of the short average stay of only about ten months. Some have said that the presence of these troops, well ahead of any build-up of Allied forces, was a morale-booster, but who is to judge that?

[*Note*: Dr John H. Bryant, research scientist at the Radiation Laboratory of the College of Engineering, University of Michigan, is currently active in assembling data relating to the history of radar for military applications.]

CHAPTER NINE

As We Were

Anne Stobbs *(née Miller), Radar Operator on CH, 700 and 7K*:

Anne Stobbs

Life on a UK radar station was unique: I doubt if any other RAF or WAAF personnel experienced anything quite like it. Most stations were very small and had comparatively few officers and NCOs. In fact, 'you'll get no promotion this side of the ocean' very much applied to the trade of radar! The vast majority of mechanics and operators never got higher than LAC/LACW in rank; I doubt if any employer ever got such a bargain when you consider the qualities the RAF demanded.

It was nobody's fault that we got no promotion this side of the ocean (nor, for that matter, on the other side of the ocean). There simply wasn't 'room at the top': each station had its requirement of different ranks, and once they were *in situ*, that was that.

One of the strangest aspects of life on a radar station was the total division between tech. and non-tech. personnel, and between A-site and B-site. A-site was where the radar itself was, and B-site was where we all lived, and never the twain did meet. They were usually at least a mile apart, in case of air attack, but they were a million miles apart metaphorically speaking. No non-tech. people were ever allowed anywhere near A-site, and this included all non-tech. officers – the adjutant, the WAAF admin. officer, the RAF Regiment Officer, etc.

So you had a situation where everybody wearing a sparks badge on their arm would be spending three-quarters of their lives within a compound which some of their own officers and all the clerks, cooks, drivers, etc. on the camp were forbidden to enter and knew next to nothing about. Sometimes this did not make for easy relations – it was bound to be a difficult situation, especially for the WAAF admin. officers who were in charge of our welfare and discipline, but who probably had a suspicion that we were happy to be out of their reach most of the time. Which was perfectly true – we were!

In spite of this, the atmosphere on most radar stations was marvellous. Within such a small group of people, everyone knew everyone else; and the even smaller groups which made up the watches became very close-knit; friendships were formed which often lasted for life. We also had good friendships with our own mechanics, who looked after the equipment and shared our 'tea-swindle' suppers on the nightwatch. Marriages between radar folk were quite common.

The level of hardship resulting from the climatic conditions on most radar sites generated a terrific cameraderie – you *had* to cope, so you did cope, but you were glad of a willing pair of hands to help you.

On most stations, some of this hardship, plus the effects of working a watch system, were counteracted by organizing little concert parties and shows. All the local talent was pressed into service, and a lot of fun ensued, for both the performers and the audiences. There were always camp dances too, and liberty runs into the nearest town, with happy sing-songs in the back of the transport on the way home.

On watch, we could relax in the rest rooms, where we all spent time 'off the tube'. One hour on was the norm for operators; somebody had decided, quite rightly, that an hour at a time of staring into a CRT was enough for your eyes and your powers of concentration. So some of the watch was always in the quite comfortable little rest room brewing up tea, chatting, knitting, reading, writing letters and, on nightwatches, frying up eggs and bacon to keep body and soul together.

Nobody who worked on radar is likely to forget that miserable feeling around two in the morning, when your body was at its lowest ebb, crying out to be asleep, yet having to force itself to stay awake. The atmosphere, especially in an underground ops room, was really awful – dry and soporific, with incessant humming from electrical apparatus.

And yet there were many compensations, not least the feeling of intense pride we all had from doing a difficult, technical and highly-secret job. Everybody on radar felt that they were doing *the* job and wouldn't have done any other. And as far as one knows, every single soul kept their mouths shut throughout the war about what they were doing. (Even within one station, where there were different radars, one didn't discuss what one was doing with people working on a different radar.)

This special ethos was quite amazingly rekindled fifty years later, when we started the big reunions, 700-strong or more, with ex-radar folk coming from Canada, the US, New Zealand, South Africa – all suddenly re-experiencing that feeling of pride in ourselves and in the job we had done all those years before.

The reunions also served as a reminder of some of the enchanting names of the radar stations, which will surely ring a nostalgic bell with all who ever heard them, either through serving on some of them or talking to them on the intercom. Most of them were the names of tiny villages or simply local areas known by those names. How about Tilly Whim, Stoke Holy Cross, High Street, Stenigot, Gibbet Hill, Canewdon, Truleigh Hill, School Hill, Windyhead Hill, Burifa Hill, Sligo, Brandy Bay, Rosehearty, Ottercops, Bawdsey – names to bring the memories back?

Fred Moore, *ex-Radar Mechanic, remembers his days on 7K at Windyhead Hill in the middle of Aberdeenshire, 1942–4*:

I remember the contractors drilling for water outside our sleeping quarters at all hours of the day and night. They never found any, and so we continued to be supplied by tanker for a short period, then the Powers That Be decided it would

Fred Moore

be cheaper to pump water from the *dhustrath*,[1] and we could make do with that. The water was fine for washing in, but the taste was foul, and it turned tea into a muddy purple liquid with an appalling taste.

I remember coming out of the mess after breakfast one windy morning in time to see the roof of the MT garage take off like a gigantic albatross and fly away out to sea in the Moray Firth.

I remember the pub in Pennan, which was so small that six bods made a crowd. I made a return visit recently, and it will now hold about twenty! All the fishing boats have gone from the little harbour, and the cottages are now mostly occupied by weekenders from Aberdeen.

I remember collecting seagulls' eggs on the cliffs near Pennan, and I had a very near squeak there, almost plunging down 500 ft below. The seagulls' eggs were really excellent with chips, which we fried in any fat we could scrounge from the cookhouse.

One day the CO gave a party for exceeding 100 days without a DOR (Daily Occurrence Report). On the very day of the party, the afternoon watch managed to slip up and receive one. (A DOR reported an occurrence of over two minutes' duration whenever the station was unserviceable for any reason, or out of phase – usually the Tx had tripped and we were unable to get it back in phase in time.)

Ernie Johnson, *Canadian Technical Officer*:

Ernie Johnson

I was always intrigued by radio. In the 1920s my older brother, on a farm 20 miles north of Winnipeg, put together a crystal set. This consisted of a copper wire 50 yards long, strung up in an east-west direction between the tops of two trees; a lead-in wire connected to a coil, cat's whisker, crystal, and earphones. Out of the contraption, wonder of wonders, came faintly, through earphones clamped tightly to your head, words and music.

Later on, a neighbour got a semicircular box that had glass tubes, wires and a speaker in it – all hooked up to a battery and a wire stretched between the tops of two trees in a north-south direction. With this device, a roomful of people could listen to old-time fiddling emanating from Shenandoah, Iowa.

Wonderment in my mind at this phenomenon continued, so when in 1941, the call went out for interested people to be trained as RCAF radio mechanics, I jumped at the chance.

Many radio and radar courses later, I became Technical Officer (TO) at Start Point, in south-west England. The station consisted of a 200 ft tower with a rotating

[1] The *dhustrath* was a heather-filled hollow where young men and maidens used to disappear on warm summer evenings!

microwave dish at the top and an operations hut at the bottom, full of WAAF bods gazing at cathode ray tubes. From the ops hut a 50 yard telephone wire stretched in a westerly direction to a Nissen hut and the telephone on my desk.

This was at the beginning of June 1944. The weather was stormy, and a flotilla of British warships proceeded westerly down the English Channel, then on 5 June came back again. On 6 June, masses of Allied aircraft passed overhead, heading for Normandy, directly across the Channel. D-Day was on, and RAF Start Point had a ringside seat, electronically speaking.

It was the next day – or perhaps two days later – that I sat in my office and decided to make a phone call. The PBX didn't respond when I lifted the receiver, so I impatiently flicked the cradle up and down with my finger. My finger *sizzled!*

Suspecting that a high-voltage wire had shorted to the phone line, I disconnected the incoming wire. In the process, the end of the disconnected wire passed close to a grounded metal pipe, resulting in an electric arc between the wire and the pipe. And lo and behold! a note of music – loud and clear – burst forth from the brilliant flash!

The explanation was simple. The BBC, a quarter of a mile inland from our station, was beaming radio programmes to the troops in Normandy, and our telephone line was picking up the full force of those powerful transmissions. The arc to the grounded pipe had acted as rectifier of the radio waves – hence the note of music!

Out of this elementary situation of course, a state-of-the-art radio had to be developed: a metal washbasin was duly grounded and half-filled with water, with a piece of cardboard floating in the middle. When the wire was allowed to arc to the piece of cardboard, a roomful of people could listen to the up-to-the-minute BBC news of the invasion!

'Deja-vu,' I mused, harking back to the copper wire stretched between the tops of two trees.

Squadron Leader Joe Pratt, *ex-Navigator/Bomb Aimer (Radar Operator Course, Yatesbury, 1945)*:

During 1945, when Schoolhill was due to close, I was sent to Longside, near Peterhead, with a dozen or so airmen to evacuate all stores from Cruden Bay (a Loran station). I headed this 'chain gang', and eventually I received orders from Group to dispose of all furniture, beds, chairs, settees and tons of coal over the cliff and into the sea.

Joe Pratt

I was very annoyed, and arranged for all stores to be placed in the coal compound (which was large, with plenty of space for the furniture, etc.). Then I went to see the only 'bobby' for miles around and told him that the coal compound was now full of goodies and would not be locked, and furthermore that the duty guard would not interfere with the removal of all items in the compound after dark that night.

It worked!

Pat Evans *(née Twohy), ex-WAAF Radar Operator at Brandy Bay*:

Pat Evans

It was in 1942 that I arrived in a remote Dorset village called Tyneham, with a radar station perched high on a hill overlooking it – the nearest railway station being Corfe Castle, and no public transport, so we spent our spare time walking, cycling or swimming in the cove called Worbarrow Bay which, although surrounded by barbed-wire, was not mined, so we could use the beach.

Just above the beach was a stone cottage where sisters Beattie and Wynne dispensed tea and buns to ever-hungry WAAF and RAF personnel. Many a romance flourished in that primitive cafe, where we sat at trestle tables, lit only by flickering oil lamps, sipping our tea or Camp coffee, with the occasional rare treat of a boiled egg.

I remember the path through the woods where the wild garlic scented the air and tainted the milk when the cows had strayed from their usual pastures.

There was a constant shortage of water – after all, the well, used to coping with the needs of a normal family, could hardly be expected to serve fifty or more women. Once a week a special 'bath-run' took us by truck to the Black Bear in Wareham for a welcome soak.

Over the hill at Lulworth Cove was, and still is, an Army Camp, and here we used to go to dances, to the music of Glenn Miller played by a superb Army dance band. After the last waltz there would be a roll call to round up stray WAAFs dallying with Army boyfriends before the lorry could return to Tyneham.

In 1943 the Army decreed that the village should be evacuated and henceforth used as a gunnery range. I learned with sadness that the villagers were forced to leave their homes and the whole area was closed. Nowadays it is possible most weekends to visit this once-idyllic place – the church has been fully restored and is full of photographs and other memorabilia of Tyneham's past.

Con Nottridge (née Robinson), *Shorthand-Typist at 60 Group, tells how the 'stuff' came on stream*:

Con Nottridge

60 Group headquarters was in a beautiful country house called Oxendon, near Leighton Buzzard in Bedfordshire. Only the very senior officers worked in the house itself, with the AOC occupying what would have been the main bedroom. The rest of us worked in Nissen huts built discreetly under trees in the grounds. My job was fascinating, working as a shorthand-typist to the officers at Group; none of us were ever posted if we had worked on the top-secret radar stuff (for fear of us talking).

My particular mob worked in technical group equipment, which meant our officers worked closely with the technical people, and as radar was changing all the time there were terrific panics to modify and rebuild radar units. All the stuff should have been obtained through usual channels, but that all went by the board and stuff was canibalized from all over the place. Even the sacred boffins at TRE Malvern released material after panic requests.

It was exciting work, and we had times when we worked very long hours, but it was so rewarding when target dates were met. One of the biggest panics was 72 Wing, which went over on D-Day plus three and was destined to be 5 miles behind enemy lines in mobile convoys. What rows there were at Group, between the technical people wanting a certain level of spares to go with them, and others wanting to be as light and mobile as possible.

Such rushes to get the equipment, and sighs of relief when it all got over there on schedule! But just before Christmas 1944, the Germans broke through the lines and 72 Wing blew up equipment to avoid it falling into enemy hands. The air was blue for a time as signals kept coming in reporting more equipment gone.

Maybe not many people know that the Powers That Be thought the Germans would react to the D-Day landings by bombing those radar stations in the south-east corner of England. To meet this possibility, those stations were duplicated, and all the bits and pieces comprising a duplicate station were hidden in obscure places like churches and cellars, so that at a given word it could all be assembled and the site put back on the air again. Thankfully, this was never necessary, but the work involved was enormous.

The Flight Lieutenant I worked for had the walls of his office lined with special graphs, and every bit of equipment was there. It was my first job each morning to insert coloured markers on each bit of equipment from signals which came in. Certain colours meant it was in hand, another colour meant on the way, and red meant it was actually on site. Before they all showed red, there were many panics. Fl. Lt. Venus himself went to some of the factories to try to hurry things up, and once he even sent me to TRE to pick up a special cathode ray tube.

Ken Humphries *recalls a filter room in the Orkneys*:

I was stationed at Kirkwall, in the Orkneys, in a filter room during the Battle of Britain. One day we had a hostile aircraft over Scapa Flow at a considerable height. He was so high that the ack-ack couldn't reach him, and it would have taken the Spitfires something like ten minutes to reach that height. He was known on the table as 'Hostile Photo Freddie'. He would take what photos he wanted to and then set off in a shallow dive back to Norway, reaching something like 500 m.p.h. He carried no guns – only a camera.

Ken Humphries

Of course, we also used to have our own 'Photo Freddie', going from Wick over Norway, similarly fitted out, but the hostile pilot got on to our wavelength one day, and over our loudspeakers came his voice. Our call-sign was 'Sinclair Control' (after Archibald Sinclair, who was Air Minister at the time), and loud and clear came the German pilot, in perfect English, saying: 'Hello, Sinclair Control, this is Fruity calling. Are your fighters going to intercept me?' Then he laughed like mad, knowing full well that they couldn't catch him.

Note: Ken Humphries was later a member of 8009 AMES (see pp. 127 and 181).

Colin Latham, *ex-Mechanic Instructor at Yatesbury*:

Colin Latham

The first and most obvious impression at an east coast CH was undoubtedly the appearance of the aerial towers. But even the relatively modest masts of the west coast pattern made their presence felt. In either case, one could have no doubt that here was an installation of some significance.

Probably the first building you would see inside would be the R-block. A narrow gap in the thick concrete anti-blast walls, a blackout light-trap, airlock doors and a narrow passage would lead at last to the door of the receiver room. First thought – what a lot of equipment, and what are these half-dozen or so RAF and WAAF bods up to, working quietly and intently in the carefully-graded low lighting, just sufficient for those writing or reading; the library-like hush broken only by calm voices giving ranges, bearings, heights and plots against the background of a low-level 50 Hz hum from sundry power transformers, and the warmish, faintly sickly aroma from the brown, polished linoleum floor.

After a bit, you would realize that the equipment was duplicated: only one of the RF6/7 sets was in use and the centre of attention. A mechanic was playing with controls on the standby set, which was also running, but nobody paid attention to him. The girl at the main receiver was quietly attending to her tubeful of echoes, not only d/f-ing and checking the range of each in turn, but managing as well to flick height buttons, take a gonio reading of theta-H, and flick again to give the calculator angle plus range to work on before she passed on to the next.

Her voice was feeding data into her mouthpiece: how did she remember the idents of each and at the same time keep alert for new, unidentified echoes coming in, mainly at longer ranges?

Somehow she did. Her telephone headset was connected to that other girl, across the room, bent over the plotting table. With a ruler pivoted against a scale of degrees, and calibrated in miles, she was plotting every range/bearing combination, adding height and ident.

Her partner, with headset connected to far-away Filter Room, passed the National Grid Reference plots down the line and received back idents for new echoes. She would have no difficulty in this. Some far-sighted person had wisely called for the installation of high-quality secure landline circuits, many of them even before the war.

The tactile nature of CH work was part of its attraction. For operators, the gonio and the range tube became extensions of the body. The successful detection of a distant echo, at first hardly discernible from 'noise'; the formation of its track; its identification as a genuine hostile, and – if things went well – news of its interception, formed a sequence as satisfying as any fisherman's golden dream.

For mechanics, there was joy in setting up the receivers where every control worked smoothly and well; and as for the transmitters, one could feel one had achieved something worthwhile in running them up and keeping them on the air.

If you were to stand still, perhaps at the close of a fine summer's day, and gaze up into the vast array of dipoles that made up the CH transmitting curtain, you would most probably hear the sound of the light evening wind singing through the wires. But you'd also hear a curious ticking – not locatable by turning the head, but all around, faint yet unmistakable: twenty-five ticks per second – presumably the combined result of countless tiny movements and discharges for every multi-hundred-kilowatt pulse. It was as if the CH were some great live and friendly guardian beast.

And if you were anywhere on the east or south coasts of England after the fall of France, and you looked out in the direction of the line of shoot, you would have been facing enemy territory. Raids could come from any part of it at any time and it was comforting that not only your CH but its fellows, and the CHLs, and all the others too, were all on the air – the whole vast chain, linked up and running.

If it is possible to feel genuine affection for inanimate equipment, then we certainly felt it for CH. At times, long hours and watch systems resulted in much weariness. But the very special cameraderie of the RAF/WAAF teams made it all worthwhile.

The camaraderie of radar personnel.

Gerry Funston, *RCAF Radar Mechanic*:

[*Note*: Gerry served in the UK in the Second World War and is nowadays active in Canada, maintaining wartime radar memories. Like many Canadians, he served on a wide variety of equipments and stations.]

Gerry Funston

After I joined up in June 1942, I was directed to the Central Technical School in Toronto for basic electrical/electronic training. In addition to this school, many universities across Canada provided similar courses – for instance, McMaster in Hamilton, Queen's in Kingston, and the University of Toronto, where all the first Radio Direction Finding Technicians (as they were then called) took their basic course. This took from ten to twelve weeks, during which most of us lived at home and wore civvies. Our working uniform was Air Force-issue overalls. While officially in the Royal Canadian Air Force, we were assigned to the War Emergency Training Program for the duration of the course.

My time at Central Tech. was extended by several weeks to do some instructing: a bit like the blind leading the blind. In mid-December 1942, I was required to report to No. 1 Manning Depot, RCAF, occupying the Coliseum and other adjacent buildings at the Canadian National Exhibition, Toronto, for indoctrination into the regular Air Force. Here we had square-bashing, inoculations, uniform and equipment issue, and the exalted rank of LAC was bestowed upon us.

The Coliseum and the adjacent sheep pens had been converted into sleeping quarters. Double-tiered bunks lined the pens, and the air was heavy with disinfectant. The Coliseum and sheep display rings were used for the daily drill exercises (which was at least preferable to being out of doors in the wintry blast).

March 1943 saw me in transit to No. 31 RDF School at Clinton, Ontario, where most Canadian mechs took their training. In addition, there was a small contingent of Americans representing their four segments of the Armed Forces. At that time, Clinton was under the direction and control of the RAF.

During the next few months we were exposed to the wonders of AI, ASV, (air-to-surface radar), IFF, BABS, CH and CHL – six weeks on airborne radar, and eight on ground radar.

At the end of the course, in June 1943, I was posted to the UK on the troopship *Queen Elizabeth*. After two months' familiarization at St Bees, near Whitehaven in Cumberland, I was en route to RAF Doonies Hill, a CHL station on the coast, just south of the mouth of the Dee, at the entrance to Aberdeen harbour. Doonies was one of the satellites of the CH at School Hill, near Portlethan. After only three months here, I was posted in December 1943 to the CH station at Loth. This was on the east coast in Sutherlandshire, between Brora and Helmsdale, about halfway between Wick and Inverness.

[*Note*: In his recollections, Gerry goes on to describe how, like many in the

RAF, he underwent a frantic series of radar postings including CHL St Bees; CHL Doonies Hill; CH Loth; CHL Cocklaw and then the Yatesbury Centimetre Course where he met Canadian chaps he'd sailed over with, though they, being on the super-secret 9K course, were billeted separately.

He was then whizzed off to Scotland (The Law, near Douglas Wood CH) en route to a centimetre station, Lamberton Moor. He actually achieved a whole year there before undergoing an RAF Regiment battle course at Staines as a forerunner to a commissioning course. But the demand for officers then fell, and it was back to Lamberton Manor, before a Gee course at Yatesbury and posting to Stenigot 7K.

A head-spinning career, but worth it, for of Stenigot he says: 'It was there that I met Freda, a 7K Operator and my wife-to-be.']

Gerry continues:

I was always amused at the extent of our protection while on duty in the operational Tx unit – a lone Sten gun! A German commando raid on the station would have met little resistance – one hand grenade in the doorway would have sufficed. The fact that the defence authorities probably knew more about the likelihood of this occurring than we did offered little reassurance that it might not happen. Admission to the tech. blocks was strictly controlled by a password, which was changed daily – a dubious requirement.

Because of surges and variations in the electrical power, you had to be alert to the possibility of the Tx 'tripping'. This occurred whenever there was a power overload and the safety overload switches cut the H.T. power to the main output valves. When this happened, the mech. on duty had to re-set the H.T. to get the Tx and the station back on the air within one minute. If not, the officer or sergeant i/c watch would be on the blower from the Rx block for an explanation.

We developed a system that would ring a bell whenever the H.T. power went off, and this allowed us to put the first-aid stretcher behind the Tx and have a nap. Our reflexes became so highly tuned that we would wake up at the sound of the click of the overload switch cutting out, and be up and around to the front of the Tx winding up the H.T. almost before the bell sounded.

At Doonies Hill we were all billeted off site. I was put in a flat in Torry, an area of Aberdeen near the harbour. For the first time I was supplied with ration coupons and exposed to the meagre civilian rations, with mine having to be shared out with the landlady and her two young children. The weekly ration per person was 2 oz of butter, ½ lb of margarine and lard, ½ lb of sugar, one egg (if lucky) or egg powder, ½ lb of bacon and ½ lb of meat. Biscuits, tea and sweets were all on coupons, and if you used them all in the first week you had to wait another three weeks before you got the next lot.

During my brief stay at Cocklaw, on only one occasion did I observe any action on the GCI unit. This was when a German aircraft was picked up at about 150 miles and subsequently identified as a weather observation plane, or 'Weather Willie'. These planes made periodic sorties from Norway. As this one closed in towards the coast, the controller scrambled three Spitfires from Peterhead. He was using a form of slide rule calculator (the Craig Calculator) which was mounted on the PPI console and was made up of several circular and semi-circular calibrated segments. The bearing, range, estimated speed and height of the 'Weather Willie', derived from the plots, was quickly locked into this calculator mechanism. The controller, who had by then established radio contact with the Spitfires, began to read off the bearing or vector, speed and height for the pilots to follow and intercept the hostile.

The conversation between the controller and pilots could be heard on a speaker, and it quickly became evident that for some unknown reason one of the 'Spits' had crashed on take-off – only two 'friendly' blips were appearing on the PPI. It was intriguing to watch these blips gradually close in on the hostile as the controller revised his calculations and gave corrections to the pilots. While the calculator was primitive by today's standards, it did its job.

Finally, at a range of about 4 miles, one of the pilots yelled 'Tally-ho!', confirming visual contact. A few seconds later we heard the sound of machine-guns being fired, and then 'Weather Willie' disappeared from the screen.

In September, off I went again for a repatriation posting to Torquay! Believing that this posting would result in a fairly quick return to Canada, we decided that Freda would join me in Canada, where we would get married. But I languished in Torquay until December, and so we decided to be married on 10 December 1945. Following our honeymoon in Edinburgh, I returned to Torquay on 21 January 1946, and a group of us left on the *Isle de France* for Halifax, Nova Scotia.

Delayed by severe North Atlantic gales, we finally arrived in Halifax on 27 January. Thence by train to Lachine, and at last, on 1 February, I arrived at Union Station, Toronto, to a great family welcome. Three years and eight months, and *fourteen* postings after I joined up!

I was demobbed at No. 1 Manning Depot on 12 February, and Freda followed on the *Aquitania* on 27 July, as a war bride. And half a century on, we are still happily married!

Bob Clifford, *Radar Mechanic, English – yet serving in the Royal Canadian Air Force*:

Bob Clifford

The outbreak of war saw me at an American school on one of the exchanges organized by the English Speaking Union. I did a year at Phillips Academy in Massachusetts, followed by another year at Harvard. I was 19 in the summer of 1941, and well aware that my age group was being called up at home. But I couldn't get home!

So the next best thing seemed to be to enlist in Canada. I applied to join the RCAF, intending to transfer to the RAF when I got back to

England. (That idea was quickly forgotten when I compared the pay and conditions of service in the RCAF overseas with those of the RAF.)

Rejected for aircrew through an eye defect, I was offered a course in RDF – very hush-hush. We started out at Quebec, with new uniforms and boots, at Valcartier square-bashing camp, where I met quite a number of Americans joining the Canadian forces: some out of deep conviction for the Allies' cause; some for the hell of it, and a good many to escape the embarrassing attentions of the US police.

After several weeks of footslogging through the woods, we were posted to the Royal Military College at Kingston, with marvellous views over Lake Ontario, for six weeks' instruction in electricity and magnetic fields, but our more serious radio training started in January 1942, at the University of New Brunswick at Fredericton, where the course was intensive and we all had to build a radio set from a boxful of components. What a relief when it actually worked and could be tuned through its wavebands – how brilliant we were! We were lodged in the basement of the gymnasium, with snow well up over the little windows every morning and temperatures down to forty below outside.

My next destination was the RAF Training School for Radar at Clinton, Ontario, where we were introduced to real transmitters and receivers, oscilloscopes and square waves, calibrations and the lethal potential of 18,000 volts of high tension.

The canteen was dreadful, but fortunately, the Canadians made complaints, and in May an energetic RCAF Flight Lieutenant made a three-day visit observing conditions. Two weeks later, the existing RAF canteen staff departed, to be replaced by trained RCAF canteen staff and admin. liaison. The standard of food and cleanliness shot up, and our morale with it.

Having successfully passed, we found ourselves in due course taking the long journey to Halifax, Nova Scotia, where we would set sail for the UK. Our ship was a modern Empress-class passenger and cargo boat built for the meat trade; needless to say, our bunks were in the lowest of the refrigerator holds, way below the water line, with vertical steel ladders to climb if a hasty exit might be required.

I spent my first night back in my own country sleeping on the floor of a school. Then next day, our RDF contingent – about fifty of us – were put on a train which took us through the gardens of Kent (early August) and down to Hastings. A week later found us in Bournemouth, sharing some of the finest hotels with other services (Free French, Norwegians, Poles, etc.). We heard Lord Haw-Haw speaking from Germany and assuring us that he knew all our moves – most comforting.

At this time I managed to wangle three days' leave and saw my parents again for the first time in three years; and my sister and brother soon arrived too. It was a marvellous reunion, even if my mother did vow to leave home if my trans-Atlantic accent didn't disappear.

I returned to Bournemouth to learn that another mechanic and I were posted to Seaham Harbour in County Durham – just about as far from home as it could be!

But after a short while a posting came through for me to Ventnor, and I spent my twenty-first birthday travelling to and from 75 Wing HQ, somewhere in Kent; thence to the Portsmouth ferry – past the stacks and masts of sunken boats off Ryde – then by train across the island, through the final tunnel into Ventnor station.

At the camp I met several 'veteran' Canadians (who all demanded an explanation of my Canadian status) and an unfeeling sergeant who refused my plea for leave to make up for my lost coming-of-age birthday ('Don't yer know there's a war on?').

A-site was surrounded by a high spiked fence with coils of barbed wire, the gate bolted and guarded by armed soldiers. There were large, well-lit underground rooms for the WAAF operators, and sleeping bunks and toilets and electric rings for kettles and toast – such luxury, after Seaham with its little gaggle of two trailers and two huts.

My first job was with a Type 271 transmitter (CHEL) under a New Zealand sergeant and a Canadian corporal, who both seemed to know every nut and bolt and every possible fault and how to keep things working.

There were always parties of boffins visiting from TRE Malvern. One such was followed by two truckloads of an experimental outfit which I believe was the first of the ultra-short-wave units which quickly came to dominate the range of equipment. Reception at all altitudes down to sea level was fantastic: we could almost monitor the enemy airfields across the Channel. When we reported to the Navy at Portsmouth that we were tracking a group of German E-boats coming to raid in the Solent we were met with disbelief and no response until too late when a dozen small ships were burning and the Germans safely away again.

The following year, a special heightfinder arrived, with a sliced parabola instead of a dish, and by then, of course, the magnetron had become the standard power output device, supplanting those cumbersome thermionic valves. The heightfinder was mounted on a turntable so that it could 'look' or 'sweep' from side to side as well as up and down.

One day, a report came through of an American bomber down in the Channel, with an approximate fix. So the jolly rig was dusted off and re-tuned and calibrated, and after searching a choppy sea for fifteen minutes, we found the bomber, and for once the Navy sent a boat in the right direction quickly, and the crew got safely back.

We had a pleasant off-duty life at Ventnor, aided and abetted by our admin. officer, who took the view that a mech's time off-duty required the minimum of chores. So there were trips round the coast on the little scenic railways, regular dances at the Winter Gardens, a good local cinema, and pubs and cafes, especially the Café Suisse, where Madame Zucker somehow managed to produce sugared pastries and creamy delights. There were no summer holidaymakers, of course, and the beaches were festooned with anti-landing-boat spikes and tank-traps; but we had the place to ourselves, and the tides came in through the spikes for many sunny days of swimming.

My last year of service was spent on the Suffolk coast at Greyfriars, near the old sunken capital town of Dunwich, where the wind off the North Sea eroded the cliff face a few feet every year and the old monks' cemetery yielded up a few bones rolling in on the sands below almost every week.

Here we were mainly engaged with the Doodlebugs, which we had already seen on the south coast, of course. By late autumn 1944 some of the gunners had moved to the Suffolk coast and achieved really first-class shooting success.

Being an overseas Canadian brought unexpectedly early demob for me, with generous offers of either farming land or college courses in Canada, or remaining in England. I took my demob suit off the rack at Canada House in Trafalgar Square, and they paid my college fees at Oxford, and again at music college. In addition, I received a married living allowance for three years; we have recently had our forty-eighth anniversary, and the grandchildren are super. Thank you, RCAF.

Alfred ('Bill') Evans, *Radar Mechanic, UK and France*:

In 1939 I was 16 and mad about aeroplanes; I knew every detail and was an ace spotter. My father, the local police inspector/ARP boss had to visit the Observer Corps posts, and when he took me with him, you can imagine how pleased they all were when a spotty character with 16-year-old eyes would identify aircraft every time better and faster than they could! I still cringe at the thought.

So at 17¾, off I went to Shrewsbury to join as aircrew. They failed me with a 'lazy' eye, and I cried all the way home. But at 18 I joined up at Padgate, then did square-bashing at Blackpool, where Max Wall was our corporal (I still walk slightly eccentrically).

February 1942 saw me at Wythall, HQ of Barrage Balloons, where they also looked after the *ab initio* RAF courses at Birmingham Tech. Here I did a seventeen-week course of basic electrical/electronic engineering, and a very good course it was.

Then it was off to Yatesbury for training on CH (RF7, RM3A and MB2). We were a mixture of 18-year-olds like myself (who knew nothing about anything but had minds like sponges ready to learn anything) and rather older bods from radio repair shops, who were brilliant at 'hands-on' work, but had got fixed (and in some cases slightly wrong) ideas of how, say, a pentode worked. Consequently, many of us sailed through the exams, becoming AC1s, while some much better practical mechanics had a bit of a struggle.

Out of a total of 20 passing out, 19 English and Welsh were posted north of Inverness, and the lone Scot to Bournemouth! I went off to Sango, east of Cape Wrath. It was winter 1942. Horizontal rain. A man beside me was literally blown to the ground by the gale. We had all hoped to find WAAFs there, but they never did appear (thanks to the horizontal rain and gales perhaps?). So I passed the time in studying the history of the clans of the far north, the topography (Sango is pure Scandinavian) and the Ossianic folk stories. There was a corporal there who had given his religion as 'Cathode Follower', and he was excused all church parades.

Presently, we had a trade test. The CO (Flt. Lt. Goldhamer, a Canadian) sat on his desk with legs swinging, and the mechs all lined up in front of him. He asked me: 'How do you run up an MB2?' That was my only question. We all passed, and the resultant exalted rank of LAC had to last me right through to demob.

We were working on a plan to build a sand-yacht and run it on the superb strand of nearby Balnakill Bay when fate intervened and I was posted to the Outer Hebrides.

Later, I went to Clee Hill – unbelievable, a Salopian posted to Shropshire! But not for long, of course – one forty-eight-hour pass later I was hustled off to RAF Grangewood near Hastings. Here we learned that there would be no course on the gear, which turned out to be the new fixed Gee-H (or 'Heavy Hundred') station, sited to work with High Street in East Anglia, to 'do' for the Germans in the Pas de Calais and beyond.

At age 20, more exciting than the equipment was the delightful novelty of working with real female operators! We were in billets in Hastings, with the technical site on the cliffs at Fairlight. This was exposed to more than the elements, as we found when the V1s started, Fairlight being on a direct line between many of their launch sites and London. The V1s were mass-produced and not always reliable – some flew so low that they thumped into our cliffs and exploded.

On 4 July 1944, the control of the V1 defence was assigned to ADGB and a high-power MEW No. 2 set up by us at Fairlight. It could 'see' low down, and it picked up the V1s between 25 and 50 miles from the coast. AA guns moved in around the site, and after Sango and Broad Bay, I felt in the midst of things.

But we still found time off duty for long bike rides, rambles, cricket matches and visits to places such as Bodiam Castle, which though closed for the duration, would open up when five or six RAF characters appeared. The St Leonards squash courts, also closed, nevertheless allowed us to play.

Together with TAF2, using Mosquitoes and Mitchells, we helped to disrupt communications and German Army HQ in the Pas de Calais. Some of the bombing, according to aircrew who (all too infrequently) visited us, was amazingly accurate. The 'Mossies' were fast but vulnerable; the Mitchells were lumbering but could carry a lot of shot. If we went off the air two minutes before 'time over target' and the Mossies had to go round twice, the accurate AA fire often got them. It certainly made us mechs work quickly (and burn our hands) after hearing that piece of feedback.

D-Day came without us initially knowing any more than anyone else, although an extended exercise in the Channel seemed strange. This turned out to be the famous phantom invasion fleet proceeding steadily across the narrow strait, produced by 'window' which was dropped by expert bomber crews flying in large circles, so that their creeping curtain of window appeared on German radar screens to be an advancing fleet. (see p. 137).

We received General Eisenhower's message, and we men wondered if we would be crossing the straits shortly ourselves, leaving our lovely WAAFs behind.

It was October/November before Austin six-wheeler trucks arrived and the CO (Flt. Lt. Peter Harrild, see p. 155) and several of us were posted as the core of AMES 117 – a 'Heavy Hundred' or Mobile Gee-H unit.

An Rx and a Tx were shoehorned into trucks and got going. I foolishly painted, very neatly, 'TAF60/117' on the front of my own truck, only to be told promptly to paint the other seven!

There was a spate of marriages before we left, including the CO, whose wife Joy made me promise to write to her regularly and tell her how her new husband was faring. I had known Joy longer than he had, and I carried out her request faithfully, which led to a piquant situation, since her husband had to censor all our letters!

Some truly sad goodbyes later, we moved off to Renscombe to be united with more bods and trucks. Conditions here were primitive. Twenty of us in a Nissen hut miles from anywhere were woken up by a man putting a bucket of water in the hut and indicating that this was ablutions (I was about the seventh to wash in it).

BAWDSEY – WHERE IT ALL BEGAN

Note: The following is an extract from a guide for visitors produced by the last commanding officer of RAF Bawdsey, **Squadron Leader D. Rothery**, by whose kind permission it is reproduced.

Serious Radar research started in May 1935 at Orfordness, a site quickly found to be far from ideal. The scientists soon 'discovered' Bawdsey; the Air Ministry bought the manor and grounds from the second Sir Cuthbert Quilter for £24,000, and the team moved there in February 1936. The radar station was handed over to the RAF in May 1937, but scientists continued to develop it as not only the first operational but also the most comprehensive radar station, serving as a model for the three varieties which were hurriedly erected in various combinations to face the growing threat: 19 covering the east coast and 6 the south.

Simultaneously, work went on to compress the bulky equipment to fit into an aircraft. This enabled a radar-equipped nightfighter Blenheim to be airborne over London on the first night of the war. That day, the research establishment was evacuated to Dundee.

The radar chain became the crucial element in the great air battle fought over Britain in the summer and autumn of 1940. It allowed Fighter Command so to conserve its effort that a numerically inferior force was able to beat back an enemy which would otherwise have overwhelmed it. The German commander later said: 'the British had an extraordinary advantage: their radar and fighter-control network. It was for us a very bitter surprise; we had nothing like it.' It had involved an enormous effort: all the work was done, supervised or inspired by the Bawdsey team.

Postwar, Bawdsey remained a major radar station and training school until 1974. Then, after nearly five years, it re-opened in July 1979 as an air defence surface-to-air Bloodhound missile unit: C Flight of No. 85 Squadron. The only reminders now of the early radar days are the porch plaque and 325 ft of one of the original masts.

Olive Carlisle *(née Marshall) remembers Bawdsey*:

Little cameos of half a century ago come popping through the cobwebs of a neglected memory, and once again I can smell the lavender on the terraces in front of Bawdsey Manor, and the leather and polished wood inside, and roam down the winding passage through the rocks towards the sea, or chug across on the ferry to Felixstowe. What a contrast from the straitjacket of Yatesbury – and a fairytale stepping stone to a wonderfully exciting life of travel, finishing in 1945 in Mons and Bonn as Signals Radar Officer.

Colin Latham *recalls*:

Most ex-RAF/WAAF folk have their favourite station – usually where they were happiest in wartime or did their most memorable work. One person's choice is not always another's, but one station whose charms no one seems to dispute is Bawdsey.

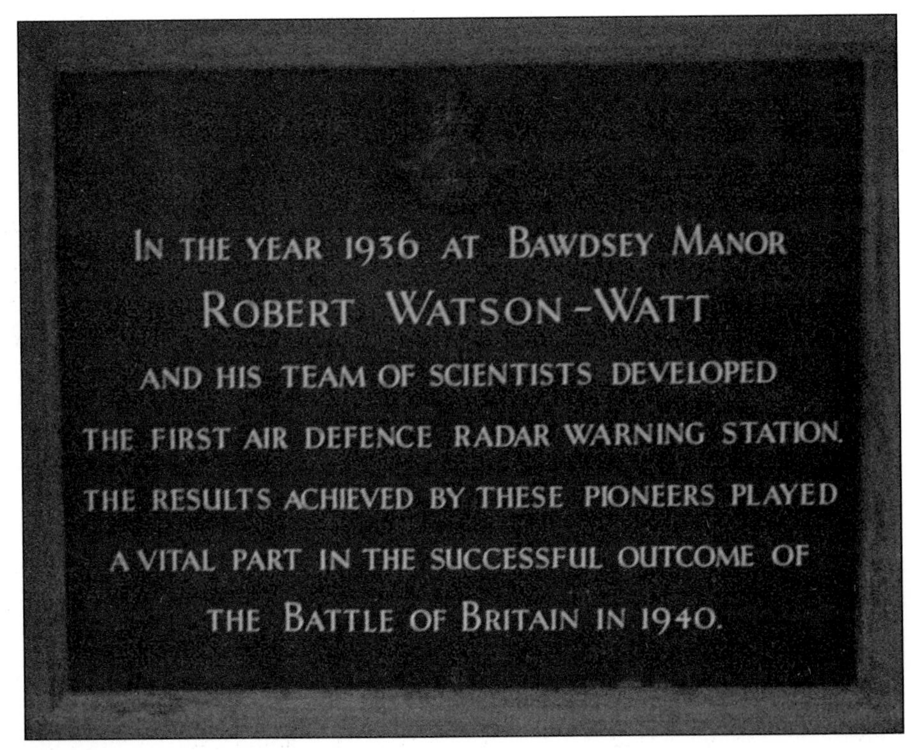

The memorial plaque at Bawdsey Manor.

Not only was Bawdsey the home of the early pioneers before the war, it was also a leading radar station throughout the war and on through the cold war. In wartime it had CH, CHL, centimetric radars, J-Watch and other novelties – all in the unique setting of the Manor, with its turrets, attractive outbuildings and exotic gardens. It faced the sea, backed by soft Suffolk countryside, and the traditional access by ferryboat across the River Deben enhanced the sense of charm and mystery.

Where else could airmen eat in such an unservicelike dining hall, be billeted in attractive huts beneath sweet-smelling pine trees, or WAAFs sleep in a Manor House with views of the sea or river? What other RAF station had gardens with nooks and crannies and grottoes in which to wander freely when off duty or seek out hidden paths down to the sea – and all within the one enchanting technical-domestic site?

Accounts of the pioneering work at Bawdsey show that the team was hard at it, striving round the clock to develop ground-based and airborne radar for the inevitable war. Yet the spirit was far from oppressive, as the following anecdotes from Sidney Jefferson illustrate.

Before the war, Sidney drew up the specifications to which the CH receivers were built. He also set the trend for the many successful marriages between radar men and women which were to follow, by marrying Nellie Boyce, one of the first three women radar operators, picked personally from the civilian secretarial staff by Watson Watt; his confidence was amply justified by their performance, and led directly to operator training for service women.

Sidney Jefferson, *a member of Watson Watt's technical staff:*

The ferryman at Bawdsey achieved undying fame. There was an item which appeared in the official list of equipment at radar stations called the 'Brinkley'. It was an earthing device to discharge high-voltage capacitors to avoid accidental shocks. It consisted of a metal hook, connected to 'ground' by means of a thick cable on the end of a stick. It was named after Charlie Brinkley, Bawdsey's ferryman, who had lost a hand which had been replaced by a hook.

Sidney and Nellie Jefferson

When A.P. Rowe replaced Watson Watt as superintendent at Bawdsey, he thought the habits of the mess (about twenty young men) were too casual, so he thought he would instigate dressing for dinner! When this became known there was unanimous revolt – not surprising, since some of us went back to work after dinner and very few had dinner jackets. As Mess Secretary, I had to point out to Rowe that it was 'no go'. Some long time later, he reminded me of the incident, saying: 'You were the leader of the anti-Rowe brigade.' However, this did not prevent him – later on, when we had moved to Dundee and afterwards to Swanage – from asking me to play golf with him almost every weekend, and to help him to choose a motor car.

Razor-sharp wit

One evening, Burge brought an electric razor into the lounge and announced that he had just bought it from Bainbridge-Bell (a senior pre-war scientist at Bawdsey). He put it down on the mantlepiece and left the room – just long enough for someone to put a piece of wire in the razor's main socket to produce a dead short.

Next morning, we were ready and waiting for Burge to announce that he had blown the fuse in his bedroom. While he was busy explaining this, the shorting wire was being removed from the razor. We recommended him to complain to Bainbridge-Bell, and suggested that the razor might have a heavy starting current!

Bainbridge-Bell was sympathetic and set up a CRT to measure the starting current, which was less than 200 mA and usually no greater than the running current. The shorting wire was replaced and removed on a random schedule, and one evening I found Burge crouching in a corner of the dining room. He explained that he had an important date that evening and thought he was more likely to get a shave if he used a 15 amp socket!

THE DAY WINSTON CHURCHILL CAME TO BAWDSEY

Sir Edward Fennessy, CBE, *Bawdsey Research Station and Staff 60 Group, recalls*:

It was 20 June 1939 – just another busy day of research and development at Bawdsey. But arriving in our various labs, we found a message awaiting us from A.P. Rowe, our chief. As best I can remember, it read: 'Mr Winston Churchill who is interested in the air defence of Great Britain will visit Bawdsey today.' There followed details of demonstrations to be given. We were all to lunch in the Manor with our distinguished guest.

Churchill arrived, and the Bawdsey CH was demonstrated, an interception flown and lively discussions held on our future plans.

Following lunch in the mess, Churchill addressed us, and after fifty-five years I still recall the essence of his speech:

'Today has been one of the most exciting days of my life, for you have shown me the weapon with which we shall defeat the Nazis. But gentlemen, you still have one problem to solve. Let me illustrate it for you. I am a German pilot flying across the North Sea, briefed to bomb London. I am a very frightened pilot, for I know that with your wonderful invention you are watching my every move. But I cross the English coast and I am a very happy pilot. Why is that? Because I have flown from the 20th Century into the early Stone Age. And that, Gentlemen, is the problem you must solve.'

Now Churchill was telling us nothing we did not know. CH tracking was excellent until the target crossed the coast, but once inland, accuracy fell off badly, and Observer Corps watchers peering out from hilltops like primitive man had to try and pick up the track. Churchill's graphic illustration brought it vividly home to us and encouraged our further work.

Exhilarated by what we had shown him (though not by the lunch, which I recall lacked any stimulants), Churchill departed to visit Dr 'Taffy' Bowen at Martlesham, to be shown the early airborne radar development.

Taffy Bowen recalls how – when offered tea – the great man called for a large brandy (perhaps to celebrate what he had been shown), which the mess promptly provided.

Within the year, Churchill was Prime Minister and taking a very lively direct interest in all our work.

[*Note*: Mr Churchill's valid concern about the lack of inland radar cover in 1939 was laid to rest a little later on as the all-round-looking CHL and GCI stations, described in Chapters 3 and 4, became operational.]

A NOTE ABOUT BAWDSEY TODAY

The Manor with its surrounding grounds, recently sold by the Ministry of Defence into private ownership, has now become Bawdsey College, where young people from many countries throughout the world are boarded and taught the English language.

The college's declared policy is to preserve the history of Bawdsey's unique part in radar development and to bring it to the attention of their students. Some may well be descendents of those who in the past have been this country's adversaries; thus Bawdsey has passed from being an instrument of war to one of peace and goodwill.

It is the intention of the college management to maintain close contact with the Bawdsey Reunion Association and to build up a collection of wartime radar memorabilia for the benefit of all who may be interested.

The Bawdsey Reunion Association still meets for an annual lunch. Details of the Association may be obtained from: Squadron Leader F.L. Fear, Julians, Colchester Road, Wakes Colne, Colchester, CO6 2AF.

EPILOGUE

How Radar Has Matured Since the War

In little more than a decade after Arnold Wilkins's Daventry demonstration, the war ended. In that brief historic period a new and vast technology had been built up. Designs were established for equipments capable of early warning, heightfinding, airborne interception, precise navigation and the auto-following of targets for anti-aircraft gunnery, and much more. Wide operational experience had been gained, much data amassed and many engineering and scientific papers prepared. Radar had come of age.

What, then, of the next fifty years? How, after all that concerted, high-pressure effort, could any goals of significance have remained?

A parallel can be seen in the evolution of motor cars. The most up-to-date mass-produced models in 1945 (actually, pre-war designs) could be described in general terms still valid today: 'integral steel body/chassis, independent front suspension, water-cooled overhead-valve petrol engine, 12 V electrical system with automatic regulator, dry single-plate clutch, synchromesh gearbox, hydraulic brakes, sun-roof and radio, safety glass all round'. Yet, within that same description, the production car of today is vastly superior in so many ways. It is faster, quieter, handles better, is roomier, less thirsty and covers comparatively enormous mileages with less maintenance. The transformation is not the result of a radically different concept but of steady development in which every detail, from the way the fuel enters the engine to the rubber that contacts the road, has been examined and improved.

So has it been with radar. While the basic principles remain, every item and detail has been improved step by step. While modern long-range early-warning radars – the descendants of CH – do not provide enormously increased maximum range, since the curvature of the earth is a limitation, they do give strong, consistent and accurate plots on quite small aircraft at all heights and out to distances where CH echoes, if seen at all, would have been weak, unreliable and of poor bearing accuracy. Consequently, the total amount of radar data produced is considerably higher.

With a few special exceptions, most modern radars – whether for defensive early-warning purposes or for civil air traffic control – work on wavelengths substantially less than 1 m, i.e. they are microwave radars. Thus, well-defined beams of radiation may be achieved with aerial arrays of manageable size. Ten centimetres, the wavelength of the original wartime microwave radars, continues to be popular, although for long-range work it may sometimes be at a disadvantage in seeing small targets through dense rain. For this and other reasons, wavelengths around 25 cm are sometimes preferred for long-range early warning (see Appendix).

Probably the major and most obvious improvements since the war have been in clutter reduction – the ability to see targets against a background of unwanted returns, whether fixed ('permanent echoes') or as a result of slowly-moving precipitation. This is the main reason why modern radar displays are so clean and easy to observe; but, hand in hand with this, there have been numerous significant improvements in the design of the displays themselves. Brightness is high enough for viewing without recourse to dimmed or special lighting; focus and definition are excellent, and the introduction of what was first termed 'intertrace marking' allows much additional information to be presented directly on the PPI, close to each echo. Thus the observer, whether military operator or civil air traffic controller, is aided by 'labels' against each response on the radar screen to indicate the identity and height of aircraft, together with outline maps of features such as coastlines or civil air lanes. Defence radars may produce heights automatically; ATC radars obtain height from the aircraft itself by interrogation and coded reply, using secondary surveillance radar (SSR), the descendant of wartime IFF.

The picture actually presented on the radar screen is rarely, these days, painted directly by the signals of the received echoes, as was the case with earlier PPI displays. Most modern displays are 'synthetic', in the sense that bright marks on the screen are produced by precise pulse-generating circuits activated by the received echoes. The circuits that do this ensure a constant and uniform displayed brightness for all echoes and are carefully designed to avoid missing the weaker ones. Such parts of the radar can be complex and come under the general heading of 'signal processing and plot extraction'. In recent years the stability and reliability of these circuits has been enhanced by the use of technology similar to that of digital computers. Computers provide backup to the operator in many ways, especially in modern GCI, where software programs take into account many relevant factors, including the known performance of the intercepting aircraft.

Reverting to the analogy of the motor car, many drivers are possibly unaware of the costly and protracted technical developments that enable them to hum along motorways at high speeds for hours on end. In the same way, not all who see radar screens may realise the extent to which development engineering has led to such fine all-round performance.

APPENDIX

The Choice of Wavelength for Radar

On encountering an object such as an aircraft, radio waves of any wavelength will be reflected to some extent; but the efficiency of reflection is diminished if the size of the target is small in relation to the wavelength. However, in practice, the dimensions of typical aircraft usually encompass many radar wavelengths, and so useful echo strengths are achievable.

Today, after six decades of practical radar technology, most long-range, early-warning radars for defence and air traffic control operate at wavelengths of less than 1 m. Ten cm and 25 cm are popular choices, but 50 cm and 75 cm have been shown to be effective, and sets at 1½ m are still in use. For small marine radars, 3 cm is commonly used, while for some short-range, high-precision radars, wavelengths of 1 cm or less may be used. On the other hand, in modern, very long-range, over-the-horizon radars, wavelengths amounting to several tens of metres may be found. The span is wide. (Wavelengths significantly less than 1 m are generally classed as 'microwaves'. Microwave ovens operate at about 12 cm.)

Modern technology now permits a choice of wavelengths for a given application, but the choice is not always easy. In considering a new specification for a long-range, early-warning radar, engineers debate – often at great length – the pros and cons of different wavelengths by raising valid arguments in support of one extreme or the other.

The matter is complex because there are so many trade-offs: the allowable weight and size of the final equipment; the susceptibility of radar performance to dense clouds and heavy rain; the ability to discriminate between close targets in both range and bearing; the accuracy of heightfinding; the resistance to jamming; the ability to select moving from fixed targets: these are just some of the aspects that vary with wavelength. No wavelength gives the ideal solution to each and every need. It is the designer's job to find the best compromise for the case in question, within imposed limits, whether physical, financial or the time available to get the job done (usually all three – and more!).

In the course of radio engineering up to the mid-1930s, when radar began to be tackled seriously in several countries, much attraction had been perceived in the use of short wavelengths for various communication purposes: radar was another example of an application that might do so with advantage. But, with the valve technology of the day, higher frequencies were difficult to generate at any great power level; thus transmitters were limited. Receivers, too, were difficult: they generated sufficient noise at the higher frequencies to mask weak signals. Wherever radio technology was in development, continuous efforts were made to solve these problems.

Radar designers before the war had to take these matters into account. Should they take advantage of the smaller aerials with more precise radiation patterns that could result from shorter wavelengths, while making the best of modest transmitter power and possibly noisy receivers, or should they use, both for transmission and reception, the more established and powerful technology of lower frequencies and accept the necessarily larger aerial arrays and less well-defined radar beams?

Broadly speaking, the answer seems to be that Germany, concentrating on 2.4 m and 50 cm, took the former course, and Britain the latter. One result was that some early German radars, such as the Würzburg, bore a remarkable superficial resemblance to later radars built by Britain and the Allies; another consequence was that the first type of British operational radar – the CH – was quite unlike subsequent radars of either side. As it turned out, this brought at least two unforeseen bonuses: first, as we have seen (p. 1), resistance to the Zeppelin spying mission of 1939; and second, much later in the war, the high-angle radiation resulting from this longish wavelength was instrumental in tracking the high-flying, supersonic V2 missiles and assisted in the location of their launching sites.

The British approach to radar design in 1935 was conditioned by the overriding preoccupation with the threat of bombing. German aircraft had previously bombed London, and therefore, in the likely event of another war, would surely do so again, and without delay. Modern high-speed bombers could attack the capital much more heavily than before. The outstanding need, therefore, was for reliable long-range early warning of approaching intruders. That was crucial.

In hindsight we know that for those starting work on radar defences in 1935, the actual need did not come at once: there was to be a period of four-and-a-half years of uneasy peace. But they could not know that. So they took the wisest and most obvious course by adapting, as far as possible, established and proven radio technology to build a system working on wavelengths of several metres. This permitted good designs of high-power transmitters and sensitive receivers, thereby giving the best guarantee of long-range performance and reliable operation.

THE NEED FOR HIGH-POWER TRANSMITTERS

In case it may be wondered why this has been stressed, a little explanation may be in order. Anyone who has set up a home projector for films or holiday slides will know that as the screen is moved back, the picture gets larger and dimmer. If the distance from projector to screen is doubled, the picture size doubles in both breadth and height; thus its area quadruples, and the brightness at any point on the screen falls to a quarter of its previous intensity. This is an example of the general 'inverse square law' applicable to the radiation of light and radio waves.

In radar the effect is even more marked because it applies in both directions – from radar transmitter to target, and again from target back to radar receiver. Thus, if we double the distance, the echo strength falls to a quarter of a quarter of its original strength – a sixteenth! Or, to put it another way, if we want to double the detection range of a radar by increasing the transmitter power, we have to do so by sixteen times. To treble the range by the same method would mean an eighty-one fold increase ($3\times3\times3\times3 = 81$). No wonder the 1935 designers, with long ranges firmly in mind for maximum early warning, opted for techniques that would ensure high powers.

SPREADING THE WARTIME RADAR SPECTRUM

When the wartime radar chain was fully established (see the map on p. 223) a wide range of wavelengths was in constant use:

- CH fixed stations (Type 1): generally around 12 m;
- Mobile CH (Type 9): around 7 m;
- CHL (Type 2): 1.5 m;
- GCI (Types 7 & 15): around 1.5 m;
- Auxiliary CHL/GCI (Type 11): 50 cm;
- Low-looking surveillance (Type 14 and many more): 10 cm;
- Centimetric heightfinding (Type 13): 10 cm.

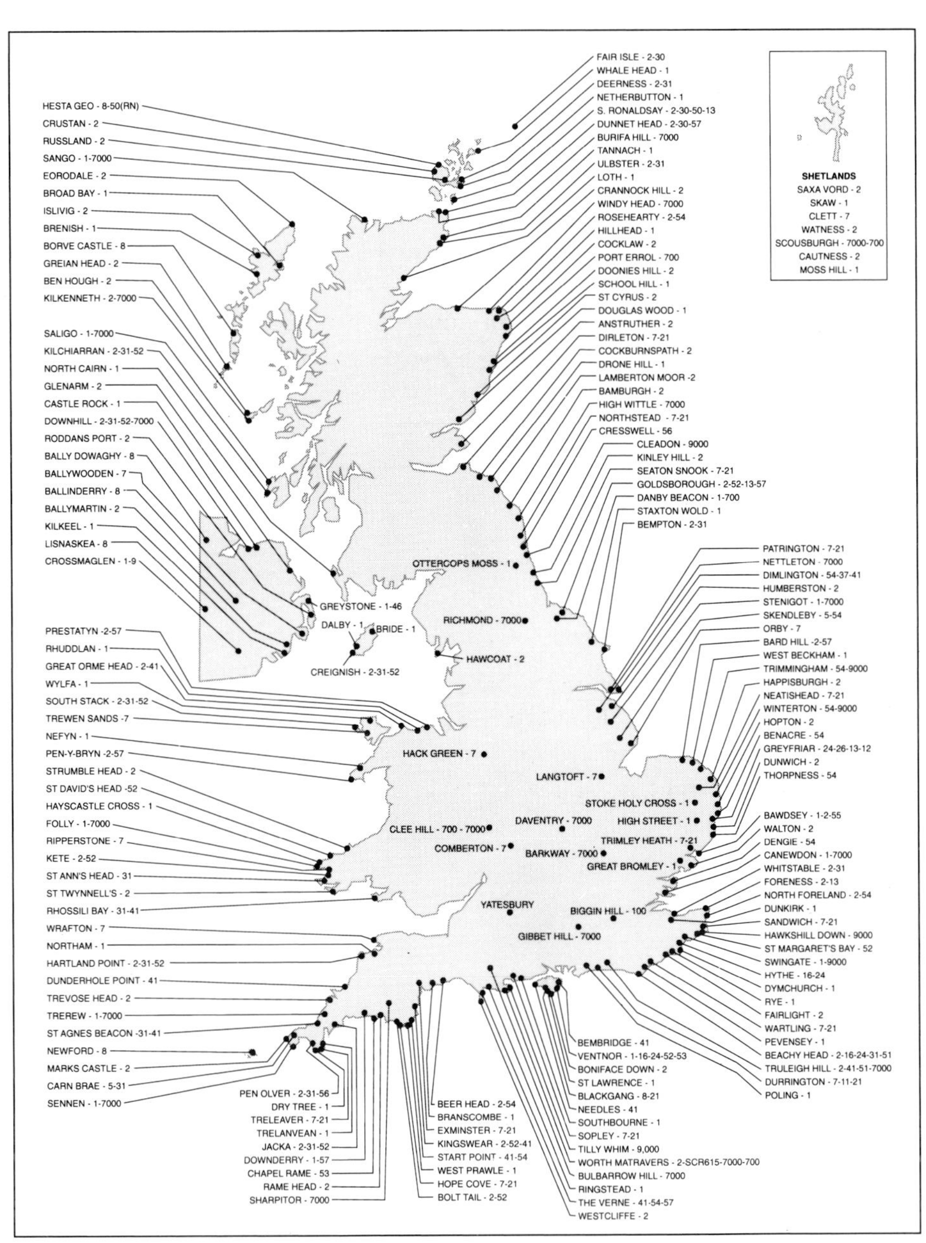

Approximate locations of RAF radar and navaid stations during the Second World War (omitting some temporary sites and test areas). The figures following the names indicate AMES types – see key on pp. 224–5.

KEY TO THE MAP – THE HOME CHAIN, 1945

The type numbers given follow the pattern, initiated early in the war, of designating the radar sites as Air Ministry Experimental Stations. The first was AMES Type 1, but subsequent equipments did not necessarily enter service in exact numerical order.

Type 1: CH stations of either east or west coast type.

Type 2: CHL – Various aerial mounting arrangements – on low or high towers or platforms of east coast CH towers.

Type 5: COL – Chain Overseas, Low – a version of Type 2 for use overseas, but a few were installed in UK.

Type 7: 'Final' static GCI station (the 'Happidrome').

Type 8: Various marks of early GCI radars, mobile and semi-static. A few at 250–300 MHz as insurance against jamming on normal 209 MHz GCI frequency. Superseded by Type 7 (static) and Type 15 (mobile).

Type 9: Mobile CH with 105 ft telescopic wooden aerial masts. Used overseas and in UK while main CH stations under construction or out of action.

Type 11: Mobile sets as possible standbys should the 1.5 m CHL/GCI radars be jammed. 50 cm wavelength, as used by Germany, reduced risk of jamming.

Type 13: 10 cm 'Nodding' heightfinder. Tx and Rx of Naval Type 277.

Type 14: 10 cm surveillance radar. Similar electronics to Type 13.

Type 15: GCI radar – mobile version of Type 7.

Type 16: Fighter Direction Station. A form of long-range 50 cm GCI.

Type 21: Five-vehicle GCI convoy comprising Types 13 and 14, control centre and two diesel generators.

Type 24: Long-range 10 cm heightfinder based on Type 13, used with Type 16.

Type 26: GCI. British-built version of American 10 cm radar.

Types 30–37 & 40–47: Variants of low- and medium-power coast-watching radars. Based on naval 10 cm sets (e.g. NT271).

Types 50–57: Variants of higher-powered 10 cm sets based on NT277, e.g.:

52: Circular, parabolic dish aerial on gantry over hut containing Tx/Rx, etc.

53: Similar to 52 but with horizontal 'cheese' aerial.

54a: Circular dish on 200 ft tower. Short waveguide from Tx just below.

54b: Similar to 54a, but long wavelength from Tx at base of tower.

55: Circular dish on 200 ft platform of 360 ft east coast CH tower. Tx in hut at ground level.

56: Circular dish on 185 ft wooden tower. Tx in ground-level Nissen hut.

57: Self-contained mobile radar. Horizontal 'cheese' mounted on box trailer containing Tx, Rx and all electronics.

Type 100: Ground-based beacon for 'H' high-precision navaid system. Three versions: fixed; heavy mobile; light mobile (the latter also capable of operating as any station of a Gee chain, for Gee-H).

Type 700: RAF designation for American Loran ground stations.

Type 7000: Gee ground stations. Master or any slave.

Type 9000: Oboe ground station, either Cat or Mouse function.

SCR 615/615A: American radar (also known as AMES Type 66).

Glossary

A	Ampère. Unit of current.
AC	Aircraftman; Alternating Current.
ACW	Aircraftwoman.
ADGB	Air Defence of Great Britain.
AI	Air Interception.
AJBO	Anti-Jamming Blackout Unit.
AMES	Air Ministry Experimental Station.
AP	Air Publication. Official document – often secret – describing aspects of RAF equipment.
ARP	Air Raid Precautions.
A-Site	The technical part of an RAF radar station, accessible only by authorized personnel holding appropriate passes.
ASR	Air-Sea Rescue.
ASV	Air-to-Surface (or Anti-Surface-Vessel) radar.
ATC	Air Traffic Control. A term rather more frequently heard in civil than military contexts, it is a descendant of GCI, in that aircraft movements are controlled by radar and radio communication.
ATS	Auxiliary Territorial Service.
AVO	Short for avometer, a famous multi-range test instrument for measuring electrical current, voltage and resistance. Hence AVO: Amps, Volts, Ohms.
BABS	Blind Approach Beacon System.
Bandwidth	The range of frequencies to which a system can respond without recourse to re-tuning.
B-Site	The 'domestic site' of an RAF radar station providing accommodation, meals, transport, administration, usually far from A-site.

CA	Coastal Artillery.
CD	Coastal Defence.
CH	Chain, Home (see Chapter 2).
CHEL	Chain, Home, Extra Low (see Chapter 3).
CHL	Chain, Home, Low (see Chapter 3).
Clerk SD	Cover name for radar plotter.
CME	Calculator Maintenance Engineer.
CO	Commanding Officer; Chain, Overseas.
COL	Chain, Overseas, Low.
Crossley	In RAF radar context, this usually implies the massive four-wheel vehicles of that make commonly used to accommodate mobile equipment. The Crossley truck had a large petrol engine with prodigious power and could tow almost anything.
CRT	Cathode ray tube.
CW	Continuous wave.
D/F	Direction-finding.
Dipole	The simplest element of an aerial array (antenna). Often a straight wire or rod having a length proportional to some fraction of the wave-length. Half-wave dipoles are common.
Echo Box	A piece of test gear which, when placed some distance from a radar, can be instrumental in assessing overall performance.
ELW	Early Light Warning.
FDT	Fighter Direction Tender. Floating GCI Stations for the D-Day invasion.
FFI	Free From Infection inspection.
Flt. Lt.	Flight Lieutenant.
F/O	Flying Officer.
GCI	Ground-Controlled Interception.

Gee	Pulsed hyperbolic navigational system.
Gee-H	Navigational aid of greater accuracy than Gee.
Halicrafter	An American make of receiver for radio communications. There were several models in the prewar range, highly esteemed by amateurs, but also much used by official organisations for professional applications.
HFDF	High-Frequency Direction-Finding.
Hz	Hertz. Unit of frequency. (1 Hz = 1 cycle per second).
i/c	In charge.
i.f.	Intermediate frequency.
H.T.	High Tension. ('Tension' is an alternative term for voltage.)
IFF	Identification, Friend or Foe. Not to be confused with IF (or, more usually now, i.f.) for the intermediate frequency stage(s) of a superheterodyne receiver.
IFRU	Intermediate Frequency Rejection Unit.
IJAJ	Intentional Jitter Anti-Jamming Unit.
kHz	KiloHertz. (1 kHz = 1,000 Hz.)
kV	Kilovolt. (1 kV = 1,000 V.)
kW	Kilowatt. (1 kW = 1,000 W.)
LAC	Leading Aircraftman
LACW	Leading Aircraftwoman
Line of Shoot (LOS)	(Not to be confused with 'shooting a line', this applied to CH stations.) The LOS was the bearing, quoted in degrees of the compass, of the centre of the broad forward transmitting lobe. Theoretically, the direction of maximum sensitivity.
Loran	Long Range Navigational System.
LST	Landing Ship (Tank). A form of special craft, designed to carry tanks to be beached in Normandy. Some, modified, became FDTs.
Magnetron	A diode with integral resonant cavities formed in its anode, and

	operating in a magnetic field. Powerful generator of microwaves. Heart of many radar transmitters.
MB2 (& MB3)	Compact, high-power radar pulse transmitter used on various ground stations of the CH type, both mobile and static (MB = mobile base).
MCU	Mobile Calibration Unit.
MEW	Microwave Early Warning (American term).
MHz	Mega Hertz. (1 MHz = 1,000,000 Hz.)
MU	Maintenance Unit.
Multivibrator	An electronic circuit producing waveshapes of approximately square or rectangular form. A pair of valves (or transistors now) required.
Noise	Random electrical disturbances, of no specific frequency, masking wanted signals. May be receiver-generated or picked up.
Oboe	Precision navigational aid.
Paralysis	In a pulsed radar system the receiver may suffer from temporary insensitivity immediately after the transmitter pulse, thus preventing short-range echoes from being observed.
PBX	Private Branch Exchange (telephone).
Pentode	A valve (known as a vacuum tube in the USA) having five electrodes – cathode, control grid, screen grid, suppresser grid, anode. Many forms, and used in a wide variety of electronic circuit applications. Noted for very high amplification in appropriate circuits.
Phantastron	A particular form of valve circuit used for generating short pulses of specific shapes.
Phase Shift Oscillator	A circuit capable of producing pure tones (sine waves) without the usual components of electrical capacitance and inductance which store energy and form the basis of most oscillators. Credited to R.J. Dippy, inventor of Gee.
P/O	Pilot Officer.
PPI	Plan Position Indicator.
PRF	Pulse recurrence frequency. The number of pulses transmitted by a radar in one second. PRF of CH was 25; CHL and CHEL, some hundreds, according to how set up; modern long-range radars,

	typically 250; medium-range ATC radars, typically 1,000; short-range radars for ship navigation and for close airport movements, up to many thousand pulses per second.
PW	Pulse width (pulse duration). Normally quoted in microseconds. CH was variable up to about 40, but normally set to less. 1–10 typical of many modern radars, but some transmit much longer pulses (hundreds of microseconds) with a pulse compression system in the receiver. Very close-range radars work with sub-microsecond pulses.
'Queen Mary'	RAF term for extra-long road vehicles designed for transporting airframes but also used for carrying sections of radar towers.
R1155	An RAF radio communications receiver, much used both in the air and on the ground. Included direction-finding circuits.
Railings	The name given, because of its appearance on oscilloscope or radar tube, to regular impulsive interference. May be a form of deliberate jamming.
RCAF	Royal Canadian Air Force.
RDF	The first title given to radar in UK. Generally understood to stand for Radio Direction Finding (alternatively, Reflected) Direction Finding. Announced publicly as 'Radiolocation' in 1941, but this term was soon superseded by 'radar'.
RE	Royal Engineer ('sapper').
Rebecca/ Eureka	A coded homing system for aircraft. Signals from a small lightweight Eureka beacon on the ground were received by airborne Rebecca. Much used for Allied landings and supply drops.
R/T	Radiotelephone; radiotelephony.
Rx	Abbreviation for 'receiver'.
SD	Secret Document. Often an AP.
Skiatron	A large, bright, radar display having a horizontal PPI face. Set in centre of a low table, it may be viewed by those looking down upon it. Used in GCI stations.
SP	Service Police.
Sprog	A new recruit.

Squegging Oscillator	An electronic circuit producing a radio-frequency output which is automatically broken up into a series of short, repetitive bursts. Applications include use as a simple pulsed signal generator (in effect, a low-power transmitter) during trials of radar equipment.
Strobe	Noun or verb – in radar, implies the close or special examination, or emphasis, of a particular portion of a display.
Superhet	Short for 'superheterodyne', itself a contraction of supersonic heterodyne. The principle by which most radio and radar receivers work, in which the incoming signal is changed to a lower and more convenient frequency for amplification and control of bandwidth.
TAF	Tactical Air Force (American term).
Theta-H	The reading indicated on the goniometer's degree scale on CH receivers when in the heightfinding mode.
Thorneycroft	Another large RAF transport vehicle complementing the Crossley.
Thyratron	A thermionic valve (electron tube in USA) containing gas at low pressure. Used as electronic switch of heavy currents, often at high voltages, in radar pulse generation. Wartime mercury-vapour, sensitive to temperature, now displaced by hydrogen.
TLC	Tank Landing Craft.
T/R	Transmit/receive.
TRE	Telecommunications Research Establishment.
Tx	Abbreviation for 'transmitter'.
Uniselector	A form of motor-driven rotary switch with a very large number of contacts which formed the basis of automatic telephone exchanges prior to modern solid-state technology.
V	Volt. Unit of electrical potential.
VHF	Very High Frequency.
Wheatstone Bridge	Classical electrical device for measuring electrical resistance, named after its famous inventor, pioneer of the electric telegraph.

W	Watt. Unit of power.
WAAF	Women's Auxiliary Air Force.
Window	Code name for metal foil dropped from aircraft to confuse enemy radar.
W/O	Warrant Officer. The highest RAF non-commissioned rank.
W/T	Wireless telegraph; wireless telegraphy.

Bibliography

Some recommended books for further reading:

Bawdsey – Birth of the Beam, Gordon Kinsey, Terence Dalton, 1983.
Boffin, R. Hanbury Brown, Adam Hilger, 1991.
Echoes of War, Sir Bernard Lovell, Adam Hilger, 1991.
Instruments of Darkness, Alfred Price, MacDonald & Janes, 1966.
LZ130 Graf Zeppelin and the End of Commercial Airship Travel, Duggan and Bauer, Zeppelin Museum, Friedrichshafen, 1996.
Most Secret War, R.V. Jones, Hamish Hamilton, 1978.
Orfordness – Secret Site, Gordon Kinsey, Terence Dalton, 1988.
Radar Days, E.G. Bowen, Adam Hilger, 1987.
The Bruneval Raid, George Millar, The Bodley Head, 1974.
The Challenge of War, Guy Hartcup, David & Charles, 1970.
The Radar Army, Reg Batt, Robert Hale, 1991.
Tizard, R.W. Clarke, Methuen, 1965.

Index